W9-CSE-973

SUBMILLIMETRE SPECTROSCOPY

SUBMILLIMETRE SPECTROSCOPY

A guide to the theoretical and experimental physics of the far infrared

G. W. CHANTRY

National Physical Laboratory
Teddington, Middlesex

1971
ACADEMIC PRESS
London and New York

ACADEMIC PRESS INC. (LONDON) LTD.
24–28 Oval Road,
London, NW1

US edition published by
ACADEMIC PRESS INC.
111 Fifth Avenue,
New York, New York 10003

Copyright © 1971 by Academic Press Inc. (London) Ltd.

All Rights Reserved
No part of this book may be reproduced in any form,
by photostat, microfilm or any other means,
without written permission from the publishers

Library of Congress Catalog Card Number: 75–149696
ISBN: 0–12–170550–1

PRINTED IN GREAT BRITAIN BY
ADLARD AND SON LTD, BARTHOLOMEW PRESS, DORKING

QC 457
C 48
PHYSICS

Preface

The far infrared or submillimetre region, the basis of which is the range of wavelengths between 1 and 0·1 mm, was for many decades one of the most difficult parts of the electromagnetic spectrum for experimentalists to work in. The wavelengths were too short for the available radio techniques to give detectable power and too long for the then existing infrared techniques, based on the black-body source and the radiometer detector, to give acceptable signal-to-noise characteristics.

Although a few dedicated workers attempted experiments in the sub-millimetre region throughout the period from 1890 to 1940, the majority of radio engineers preferred to work at longer wavelengths, where, with the development of megawatt power vacuum-tube oscillators, radio and tele-vision were born. In a similar fashion, infrared spectroscopists preferred to develop the 2–15 μm region of the infrared in which, with copious radiation from the black-body sources and with sodium chloride prism spectrometers, the diagnostic art of infrared "fingerprinting" was developed. Nevertheless the two-pronged attack on the submillimetre region continued, with a few radio engineers attempting the construction of ultra-high-frequency spark generators, and some infrared spectroscopists trying to build still more luminous spectrometers and to make still more sensitive detectors. A good account of these early days has been given by Gordy[1] who notes that, although overlapping of the two lines of investigation occurred as early as 1924 with the work of Glagolewa-Arkadiewa[2] and of Nichols and Tear,[3] very few results of spectroscopic significance were obtained by radio methods through-out the whole era. The infrared physicists progressing to longer and longer wavelengths had more luck. As early as 1892 Rubens[4] was beginning his lengthy series of far infrared investigations and had established the method of residual rays or "reststrahlen" to produce quasi-monochromatic beams of far infrared radiation. Having made the beams, he and his colleagues used them to investigate the optical and electromagnetic properties of materials[5] and establish the polarization of far infrared radiation by metal gratings and meshes.[6] In 1911 Rubens and Baeyer[7] discovered the use of the quartz envelope mercury lamp as a far infrared source. A full list of Rubens' papers is given in the bibliography published by Palik.[8] Two things stand out on read-ing this list: firstly the relevance of much of the work to present-day research, and secondly the array of distinguished physicists who joined Rubens in his

v

investigations. One notes du Bois, Snow, Nichols, Hagen, Ladenburg, Baeyer, Trowbridge and Wood, along with several others. In 1925 Czerny[9] published his first observations of the pure rotation spectrum of HCl. This experiment can be regarded as the beginning of far infrared molecular spectroscopy and it was to prove the first instalment of a long and still continuing flood of molecular information obtained from work at these wavelengths. Badger[10] observed the rotation spectrum of ammonia in 1928. Barnes[11] and Cartwright[12] followed on with better instruments and got still more detail in their spectra. In 1933, Wright and Randall (*Phys. Rev.* **44**, 391, 1933) detected the inversion splitting of the NH_3 rotation lines and in 1934, in an experimental *tour de force*, Cleeton and Williams (*Phys. Rev.* **45**, 234, 1934) observed the corresponding absorption, near 0.8 cm^{-1}, by making use of an echellette grating spectrometer coupled to an early form of magnetron as source. Strong[13] developed an excellent spectrometer in the early 1930's and by 1938 Randall[14] was able to write a review of far infrared spectroscopy reporting a respectable list of accomplishments.

During the war years 1939–1945, the impetus towards the development of special electron tubes to generate microwaves was accelerated by the desperate need for radar. The operating wavelengths of the radar systems were progressively reduced from tens of centimetres down to several millimetres and a whole array of devices ranging from magnetrons through klystrons to travelling wave tubes was developed, capable of delivering considerable power. After the war scientists used these sources to found the new discipline of microwave spectroscopy.[15, 16] This was the first time that it had been possible to study molecular spectra with coherent radiation and the resolving power achieved was remarkable. To this day, no other physical technique can match in precision the power of microwave spectroscopy to determine molecular sizes and shapes. Not surprisingly, therefore, there was great interest in extending these methods to as high a frequency as possible. The direct generation of power at submillimetre wavelengths has proved difficult even to the sophisticated technology of the 1960's and the most successful method in practice has turned out to be harmonic multiplication of the output of a klystron by a non-linear crystal. By 1964 Gordy,[17] who has long been the chief protagonist of this technique, had reached a wavelength of 0.43 mm where he observed the $J(5) \rightarrow J(6)$ line of CO.

A similar dramatic breakthrough came in the late 1950's and early 1960's from the infrared side when the use of the Michelson (or alternatively the lamellar grating) interferometer plus computer as a spectrometer was developed by Gebbie,[18, 21] Vanasse[18, 20] and Strong.[19, 20] These devices with their multiplex and radiation throughput advantages opened up new realms of quality in far infrared spectroscopy. This, coupled with the availability of the Golay[22] pneumatic detector and later the still more sensitive carbon bolometers and indium antimonide detectors,[23] has led to the present state where high precision, high resolution spectroscopy by optical techniques is possible down to $2\,cm^{-1}$ (5 mm). Nichols and Tear may have been optimistic in declaring the submillimetre barrier to have been overcome in 1925, but it certainly has now, in 1971.

This book is intended as a survey of the field as it appears today. The treatment must necessarily be eclectic but I think I will be forgiven by anyone who reads the more recent bibliography of Bloor[24] which has over 1800 entries. The subjects treated in depth tend to be those of interest to the research group at the National Physical Laboratory at Teddington in England who pioneered the hardware of Michelson interferometry for the far infrared and made it a practical proposition. This group was led by Dr. H. A. Gebbie whose far-sightedness, enthusiasm and determination to succeed made it all possible. I would like to thank him especially for a great deal that I have learnt and also for putting the idea of this book in my mind. To my other colleagues at NPL, who have included at one time or another A. Anderson, J. R. Birch, W. J. Burroughs, C. C. Bradley, John Chamberlain, G. Duxbury, F. D. Findlay, J. W. Fleming, J. E. Gibbs, J. Harries, R. G. Jones, N. W. B. Stone and Dudley Williams, I would like to extend my thanks for their unfailing support and help. Finally I would like to thank my numerous friends throughout the world who have assisted me in preparing this book and have helped me to avoid many errors. These include Nora Hill, Bernadette Lassier, Irene Darmon, G. Birnbaum, C. Brot, Mansel Davies, W. Gordy, J. L. Rivail and G. R. Wilkinson. Only a small part of the scientific content comes from my own researches; the rest is the work of other men and women and I can but hope that my compilation does them justice.

October 1971   G. W. CHANTRY

Contents

CHAPTER 1

The Nature of Spectroscopy and the Spectroscopic Method

The science that deals with the propagation and interactions of electro-magnetic radiation is known as optics. The reason for this is historical since the first physicists to investigate the nature of light had little idea that this was a form of electromagnetic radiation confined to a narrow region of the spectrum and the title of the art comes from the only detector available to them, the human eye. The eye is a wonderfully sensitive detector and in the visible region it has only been surpassed this century with the development of sensitive photographic emulsions and photomultipliers. It is not surprising therefore that most of the fundamental discoveries in optics have been made by visual observations. The wave nature of light was established by the observation of the phenomenon of interference, and the vector nature of the radiation field by the observation of polarization effects. The enormous importance attached to visual observation still persists as was shown by the excitement generated when visible pulsations were detected from a star in the centre of the Crab nebula which had previously been shown to pulsate in the radio-frequency region.

The profound change in scientific outlook which led to the realization that the information available to us from observations confined to the visible region was only a small fraction of what could be discovered came with the development of the electromagnetic field equations by Maxwell. These equations represent a synthesis of electrostatics and electrodynamics and their solutions indicate the existence of transverse waves made up of ortho-gonal electric and magnetic vectors and propagating at a velocity identical to that found for light. It was then a small step to the realization that light was a disturbance of the electromagnetic field.

This was a wonderful synthesis of the various elements which had been accumulating under the general name of optics, not least of which was the science of spectroscopy. This too had been discovered by visual methods when the great Sir Isaac Newton allowed the light from the sun to strike one of the inclined faces of a glass prism. The refracted light emerging from the other inclined face travelled to a screen and there produced a brilliant

B

array of colours ranging from red to violet—in fact a spectrum. Not long after this it was discovered that on each side of the visible spectrum there were invisible rays—the infrared and the ultraviolet. Later, and associated principally with the names of Bunsen and Frauenhofer, came the discovery of an entirely different kind of spectrum—not continuous with the colours blending imperceptibly into one another, but sharp and discrete. How these sharp lines came to be associated with emissions from atoms is well known as is the growth of the science of spectrum analysis which had spectacular triumphs in the detection of chemical elements in the sun and other cosmic objects. For the science of spectroscopy itself, however, the more important happening was the gradual realization that each point in the spectrum corresponded to waves of a given wavelength. Interference methods allowed the wavelength of a sharp spectral line to be determined and it was shown that the visible region of the spectrum corresponded to wavelengths lying between $0 \cdot 4$ and $0 \cdot 7$ μm. After Maxwell's work came the great concept—the electromagnetic spectrum stretching from radiowaves through the infrared, visible and ultraviolet regions on to the X-rays and γ-rays.

Spectroscopy is performed nowadays in all these regions and the observation of sharp lines throughout the spectrum has been a constant experimental guide to the theorists, from Planck and Bohr to Dirac and Lamb, in the development of quantum mechanics. Line position has been the paramount quantity and not many physicists have been concerned with such questions as "What do we mean by a spectral line?" or "What is the real meaning of wavelength?" Such questions became more urgent in the period following World War II (1939–45), when physicists turned the hardware and skills which had been necessary for radar to the development of radio-frequency and microwave spectroscopy. In fact, it is now a much better and more satisfactory way of developing the theory of spectroscopy to abandon the historical approach altogether and to begin by asking what one does when one observes a spectrum in the radio-frequency region.

The first thing that strikes one is that the continuous and perfectly harmonic waves that are so much a feature of discussions of optical spectra can actually be realized in the radio-frequency region. In fact, wavetrains of arbitrary length can be generated at frequencies up to approximately 10^{11} Hz by the successive use of appropriate electronic devices. Superheterodyne detection of radio broadcasts is a commonplace, although it involves a concept which in the optical region was considered impossible until very recently, namely interference between separate discrete sources. When the words "frequency" or "wavelength" are used of waves in this region the concepts are quite clear and precise, and it is now becoming obvious that most elementary treatments of spectroscopy in the region above 10^{12} Hz are improper in that they invoke the mathematics of these long wavetrains when such trains are not commonly emitted by sources in this high-frequency region. The difference between the radiation given out by a valve oscillator and that given out by excited atoms is described in terms of the concept of coherence. If the electromagnetic disturbances are perfectly coherent then it follows that, if they are known over a small space–time region, their values at all past and future times can be explicitly derived. If the disturbances are incoherent then no such calculation can be made—the situation is one of chaotic and random fluctuations. Intermediate states exist and these can be characterized by coherence lengths or, equivalently, coherence times. When it is said that two independent light sources cannot interfere with each other what is really meant is that the interference pattern only persists for the mutual coherence time which is usually extremely short. Any detector such as the eye has a finite detection time and gives only the average over this time. Consequently no visible interference fringes can usually be seen. Very recently, highly coherent visible devices called lasers have been developed and with these fringes lasting fractions of a second have been observed when the radiation from two lasers is combined. If the radiation from a single partly coherent source is split into two or more beams which are subjected to varying delays and then recombined, a stationary interference pattern is observed, provided that the time taken to traverse the delays is less than the coherence time of the radiation. Since the velocity of light is very great, spatial delays of several centimetres can be used to produce discernible fringes when the relatively incoherent light from low pressure gas discharges is being studied. In the radio-frequency region, because of the very high coherence, interference is observable with spatial delays of many miles—a phenomenon irksomely familiar to those receiving television broadcasts in built-up areas.

The second principal difference between radio frequency and optical spectroscopy is the quality of the detectors available. In the low-frequency region, various non-linear devices such as electron tubes or crystal diodes are available which give a voltage output oscillating in the same manner as the electromagnetic radiation incident on it. In the high-frequency region ($> 10^{12}$ Hz), on the other hand, the available detectors give a d.c. output proportional to the mean power in the incident radiation. Spectroscopy at radio frequencies is thus quite straightforward. The output from the detector is passed to a frequency analyser which, when set to a frequency ν, gives the power in the frequency range $\nu \pm \delta\nu$. The plot of power versus ν is then the spectrum of the radiation. This simple procedure is varied at microwave frequencies by recourse to the superheterodyne principle in which radiation from a local oscillator is mixed with the incoming radiation to produce a much lower and much more easily handled "difference frequency" but this is merely an experimental convenience—the wave analyser remains as the spectrometer. The operation of the wave analyser must therefore be closely looked at, for the essence of the meaning of the word "spectroscopy" is therein to be found. Basically, the incoming radiation is a time-dependent fluctuating electromagnetic field. Fourier has shown that any such temporal fluctuations can be resolved into an infinite number of pure cosine and sine waves of differing frequencies. The word "spectrum" therefore means a plot of the power in the component waves lying between ν and $\nu+d\nu$ as a function of ν—in other words the spectrum is the Fourier transform of the temporal fluctuations of the field. The two variables, time and frequency, are said to be conjugate and the two functions $F(t)$ and $f(\nu)$ are said to be Fourier "mates" of one another. A perfect wave analyser does this Fourier transformation directly and its output as stated above is the spectrum. An imperfect wave analyser will have a finite discrimination $\Delta\nu$ and will report power over this finite range even if the incident radiation is a pure cosine wave and hence has only a single component. The effect of this finite discrimination is to restrict the resolution available in the spectrum, for if there are two or more components lying within the range $\Delta\nu$ they will not be separated in the output of the wave analyser. To illustrate these points we will consider the radiation from an oscillator which starts to oscillate with a gradually increasing amplitude, reaches a maximum and then gradually dies away. The output of a perfect and an imperfect wave analyser supplied with such an oscillation to its input terminals is shown in Fig. 1.1. Consider first the perfect case. The line profile, apart from the subsidiary oscillations, is what we familiarly think of as a spectral line. Its grand maximum occurs at a frequency ν_0 which is what would usually be called the line frequency and, as spelt out at length earlier, this has been the quantity most investigated by spectroscopists. The line does, however, have a finite width, the so-called "natural line-width", which can be seen from the above analysis to be a direct consequence of the finite length of the wavetrain. The curve for the

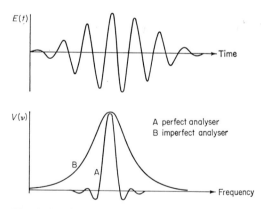

FIG. 1.1. Direct spectroscopy with a wave analyser.

imperfect case is much broader; its breadth arising as it does from instrumental imperfections is called the "instrumental line-width". Curves similar to B would be observed even if the incident wavetrain were very long indeed and its Fourier transform, therefore, confined to a very narrow region in the frequency domain. This leads us to a concept which applies to all spectroscopic devices, namely the "spectral window". This quantity is the spectral line profile produced by the instrument when perfectly monochromatic radiation is incident on it. If the incoming radiation contains two or more components which are closely spaced compared with the width of the spectral window then they cannot be separated in the output of the instrument—that is, they will not be resolved. The shape of the spectral window is thus a measure of the resolving power of the instrument.

The third principal difference between the two forms of spectroscopy concerns the available sources and is most clearly demonstrated by considering absorption spectroscopy rather than the emission type so far discussed. In an absorption experiment radiation from a suitable source passes through the specimen under investigation and then travels to a detector. The problem is to determine the amount of power absorbed by the specimen as a function of frequency. One way of doing this in the radio-frequency region would be to have a broad-band incoherent source such as a spark and to examine the output of the detector with a wave analyser in the manner outlined above. Since the source is incoherent, the detector plus wave analyser cannot give any information about the quality of the component wavetrains, but this is not any loss since it is only the total power in the components lying within the spectral window that is required. Such an experiment will yield a spectrum whose resolution is governed by the spectral window of the detector plus analyser. As will be shown later, this is precisely the method which has to be used in the high-frequency regions. However, in the lower frequency (i.e. microwave) region an alternative is available. One can use a power (in this region also called "video") detector such as a crystal diode and alter the frequency of a coherent source. A record of the d.c. output of the detector versus source frequency will be the desired spectrum. Essentially one is studying the absorption of each of the Fourier components into which the broad-band radiation can be resolved *separately* and as may be imagined the resulting resolution is very high indeed. The resolution is in fact only limited by source frequency jitter and by the amount of time (i.e. wavetrain length) available. This technique has been extensively exploited in the microwave region to study pure rotation spectra of gases in absorption and the resolution achieved has been the highest ever recorded in any spectroscopic experiment. In fact, the line positions can be observed to such high accuracy and the molecular parameters determining these positions can be so well determined that the lines of the spectrum lying at much higher frequencies,

and which are hence inaccessible to microwave techniques, can be predicted
to a higher accuracy than they can be experimentally observed using the
lower resolution techniques which are all that are available there. Very
recently electron beam devices for the submillimetre region (frequencies
lying between 3×10^{11} to 3×10^{12} Hz) have been developed and non-linear
mixers using lasers have also been developed for the optical region and these
can, in principle, be used in the same manner to give ultra-high resolution,
but in general it is true that this method is inapplicable at frequencies higher
than 10^{11} Hz.

We have seen, therefore, that spectroscopy in the radio-frequency region
is conceptually easy and experimentally quite straightforward; the question
to be asked now is: how does one do spectroscopy when one is limited to
incoherent (black-body) sources and power detectors? Clearly nothing can
be done about the source, so all the unscrambling of the Fourier components
has to be done before the radiation reaches the detector. Two methods are
possible. Firstly, one can invoke absorption in filters and make up a set of
narrow-band filters to cover the spectral range in question and then record
the power transmitted through each filter and plot this power as a function
of frequency of maximum transmission of the filter. This method has some
applications in analysis where it is sometimes called "colorimetry" but it is
not a practicable method if even moderate resolution is required. All techniques for higher resolution are based on the second method,[25] that called
"the delay principle". If the incoming wavefront is divided into a number
of beams and each of these subjected to a different temporal delay and then
all the beams recombined, a pattern results in the image plane which contains
all the spectral information about the incident radiation. The most familiar
example of this takes us back to Newton and the prism. In Fig. 1.2 is shown

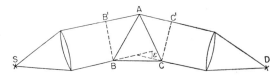

FIG. 1.2. Deviation by a prism.

a parallel beam of light incident upon and just filling one of the inclined
faces of a prism of angle α. The angle of incidence θ is so chosen that the
deviation is a minimum and hence the rays inside the prism travel parallel
to the base. Initially we will imagine the radiation to be monochromatic
and let the refractive index of the prism material be n. It can readily be shown
by applying Snell's law, namely

$$n = \sin \theta / \sin \theta' \qquad (1.1)$$

where θ' is the angle of refraction inside the prism, that

$$\epsilon = 2(\theta - \theta') \tag{1.2}$$

and that

$$AB' = AC' = \tfrac{1}{2}n \, BC. \tag{1.3}$$

Now nBC is the optical path length of the extreme ray inside the prism, so equation (1.3) brings out clearly the physical nature of the deviation by a prism. The ray *has* to be deflected through the angle ϵ so that the wavefront emerging (CC') will be cophasal, i.e. have the same phase everywhere across the wavefront. Another way of looking at the operation of the prism is to say that interference between the infinite number of beams into which the pencil is divided by the inclined faces is completely destructive at all angles of deviation except ϵ. In other words, the prism is an interferometer involving an infinite number of beams. Because the number of beams is infinite there is only one angle of deviation and the energy is focussed by the second lens to a single point. Of course strictly parallel light and point images do not exist and diffraction has to be considered and will be later on, but the general philosophy applies, namely that a prism gives a unique spectral display. To emphasize this more and to lead on to more general discussion we will consider two components of different frequencies incident on the prism. The refractive index of the prism will depend on frequency due to the phenomenon of dispersion, and therefore the angle of deviation will change so as to satisfy equation (1.3). As a consequence the two components will be imaged at different points along a line in the image plane and thus we have brought about unique spatial separation of the spectral components. This is just what Newton and his followers did and the record of intensity versus distance is what is usually called the spectrum: each point along the line corresponds to a unique frequency, apart from complications due to finite spectral windows (in this case due to non-point sources, non-point detectors and diffraction). It is not quite a spectrum in the sense defined earlier for in general the scale of distance is non linear in terms of frequency due to the non-linear characteristic of the dispersion curve, but this is a minor point and the record could be replotted with a linear abscissa.

It remains to discuss the resolution available with a given prism in a given spectral region. In practice of course S is a slit perpendicular to the plane of Fig. 1.2. The wider the slit the lower the resolution because the images of the slit formed by each component of the radiation will overlap. Suppose, however, that the slit has vanishing width—what we now need to know is the limiting resolution. Clearly under these circumstances the spectral window is governed by Fraunhofer diffraction in the image plane. The diffraction pattern produced at D is principally determined by the effects of the rectangular aperture whose base is BB′ and whose height is that of the slit. Diffraction at a rectangular aperture leads to a pattern of bright and dark fringes whose positions are given by the function[26]

$$I(\Delta\epsilon) = I(0)\{\sin \pi\bar{\nu}(BB')\Delta\epsilon/[\pi\bar{\nu}(BB')\Delta\epsilon]\}^2. \tag{1.4}$$

The first minimum thus occurs at an angular distance

$$\Delta\epsilon = 1/[\bar{\nu}(BB')]. \tag{1.5}$$

Resolution is a rather difficult concept to define explicitly but one definition widely used is that suggested by Rayleigh, namely that an instrument can be said to resolve two "monochromatic" lines when the grand maximum of the diffraction pattern of one lies on the first zero of that of the other and vice versa. Applying this and the formula for the change in angle of deviation with change of refractive index, namely

$$\Delta\epsilon = \left(\frac{BC}{BB'}\right)\frac{dn}{d\bar{\nu}}\Delta\bar{\nu} \tag{1.6}$$

leads to the result

$$\Delta\bar{\nu} = \left[\bar{\nu}(BC)\frac{dn}{d\bar{\nu}}\right]^{-1}. \tag{1.7}$$

The resolving power available with a prism depends, therefore, on the dispersion of the prism material and on the base length of the prism. This is a particular illustration of a very general result that the resolving power available with any device based on the delay principle is always determined by the maximum delay introduced. In the case of the prism the delay varies from zero at the apex to a maximum set by the base length of the prism.

The next instrument to be considered is the diffraction grating. This differs from the prism in that it is a purely optical device not invoking any such constitutive property as dispersion, but from our present viewpoint the principal difference is that in a grating instrument the delay pattern is produced by a finite number of beams. We consider a plane grating made up of N very narrow strips, either perfectly reflecting (reflection grating) or perfectly transmitting (transmission grating), separated by regions which are non reflecting and totally opaque. We ignore for the moment diffraction by the narrow strips themselves and merely consider interference between the N beams into which the incident beam is divided by the grating. The situation is illustrated in Fig. 1.3 where we have a "parallel" beam of radiation of wavenumber $\bar{\nu}$ incident at an angle θ and we consider a wavefront leaving the grating at an angle ϕ. Such a parallel beam will be imaged by the lens to a point and each point will correspond in a one-to-one fashion with a particular value of ϕ. The intensity in the image plane at a given point

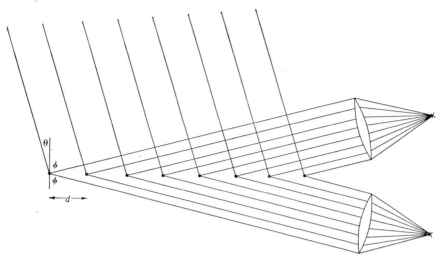

FIG. 1.3. Diffraction by a grating.

is found by squaring the electric field strength there and the electric field strength is found by adding up the contributions from the N beams. In fact if

$$\delta = 2\pi\bar{v}d(\sin\theta - \sin\phi)$$

then

$$E(\phi) = E_0[\cos 2\pi vt + \cos(2\pi vt + \delta)$$
$$+ \cos(2\pi vt + 2\delta) \ldots \cos(2\pi vt + N\delta)]. \quad (1.8)$$

This is readily shown by the use of De Moivre's theorem (see Appendix 1 for an alternative method) to be

$$E(\phi) = E_0[\sin \tfrac{1}{2}(N\delta)/\sin \tfrac{1}{2}\delta] \cos(2\pi vt + \tfrac{1}{2}N\delta) \quad (1.9)$$

and thus

$$I(\phi) \sim I(0)[\sin \tfrac{1}{2}(N\delta)/\sin \tfrac{1}{2}\delta]^2. \quad (1.10)$$

The intensity along the image line shows, therefore, strong maxima whenever the denominator vanishes, i.e. when

$$d(\sin\theta - \sin\phi) = m\lambda, \qquad m = 0 \pm 1, \pm 2. \quad (1.11)$$

The effect of the numerator is merely to make the maxima sharp. In fact the larger is N the sharper are the maxima. We thus see the profound difference between the grating and the prism. The grating produces a large number of maxima when irradiated by monochromatic light whereas the prism produces just one. This is a consequence of the finite number of beams and the various maxima are referred to as the "orders" of the grating.

When m = zero—that is the zeroth order—θ must equal ϕ and therefore there is no frequency dependence and, if the grating is irradiated with polychromatic radiation, all the power will be imaged to the same spot. If m is non zero, however, very different considerations apply and different frequencies are imaged to different spots for the same order; that is we have produced a "spectrum". An immediate complication will be noticed, for clearly the spectra produced by one order will overlap the others if the bandwidth is large or the orders closely spaced and confusion can arise. The full details of this overlapping will be postponed until the next chapter. We will here merely emphasize that reduction of the number of beams to a finite number necessarily leads to ambiguity in interpretation of the resulting spectral record.

The ultimate of this procedure is when the number of interfering beams is reduced to two—the minimum number if the delay principle is to be invoked. Instruments of this kind are therefore called two-beam interferometers and examples are the Michelson interferometer and the lamellar grating which are schematically illustrated in Fig. 1.4. The full theory of these instruments

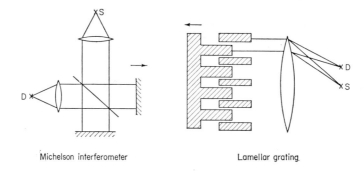

Michelson interferometer   Lamellar grating

Fig. 1.4. Two-beam interferometers. S = source. D = detector.

will be developed later. At the moment we will consider how the intensity at the image point varies with the delay introduced. The incoherent radiation from the source is, as we have seen, made up of a chaotic assembly of wavetrains of random length and phase. Each wavelet, however, is split in two (either by the beam divider in the Michelson interferometer or by the two sets of mirrors in the Lamellar grating) and then recombined so interference is possible. To calculate the mean intensity at the image point we divide each of the split wavelets into its Fourier components, add their electric vector amplitudes, square these and take a time average. Thus if the additional path length travelled by one beam is $2x$ and the wavenumber of the component is $\bar{v}$ we would have

$$E(t) = E_0 \cos 2\pi v t + E_0 \cos (2\pi v t + 4\pi \bar{v} x). \qquad (1.12)$$

The intensity contributed by this component is thus

$$dI = S(\bar{v}) [\cos 2\pi \bar{v} x]^2 d\bar{v}. \qquad (1.13)$$

The total intensity is then obtained by adding up all the Fourier components, that is

$$I(x) = \tfrac{1}{2} \int_0^\infty S(\bar{v}) [1 + \cos 4\pi \bar{v} x] d\bar{v}. \qquad (1.14)$$

This equation means that a plot of $I(x)$ against x contains all the information needed to deduce the spectral function $S(\bar{v})$ which, as will be seen on reflection, is the true spectral function since it is the Fourier transform of the radiation field. It is worth while going over what we have done again to bring out clearly what delay spectroscopy is all about. When we take the time average of the square of $E(t)$, which is

$$E(t)^2 = 4E_0^2 [\cos (2\pi v t + 2\pi \bar{v} x) \cos 2\pi \bar{v} x]^2, \qquad (1.15)$$

all the information about the time dependence of the field disappears. We have no choice in this as the detectors simply cannot follow the ultra-high frequency oscillations. But, because of the delay introduced into one of the beams, the time average depends on the wavenumber of the radiation $\bar{v} = v/c$ and the spectroscopic information is recovered even with the limitations of power detectors.

We have said that equation (1.14) contains all the spectral information: but in what form? Consider two analytical functions for $S(\bar{v})$: firstly the delta function $S(\bar{v})$ = zero for all $\bar{v}$ except $\bar{v}_0$ (in other words perfect monochromatic radiation), and secondly $S(\bar{v})$ = unity for all $\bar{v}$ up to $\bar{v}_{max}$ and is zero from thence on (in other words broad-band radiation). $I(x)$ for these two functions is shown in Fig. 1.5.

The reduction of the number of beams down to two has made the pattern, even with monochromatic radiation, hardly intelligible and that with the broad-band radiation completely unintelligible. This does not mean that the spectral information is not there and cannot be retrieved mathematically; what it does mean is that the direct intelligibility to the eye of the experimentalist is very low indeed.

It might therefore be thought that a spectroscopist would always use a prism when possible, a grating when a prism was unsuitable and that the two-beam interferometer would be relegated to the curio department of a museum. However, since the development of information theory, we are

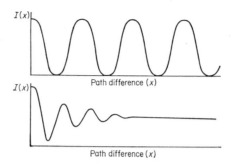

FIG. 1.5. Interferogram patterns generated by simple idealized spectral profiles; the upper curve is for monochromatic radiation, and the lower curve for broad-band radiation.

beginning to realize that the truism, "One doesn't get anything for nothing", has a less familiar converse, "One is never forced to lose something without a corresponding gain". In the case of spectrometers this takes the form that the more comprehensible is the delay pattern, the lower is the energy through-put for a given resolving power.[25] Thus, whilst the Michelson interferometer gives the least intelligible display, it has the highest throughput of any spectroscopic system.[27] This is normally only of academic interest in the visible and near infrared regions of the spectrum where sources are very bright and detectors very efficient, and one can well afford to lose the large fraction of the radiant power that is absorbed by the faces of the entrance slit. However, in the submillimetre region very different considerations apply. The sources used for absorption spectroscopy will be hot bodies heated to as high a temperature as can conveniently be used—in practice about 1000 K. If such a source is to radiate effectively in the frequency range of interest, then, by Kirchoff's law, it must absorb strongly in that range; in other words we are dealing with more or less black bodies. The spectral distribution of the radiation from a hot black body is given by the well-known formula due to Planck, namely

$$F(\bar{\nu}, T) \, d\bar{\nu} = 2\pi h c^2 \bar{\nu}^3 \, [\exp{(hc\bar{\nu}/kT)} - 1]^{-1} \, d\bar{\nu} \qquad (1.16)$$

which is illustrated in Fig. 1.6.

It will be seen from this figure that the large majority of the radiation is concentrated in the near infrared and only a small fraction of the radiation occurs in the far infrared. The total power radiated is obtained by integrating (1.16) over the entire frequency range. This leads to the expression

$$W = [2\pi^5 k^4/(15h^3 c^2)] \, T^4 = \sigma T^4 \qquad (1.17)$$

where σ is Stefan's constant and therefore

$$W = 5 \cdot 72 \times 10^{-12} \, T^4 \, \text{W cm}^{-2}.$$

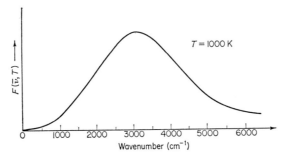

FIG. 1.6. Radiant energy distribution from a black-body radiator.

So a black body with a surface temperature of 1000 K will radiate 5·72 W cm^{-2}. The power radiated in the submillimetre (<100 cm^{-1}) region could be found by a similar integration but is more normally handled by means of an approximation, which is

if

$$hc\nu/(kT) \ll 1$$

then

$$F = 2\pi c\nu^2 kT \, d\nu \tag{1.18}$$

and

$$W = \tfrac{2}{3}\pi c\nu_0^3 kT \tag{1.19}$$

where ν_0 is the upper frequency limit of the integration. Substituting the appropriate physical quantities into (1.19) gives the answer that the total power radiated at frequencies less than 100 cm^{-1} is $\approx 4 \times 10^{-4}$ W cm^{-2}. Thus, only 1 part in 10^4 of the total radiation lies in the submillimetre band. Equation (1.18) was first given by Rayleigh and Jeans in connection with their attempt to explain the laws of radiation emission in terms of classical mechanics and, therefore, the submillimetre band is occasionally referred to as the Rayleigh–Jeans region. If the temperature of the source is raised, more radiation in the submillimetre band is obtained but vastly more in the near infrared regions. One is therefore faced with the inescapable fact that spectroscopy in the submillimetre region is always going to involve the use of dim sources and will perpetually be plagued with a vast surplus of higher frequency radiation which has somehow to be removed. Prism and grating spectrometers are wasteful of energy and particularly prone to the hazards of the inadvertent observation of stray radiation.

Further difficulties arise when we come to consider detectors.[23, 28] There is no detector available in the infrared region to match the extreme sensitivity of the photomultiplier in the visible region. In the near infrared some very fine detectors are available which, although not as good as photomultipliers, are still very sensitive. Thus a lead telluride photoconductive cell of detector area 1 mm^2 has been reported[29] with an ultimate sensitivity of 2×10^{-14} W at $2 \cdot 2$ μm. In the submillimetre region the available detectors are much less sensitive. The room temperature Golay cell (area 9 mm^2) has a sensitivity of 5×10^{-11} W and it is necessary to go to various devices operating at liquid helium temperature before this figure can be much improved. The principal reason for this is that room temperature (300 K) corresponds to a frequency of about 200 cm^{-1}, so that if a submillimetre photon is to have an energy much larger than that of the electrons in the detecting material this will have to be at a very low temperature. Another point relevant to discussions of detector performance which follows on from this is concerned with the noise characteristics to be expected. In the high-frequency regions the principal source of noise lies in the chaotic and sporadic rate at which the photons arrive, for virtually no electrons are released except by the photoelectric effect. Under these circumstances the signal-to-noise ratio is proportional to the square root of the incident intensity and the detector is said to be photon-noise limited. In the submillimetre region most of the noise comes from the detector and the signal-to-noise ratio is directly proportional to the incident power (detector-noise limited case). From this and what has been said above, it is highly desirable to choose a spectroscopic system which gives the optimum transfer of energy from the source to the detector and, this being the case, the Michelson interferometer, which does this and is also free from stray radiation problems, has come to the forefront in submillimetre spectroscopy.

Even despite all its advantages, the instrument would not have been a practical proposition were it not for the contemporaneous development of the digital computer. Looking again at equation (1.14) rewritten in the form

$$I'(x) = I(x) - \tfrac{1}{2} \int\limits_{0}^{\infty} S(\bar{v}) \, d\bar{v} = \tfrac{1}{2} \int\limits_{0}^{\infty} S(\bar{v}) \cos 4\pi\bar{v}x \, d\bar{v}, \qquad (1.20)$$

it will be seen by applying Fourier's integral theorem that

$$S(\bar{v}) = \tfrac{1}{2} \int\limits_{-\infty}^{+\infty} I'(x) \cos 4\pi\bar{v}x \, dx. \qquad (1.21)$$

In other words the spectrum can be recovered by the Fourier transformation of the modified interferogram function. The evaluation of the integral (1.21) is a very straightforward affair in a high-speed digital computer and, since these are now commonly available, the lack of immediate intelligibility in the interferogram is no longer a handicap. The ideal submillimetre spectrometer is therefore a Michelson interferometer coupled to a digital computer.

The overall system has two further advantages. Firstly the interferometer is mechanically extremely simple whereas a grating instrument, as will be shown later, is very complex. Of course, since an instrument has to disentangle a spectrum it *has* to be complex somewhere. In the interferometric case the complications are transferred to the computer and we are thus able to shift our problems to an instrument whose technological advance is remarkable and from which we can expect full theoretical performance.[25] Basically this means that instead of having to make new gratings or interference filters for a new set of observations all that is required at most is to write a new programme. The second advantage was first pointed out by Fellgett[30] and is known as the multiplex advantage. Suppose that we are to observe a spectrum made up of N elements—that is spectral intervals equal to the resolution—in a time T. Then, with any dispersive instrument, each element will be observed for a time T/N and the signal-to-noise ratio in the observed spectrum will be proportional to the square root of the observing time, namely $T^{1/2}/N^{1/2}$. However, with an interferometer each element is observed all the time so that the signal-to-noise ratio will be proportional to $T^{1/2}$. It therefore follows that the interferometric system will be superior to the dispersive system by the factor $N^{1/2}$ which may be considerable. To get the full advantage, it is important that the system be detector-noise limited and that a resolution has been decided on appropriate to the bandwidth of radiation reaching the detector. Clearly if photon noise is significant, then the fluctuations in the spectrum (also "noise" in common parlance) within each resolution interval will depend on how many intervals there are and how much radiant power there is in each. An extreme case might be a spectrum consisting of a very strong emission line accompanied by very much weaker components. If this were being studied with an interferometer featuring a photon-noise limited detector, then the transformed interferogram (i.e. the spectrum) would be very noisy all over and the noise in the vicinity of the weak components might be sufficient to swamp them altogether. The strong line itself, on the other hand, would be clearly delineated. In this case it would be better to use a dispersive instrument in front of the detector if the weak components were the principal object of study, provided that the luminosity loss could be tolerated.

It is most important to realize as Fellgett[30] has emphasized, that the multiplexing is a property of the system as a whole. Merely using an interferometer does not guarantee this advantage, nor does the need to use a dispersive instrument necessarily deny it. A spectrograph equipped with a photographic plate is a multiplex instrument since the detector is observing many channels simultaneously. The noise (i.e. grain fluctuations) induced by any given line is sensibly restricted to the region of the plate where the radiation of that frequency is brought to a focus and so, in a sense, we have a form of detector-noise limitation. The parallels with the far infrared

Michelson interferometer are quite interesting and led Gebbie[31] to remark that a photographic plate and a computer have in common that they are both wonderfully sophisticated, absolutely essential spectroscopic adjuncts that fortunately the spectroscopist did not have to invent himself.

In the far infrared, of course, detector-noise limitation prevails and the resolutions available (as high as $0 \cdot 01$ cm^{-1}) are always adequate. It therefore follows that the full multiplex advantage is available provided the experiment is properly designed. This has seldom been so in practice for the gain arising from the luminosity advantage has been so great that spectroscopists have been able to find out what they wanted to know without going to all the bother of optimizing the experimental arrangements. When subsequently the same experiment had been carefully repeated using a splendidly engineered grating instrument it was found that spectra of comparable quality resulted. This apparent discrepancy led to the debate on gratings versus interferometers which, although basically futile, did lead to an interesting issue of *Applied Optics*[32] where the matter was thrashed out. Jacquinot[33] in his summary pointed out that, although interferometers were always superior, the number of problems which could only be investigated by interferometric methods was relatively small. Very many problems could be investigated by either method and the choice lay with the operator who would choose the one most appropriate to the time and the problem. It is perhaps significant that many laboratories feature both types of spectrometer in their instrumental array. However, in the ultimate analysis, for the highest quality results, only interferometers will do. This is illustrated by Jacquinot's calculation that P. and J. Connes could have duplicated their interferometrically observed planetary spectra provided they had an uninterrupted few thousand years of grating spectrometer observing time.

CHAPTER 2

Far Infrared Spectroscopy with Non-multiplex Instruments

Non-multiplex spectroscopy in the submillimetre region can be carried out in four main ways: (1) with the use of prisms or gratings as dispersive elements; (2) by interferometric methods using, for example, the Fabry–Perot etalon; (3) by radio-frequency techniques involving harmonic multiplication; (4) by the use of special electronic oscillators of the carcinotron type. These have all at one time or another been extensively reviewed in accessible books or journals and for this reason this chapter will be principally concerned with the fundamentals of each and their most recent applications.

2.1. Submillimetre Spectroscopy with Prisms or Gratings

As we have seen earlier, the dispersion of a prism, and hence its power to produce a spread-out spectrum, depends on the magnitude of $\partial n/\partial \bar{v}$. The dispersion of n is a consequence of the existence of strong absorption bands in some regions of the spectrum (see Appendix 3) but the variations of n are not usually confined to the immediate vicinity of the absorption bands, although in truth the maximum variations of n do occur there. The principal absorption mechanisms in alkali halide materials are the reststrahlen process in the far infrared and the processes involving electronic excitation which occur in the ultraviolet. There is a minimum of dispersion at a frequency intermediate between these two—for example, the minimum for NaCl is found at 2 μm. From this it follows that an NaCl prism spectrometer will perform poorly in the near infrared but will get better and better as the wavelength increases. Ultimately, as the region of the reststrahlen band is approached, the prism will start to absorb and the performance will rapidly fall off. For this reason NaCl spectrometers are usually operated only as far down as 650 cm^{-1}. If a heavier alkali halide such as KBr is available, the spectrometer can be used as far as 400 cm^{-1} because the reststrahlen band will have shifted to a lower frequency (see Chapter 4 for details). The KBr prism will have a poorer performance in the 2–10 μm region than the NaCl prism and it is therefore common either to have a prism interchange or

17

else to use two spectrometers (not out of the question nowadays in the era of inexpensive instrumentation) to cover the full range from 2 to 25 μm. The use of still heavier alkali halides has occurred quite often in the past and at least one commercial instrument—the Beckman IR5A—is available featuring a CsBr prism and it is useful, therefore, as far down as 280 cm^{-1}. Commercial practice is, however, veering away from the use of prisms for the low-frequency region, since there is no material available for frequencies less than 180 cm^{-1}. Grating instruments on the other hand have no such limitation and replica gratings are nowadays becoming relatively inexpensive.

Grating monochromators have been described by several authors for investigations in the far infrared. Extensive review articles by Wilkinson and Martin[34] and by Kneubuhl[35] have appeared and several instruments are available commercially. The essential problem is, of course, to increase the luminous throughput of the monochromator whilst preserving the resolving power. The design of a grating monochromator normally allows a wide choice of operating parameters but the overwhelming difficulties of energy starvation so restrict the freedom of choice in the far infrared that most designs tend to look alike. High numerical apertures ($f/4$ or $f/5\cdot6$) are usual, combined with very large grating size (up to 30 cm $\times$ 35 cm), tall and curved slits and light pipes to ensure maximum transfer of energy from the exit slit to the detector. Gratings are universally ruled to the echellette[36] profile drawn in Fig. 2.1. The saw-tooth groove profile is more difficult to machine

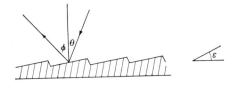

Fig. 2.1. Echellette grating for the far infrared with blaze angle ϵ.

than is the simpler profile used in the visible region but it has the enormous advantage of selectively channelling the available energy into specified orders of the grating. The full theory of reflection from an echellette (from the French word échelle = ladder) grating cannot be developed within the scalar wave[37] approach, especially when the polarization effects are under consideration, but nevertheless some valid and useful results can be stated in a simple manner. The first of these is that the echellette tends to concentrate energy into that order whose diffraction angle is nearest to specular reflection from the long edge. From the geometrical arrangements of Fig. 2.1 this leads to the result that $\theta + \epsilon$ should equal $\phi - \epsilon$ and, by substituting this in equation (1.11), the result

$$m\lambda = -2d \sin \epsilon \cos (\theta + \epsilon) \qquad (2.1)$$

is obtained. Gratings are usually used in first order ($m = -1$) and the angle ϵ is usually no more than 20°, and under these conditions λ is less than d. The smaller is λ compared to d, the more nearly correct becomes the scalar wave approach and it will be seen therefore that this method is not out of court for far infrared diffraction at a grating. Nevertheless, the distribution of intensity in the various orders is not amenable to treatment by scalar wave theory. Some experimental data have been reported by Kneubuhl[38] and his colleagues who studied the diffraction of a plane parallel beam of 337 μm radiation from an HCN laser (see Chapter 6) by a grating with $d = 500 \ \mu$m, $\epsilon = 20°$, and with source and detector so arranged that $\theta + \phi = 23°$. For these parameters $\lambda/d = 0\cdot674$ and hence, from equation (1.11), m is restricted to the values ±2, ±1 and 0. As the grating is rotated each of these five orders becomes incident on the detector and a plot of detector signal versus angle of rotation shows five sharply defined peaks:

$$m = \ \ 2 \qquad \theta = \ \ \ 54° \ 50' \qquad \phi = -31° \ 50'$$
$$m = \ \ 1 \qquad \theta = \ \ \ 31° \ 35' \qquad \phi = \ -8° \ 35'$$
$$m = \ \ 0 \qquad \theta = \ \ \ 11° \ 30' \qquad \phi = \ \ 11° \ 30'$$
$$m = -1 \qquad \theta = \ \ -8° \ 35' \qquad \phi = \ \ 31° \ 35'$$
$$m = -2 \qquad \theta = -31° \ 50' \qquad \phi = \ \ 54° \ 50'$$

The order with $m = -1$ satisfies the blaze condition very well since $\theta + \epsilon = 11° \ 25'$ and $\phi - \epsilon = 11° \ 35'$ and, not surprisingly, there is intense reflection in this order. What is most surprising is that there is very strong reflection in the order with $m = +2$. The orders with $m = 0$ and $m = +1$ are very weak but that with $m = -2$ is again intense. This erratic pattern underlines the breakdown of scalar wave theory when diffraction by objects of the same order of magnitude as the wavelength is being considered. This topic will be taken up again later in connection with the theory of the lamellar grating interferometer. An old puzzle in connection with diffraction gratings is the occurrence of the so-called "Wood anomalies"—that is anomalous energy distribution in the various orders when the grating is irradiated with radiation polarized perpendicular to the grooves.[39] It is likely that these too could be explained within an electromagnetic approach with proper boundary conditions, but this problem has not yet been solved for echellette gratings. Very recently Ritchie[40] and his co-workers related the Wood anomalies to second order surface plasmon-grating interactions. In normal specular reflection from a metallic surface a plasmon (i.e. a quantized wave of oscillation in the free electron plasma within a metal analogous to a photon or a phonon) cannot be excited, but in diffraction from a metallic grating this becomes possible due to the periodic fluctuations in electron density associated with the grooves. From an analysis of the anomalous diffraction Ritchie *et al.* have constructed dispersion diagrams (see Section 5.5 for the phonon analogues) for the surface plasmons. This approach seems of general applicability and may be extended to other metals, especially when far infrared measurements are available.

Grating monochromators have to be laid out optically so that the components introduce the least possible aberrations. Various mountings called Littrow, Paschen, Eagle, Czerny–Turner and Fastie–Ebert, after their inventors,[34] have been introduced at one time or another to realize this in practice. The commonest in home-made far infrared instruments is the Czerny–Turner[41] which is shown in Fig. 2.2.

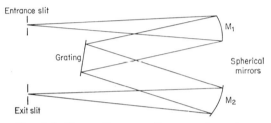

FIG. 2.2. Czerny–Turner grating monochromator.

This set-up features two spherical mirrors, M_1 and M_2, and is quite similar in operation to the long-path cell due to White (see Fig. 4.10) and like this cell it is self-compensating in operation. The Littrow arrangement is more economical in space and for this reason it appeals to commercial manufacturers. The aberrations, however, can only be removed by introducing an off-axis paraboloid mirror, but this complication is no longer a serious problem to instrument manufacturers. Because of the inapplicability of photographic recording in the far infrared and the undesirability of moving the detector window over the dispersed spectrum, it is universal practice to keep all the optics fixed and to scan the spectrum by rotating the grating. This implies that the sum of the angles θ and ϕ will be constant (usually about 20°) and therefore equation (2.1) has a unique solution for $m = -1$. This wavelength, called the blaze wavelength λ_b, is such that in strict scalar wave theory virtually all the energy would be channelled into the first order. It follows, of course, that for $\lambda = \frac{1}{2}\lambda_b$ the equation will be satisfied for $m = -2$ and essentially all the energy will be diffracted into the second order. By an analogous argument for $\lambda \gg \lambda_b$, m will have to be zero for equation (2.1) to be approximately satisfied, and this implies that the energy is more and more directed into the zero (i.e. dispersionless) order as λ increases. From this it will be realized that there is a restricted range of wavelengths near λ_b for which the grating effectively sends energy into the first order. Wilkinson[42] has proposed the useful rule of thumb that a grating can be used from $\frac{2}{3}\lambda_b$ to $\frac{3}{2}\lambda_b$. Whilst in the visible region of the spectrum such a range of wavelengths would represent an enormous frequency range, in the far infrared this is just the reverse and several gratings are necessary to cover the region. As an example Wilkinson and Martin[34] suggest that five gratings with 7·5, 15, 30, 60 and 120 lines per centimetre would suffice to cover the spectral range 5–240 cm⁻¹. Since it is usual to have ϵ and $\theta + \phi$ small, equation (2.1) shows that λ_b^{-1}, i.e. ν_b, is approximately equal to the number of lines per centimetre.

The most serious hazard facing the user of a grating monochromator in the far infrared is the problem of overlapping orders. Quite clearly if λ_b arrives at the detector in first order then λ_b/m will arrive in mth order. The grating selectivity helps to reduce the problem but the rapid rise of intensity with frequency of a black-body source aggravates it and in general very effective filtering is necessary to reject the short wavelength radiation. The problem is much worse than the corresponding interferometric case (see Chapters 3 and 4) for, although both share the requirement that visible and normal infrared radiation must be removed from the beam, grating instruments require that filters be available to split up the far infrared into narrow regions. As an example, if the 7·5 lines per centimetre grating were being used from 5 to 11 cm⁻¹ it would be necessary to have filters transparent in this region but opaque at higher frequencies. In general, such sharp cut-off filters are not available and, although the interferometric filters described in Chapter 4 can be helpful, the filtering problems are immensely difficult. This is one of the factors which influences the decision of most commercial manufacturers to restrict their low-frequency coverage to somewhere greater than 33 cm⁻¹. Even at these higher frequencies where an array of suitable filters is available and the frequency range of the gratings is larger mistakes still occur. One of the best far infrared grating monochromators has been described by Kneubuhl and his colleagues,[43] but their results have been criticized by Dowling and Hall[44] who point out that the mysterious absorption lines at 216, 202 and 199 μm reported by Kneubuhl *et al.* in the spectrum of water vapour may arise, due to the well-known lines at 108 μm (92·54 cm⁻¹, $1_{10} \rightarrow 2_{21}$), 101 μm (99·04 cm⁻¹, $1_{11} \rightarrow 2_{20}$) and 99·5 μm (100·52 cm⁻¹, $4_{14} \rightarrow 5_{05}$) appearing in the second order of the grating. This has been rejected by Kneubuhl *et al.*[45] but the fact that such a controversy can arise at all is indicative of how real a risk overlapping orders present. Stray radiation is also a hazard, especially at very long wavelengths. Again, effective filtering is the only answer but in this case the use of selective choppers, whose blades are transparent for most of the infrared and are opaque in the far infrared, are helpful. When such a chopper is being employed (alkali halides are suitable materials) only the far infrared radiation is modulated and thus leads to a signal emerging from the selective amplifier.

Despite all these difficulties an impressive array of valuable far infrared spectra has been observed using grating instruments. The Perkin–Elmer model 301 and the Beckman Company's IR 11 have been extensively employed, especially in investigations of inorganic molecular structure. Recently the Perkin–Elmer Company has introduced a new model, the FIS–3, based on a successful design of a Japanese Group.[46] This instrument can be evacuated throughout which is much better practice than the dry nitrogen purging used in some earlier instruments. The frequency range covered is 400–30 cm^{-1} and resolutions of up to 0·5 cm^{-1} are possible with low-loss samples such as gases. A feature of particular value is the facility to study samples at other than ambient temperatures. This is normally very difficult with double-beam far infrared spectrophotometers where the beam splitting and recombining generally require that chopping of the beam should occur *after* the sample. If the sample is at a different temperature than the detector there will be a net flow of modulated (and hence reported) energy and the absorption spectra indicated by the spectrophotometer will be erroneous. The FIS–3 gets round this by chopping at two different frequencies, 10 and 0·9 Hz. The low-frequency chopper is situated before the sample and when it is activated and phase-synchronous rectification at 0·9 Hz switched in, the radiation to or from the sample is ignored. This instrument, like most other commercial far infrared spectrophotometers,

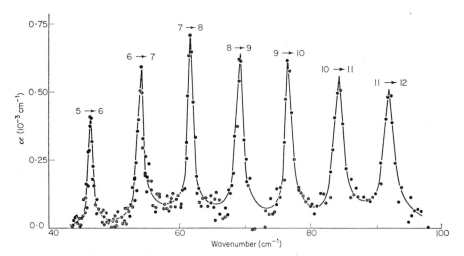

Fig. 2.3. Preliminary scan of the pure rotational spectrum of CH₃D taken in a 5·0 m cell at a density of 3·55 Amagat and a temperature of 296·5 K. A representative smooth curve has been drawn in by hand. The numbers above each line specify the initial and final rotational levels involved in the corresponding transition. (From the work of Ozier, Ho and Birnbaum.)[47]

features automatic grating and filter changes. This complexity, together with all the other problems, both instrumental and electronic, accounts for the high cost. In the near future it is certainly going to be true that it will be possible to buy an interferometer, plus all ancillary electronics and computer, for less than the cost of a recording far infrared spectrophotometer.

Grating monochromators show up best in comparison with interferometers (though even here the interferometer performance can be made incomparably better) in the situation where the sample absorbs strongly in narrow regions and is very transparent in between. The pure rotation spectrum of a gas is a good example. One of the most beautiful examples recently reported occurs in the work of Ozier, Ho and Birnbaum[47] who studied CH_3D. Now CH_4 has no dipole moment and in fact the first allowed multipole moment is an octopole (see Chapter 5) and no observable pure rotation spectrum is expected. For CH_3D a very small dipole is expected, arising from the changes in zero point vibration and electronic wave functions (see Whiffen[48] for a discussion of a similar case) and consequently a symmetric top type of pure rotation spectrum (see Chapter 5) is expected. The observed results are shown in Fig. 2.3 and from this Ozier $et\,al.$ deduce that the dipole moment is $(5\cdot68 \pm 0\cdot30) \times 10^{-3}$ D and that $B_0 = (3\cdot882 \pm 0\cdot002)$ cm^{-1} and $D_J = (7\cdot7 \pm 0\cdot3) \times 10^{-5}$ cm^{-1}.

2.2. Submillimetre Spectroscopy with Fabry–Perot Interferometers

As we have seen in Chapter 1, the ultimate resolution obtainable from any instrument is always directly proportional to the reciprocal of the maximum delay between beams. In most spectrometers the delay is introduced by making beams travel $once$ (as in simple spectrometers) or $twice$ (as in double-pass spectrometers and two-beam interferometers) along paths of varying lengths. The maximum delay is then the extra time taken by the beam which has travelled the furthest extra distance. A very economical way of introducing very long delays is to make the beam traverse a fixed distance a large number of times and this is the principle of the Fabry–Perot interferometer. This instrument nearly always consists of a medium of refractive index n and thickness d, enclosed by two plane parallel, partly reflecting, partly transmitting plates. The multiple-beam effects that go on in such a system are discussed in detail in the next chapter and in particular are illustrated by equation (3.58), but for the moment we need only note that the total transmitted power will arise from beams which have suffered 0, 2, 4, etc. internal reflections and that adding these up, taking full account of interference, leads to

$$I = I_0 T^2/(1 - 2R \cos \delta + R^2) \qquad (2.2)$$

where T is the transmittance of the plates, R the reflectance at the interface and

$$\delta = 4\pi n \bar{\nu} d \cos \theta' \qquad (2.3)$$

where θ' is the angle of refraction inside the medium. In the visible region of the spectrum the medium is usually air and the plates are made of glass or quartz. The inside surfaces of the plates are coated with dielectric layers of thickness $\lambda_0/4$ to maximize the reflectance for radiation of wavelength λ_0. The outside surfaces are usually slightly wedged to prevent multiple reflection effects inside the plates. When such an etalon (this word is used because it is not usual to vary d and the device is therefore not an interferometer in the usual sense) is irradiated by quasi-monochromatic radiation from an external source and the transmitted radiation focussed by a lens onto a screen, a series of rings is observed provided that $d \gg \lambda$. Each ring corresponds to a value of θ' which makes $\delta/2\pi$ integral. If the incident radiation contains more than one sharp component then there will be several sets of rings of differing pitches and, provided that δ is large enough, the sets of rings arising from very close lines may become separated. The form of Fabry–Perot fringes is very interesting for it will be seen from equation (2.2) that, if $T = 1 - R$ and R is close to unity, the fringes are very sharp. This contrasts with the performance of the Michelson interferometer, discussed in the next chapter, where the fringes are close to sinusoidal in profile. It is for this reason that, although a Michelson interferometer in static form—that is with fixed mirrors and photographic or visual observation—having a mirror separation of $d/2(1-R)^2$ has in principle the same resolution as the etalon, in practice this may not be so easily realizable. Michelson attempted to get round this difficulty by inventing the method of "visibility of fringes" in which he moved one of the mirrors. He then deduced the multiplet structure of certain spectral lines from the amplitude modulation or "beat" patterns in the record of intensity at the centre of the pattern versus mirror displacement. Fabry and Perot,[49] on the other hand, were able to detect the multiplet structure directly. This contrast is less impressive nowadays since Michelson's frustration at being fifty years ahead of his time does not apply to his successors who have access to computers. The most complex of interferograms can be decoded with their help, but still, as a matter of convenience rather than necessity, the etalon is the preferred instrument for ultra-high resolution in the visible region. A modern example is the detection of the microwave modulation of visible lasers by direct spectroscopic observation of the frequency-shifted side bands. The other side of the coin is that spectroscopy of broad-band sources with the Fabry–Perot interferometer is very difficult since, unlike the situation with the Michelson interferometer, there is no simple integral transform equivalent to equation (3.16).

It is for this reason that it cannot be used as a multiplex spectrometer since the problem of untangling the overlapping orders via equation (2.2) is just too formidable to be contemplated. Nevertheless, a scanning Fabry–Perot interferometer can be used as a spectrometer, provided that very efficient filters are available. The position is just the same again as that encountered with the grating where one had to remove overlapping orders with various types of filter. In the absence of filters and with normal incidence the transmitted radiation will contain components at frequencies $\bar{\nu} = m/2nd$. This is illustrated in Fig. 3.10 for a dielectric film, which can be regarded as a low finesse (i.e. $R \ll 1$) Fabry–Perot etalon. If, again with normal incidence, the interferometer starts at a setting d_0 and scans to $d_0/2$, and filters are present to eliminate all radiation of frequency greater than $\bar{\nu}_0 = (nd_0)^{-1}$, then the detector output as a function of d^{-1} will be a more or less faithful record of the spectrum between $\frac{1}{2}\bar{\nu}_0$ and $\bar{\nu}_0$. The point of this is that the Fabry–Perot interferometer, having full cylindrical symmetry, enjoys in common with the two-beam interferometers the great advantage of high luminosity which that feature confers over prism and grating instruments. It follows that Fabry–Perot interferometers should be valuable for directly scanning narrow regions of the submillimetre region.

The difficulty which has impeded the realization of this desirable programme has been the absence of highly reflecting low-loss materials in the far infrared. Metals such as aluminium or gold, which are so useful at high frequencies, are no good here where the thinnest films that can be realized are still totally opaque. Dielectric films, made for example by evaporating germanium onto a transparent substrate, have reflectivities which are too low to give the very sharp fringes which are in this connection the equivalent of the scanning slit-width of a dispersive spectrometer. None of these difficulties applies, of course, if the radiation originates inside the etalon—it is the injection which is the difficulty—and for this reason Fabry–Perot interferometers are almost universal as the resonators or cavities of lasers and masers (see Chapter 6). The variant form of interferometer with confocal mirrors, originally suggested by Connes[50] as an instrument for passive spectroscopy, has come to its full flower in this connection and the very high order fringe patterns obtained in emission from lasers have become a familiar feature of submillimetre research (see Fig. 6.3). One way round the injection difficulty has been suggested by Ulrich, Renk and Genzel.[51] They have shown that wire grids are suitable as the reflectors and that this is especially so for metal meshes where the holes have square section and polarization phenomena do not arise. The properties of metal meshes as infrared filters are discussed in Chapter 4, but here it is only necessary to remark that such a mesh shows high transmissivity for $\lambda \approx g$, where g is the edge size of the holes, and an increasing reflectivity as λ gets bigger than g. Two meshes of this type, either unsupported or embedded in a suitable matrix such as polyethylene, constitute a far infrared Fabry–Perot interferometer. The injection loss is high, except for wavelengths approximately equal to g, but this helps with the filtering for, as remarked above, the interferometer can only be used unambiguously over a narrow range of wavelength. Ulrich, Renk and Genzel have demonstrated a spectrum of the atmosphere in the range 75–25 cm^{-1} which they observed using a Fabry–Perot interferometer as a spectrometer. The general quality is only modest and, although the strong water vapour lines can be discerned, far better spectra can probably be obtained as easily using a two-beam interferometer. Where the Fabry–Perot interferometer really makes its mark is as a tunable submillimetre filter. Ulrich and his colleagues studied the output of a crystal multiplier fed by a klystron oscillator of fundamental wavelength $0 \cdot 924$ cm. Using a mesh spacing g equal to $0 \cdot 45$ mm, they were able to isolate the harmonics with very high efficiency merely by altering the separation of the meshes. The second to the sixth harmonics were observed spanning the frequency range $3 \cdot 24$–$7 \cdot 56$ cm^{-1} in orders ranging from the first to the seventh. In this regimen λ is larger than g, so the injection losses are high, but this was deliberately chosen since for $\lambda \gg g$ the curve of transmission versus wavelength for the mesh is nearly flat. If high transmission plus high selectivity at a given wavelength were desired then both g and d would be chosen appropriately. The spectral power transmission of a metal mesh Fabry–Perot interferometer is given by equation (2.2) with the modification that T is never equal to $(1 - R)$ for there is always an additional loss due to the metal and, additionally, the phase change on reflection is not exactly π. These two modifications can be allowed for by writing

$$I = \frac{I_0(1-R)^2[1-A/(1-R)]^2}{1-2R\cos\delta+R^2} \tag{2.4}$$

where $T = 1 - R - A$ and $\delta = 4\pi n\bar{v}d - 2(\phi - \pi)$.

The first of these, after suitable trigonometrical manipulation, has been given by Ulrich et al. The second has the effect of adding a constant term to δ and hence leads to a displacement of the observed frequency scale by a small additive constant.

It is unlikely that Fabry–Perot interferometers will come into wide use as broad-band absorption spectrometers, but as tunable filters and especially as devices for measuring the wavelength of coherent emissions in the sub-millimetre they will be very valuable. As an example of this, the difference frequency radiation obtained by beating the output of two ruby lasers together (see Chapter 6) was studied very conveniently with a Fabry–Perot interferometer.

2.3. Submillimetre Spectroscopy Using Harmonic Multiplication

In the microwave region, which we can roughly define as lying between 10^9 and 10^{11} Hz, spectroscopy has achieved some most remarkable successes. Ultra-high resolution is commonplace and transitions so weak that $\alpha_{max} = 10^{-9}$ neper cm^{-1} are readily observed.[16] Both of these invaluable features owe their origin to the electronic nature of microwave methods. By this we mean that:

1. very long wavetrains of accurately defined frequency and phase can be generated;
2. these wavetrains can be modulated and demodulated at will;
3. absorption effects can be multiplied up by the use of resonant cavities;
4. bridge techniques are available so the reflected power can be balanced off against the ingoing power leaving only the net absorption to be reported by the detector;
5. the video crystal detectors are not capable of giving a.c. outputs at frequencies much in excess of 10 MHz but, nevertheless, they are quite sensitive[52] ($\simeq 10^{-9}$ W for 1 Hz bandwidth) and superheterodyne techniques using a local oscillator klystron can be employed to improve the sensitivity still further. Values around 7×10^{-15} W have been quoted[52] for the noise equivalent power of such a superhet working at 2 mm wavelength. It is therefore not surprising that there have been numerous attempts to extend these techniques to higher frequencies and ultimately into the submillimetre band.

The principal difficulty which faces a straightforward attack on this problem[53] is that the resonant cavities in the electron tube oscillators have to be roughly the same size as the wavelength to be generated. The shortest wavelength klystron oscillators in common use give out 4 mm radiation. It is possible to buy 2 mm klystrons but they are expensive and much less reliable than their longer wavelength counterparts. There is virtually no prospect of making simple oscillators which will work at shorter wavelengths and it was precisely this fact which led to the idea of a "millimetre barrier" beyond which lay the submillimetre region inaccessible to radio techniques. Since direct methods fail, the recourse must be to indirect methods and all of these rely on the generation of radiation at frequencies which are integral multiples of a fundamental frequency; that is to say harmonic multiplication. This can be done in two main ways; firstly by absorption of the fundamental radiation in a non-linear element followed by re-radiation of the harmonics, and secondly by introducing periodic structure in an electron-beam device in order to bunch the electrons so that the current has Fourier components at many multiples of the fundamental oscillation frequency. The latter method offers the best prospects for high-power sub-millimetre sources suitable for communication purposes. Phillips have developed frequency multiplier klystrons which have given wavelengths as short as 430 μm at power levels of 0·1 mW. Travelling wave tubes and carcinotrons or backward wave tubes (so called because the phase and group velocities of the radiation are opposed) have given wavelengths ranging between 2000 and 345 μm at power levels varying from 1 W to 100 μW. Pulsed magnetrons operating at wavelengths of a few millimetres have given peak powers of the order of tens of kilowatts and there are many other variant types of electron-beam device which have operated successfully at millimetre and submillimetre wavelengths. Comprehensive accounts of this field have been given by Coleman,[53a] Dees,[53b] Robinson[53c] and the contributors to the book on the topic edited by Benson.[54] In spectroscopic applications, on the other hand, very high power levels are not mandatory and it is much more desirable to have the source small, cheap, easily handled and giving out CW (continuous wave) power. For these reasons the preferred route to submillimetre waves for spectroscopy has nearly always been harmonic multiplication in a non-linear device external to the electron tube.

One of the most illustrious pioneers of this branch of spectroscopy is Gordy of Duke University, who has given accounts of its history and development both to the Symposium on Millimetre Waves held in New York in 1959 and to the VIIIth European Molecular Spectroscopy Congress in Copenhagen[55] 1965. Gordy and his group have built submillimetre spectrometers in which the radiation is produced by harmonic multiplication in one silicon crystal and is video detected in another. The multiplier features an etched tungsten cat's whisker contact, but unfortunately there is still much of the trial and error characteristic of these devices even today. In general a sensitive contact once made will work moderately well for a day's work but will have to be remade the following day. It is true to say that there is still more art than science in getting these devices to work well and this is underlined by the theoretical observation that gallium arsenide should be much better than silicon. Despite this, only silicon works and without this material the exploration of the submillimetre region by radio techniques would be extremely difficult. The experimental arrangement commonly used is to have the multiplier mounted on a post near the junction of a crossed waveguide. The fundamental radiation is led in along one arm of appropriate size and the harmonics are led away along a waveguide of much smaller internal size. This latter will be too small for the fundamental to propagate in, i.e. it will be "cut-off", and therefore a good degree of filtering is available. This principle can be extended further by using even smaller waveguides if discrimination against the lower harmonics is desired. The current versus

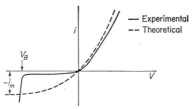

FIG. 2.4. Theoretical and experimental characteristics of an *n*-type silicon diode.

voltage characteristics of a silicon diode containing, say, phosphorus impurities (and therefore *n*-type since there is an extra electron) are shown in Fig. 2.4. In the region of positive voltage *i* is roughly an exponential function of *V* in fair agreement with the theoretical expression

$$i = i_m \{\exp [e'V/(kT)] - 1\} \tag{2.5}$$

where e' is the effective charge of the carriers, but in the negative voltage region the conduction is always less than theoretical. At large negative voltages the diode breaks down and a large current flows. When an electromagnetic wave of frequency ν_0 is incident on such a diode, currents will be induced both at d.c. and at multiples of ν_0 because of the non-linear characteristic. The rectification and consequent demodulation of radio frequencies by metal–semiconductor junctions was discovered empirically and was the basis of the early crystal sets. The efficiency of a crystal, both as an harmonic generator and as a detector, can be altered by the application of a steady d.c. voltage. Imagine that we have a completely general characteristic

$$i = f(V) \tag{2.6}$$

and that with a steady voltage V_0 across the diode it is exposed to an r.f. field

$$\Delta V = \Delta V_0 \cos 2\pi\nu_0 t. \tag{2.7}$$

We may write down the resulting current using Taylor's theorem

$$i = f(V_0) + \left(\frac{\partial f}{\partial V}\right)_{V_0} \Delta V + \left(\frac{\partial^2 f}{\partial V^2}\right)_{V_0} (\Delta V)^2 + \cdots \tag{2.8}$$

The term involving $\partial^n f/\partial V^n$ will lead to a rectified component because of the constant term in $(\Delta V)^n$ but will also lead to components at frequencies $n\nu_0$ because of the time-dependent parts of $(\Delta V)^n$. The differential coefficients of $f(V)$ will usually depend on *V*—they certainly do for the particular case of equation (2.5)—and it follows that one can improve the harmonic conversion by choosing a suitable point on the characteristic via an appropriate choice of V_0. Several workers have chosen back biasing, that is negative values of V_0 close to V_B, where the curvature is very sharp, but this requires delicate control. Others have preferred the use of special types of diode with highly non-linear characteristics. Examples of this are tunnel diodes in which V is no longer a monotonic function of i and there are maxima and minima in the positive voltage region.[56] Gordy[55] has preferred the type of silicon crystal described by Ohl[57] and made by bombarding the initial rather pure silicon with high-energy phosphorus atoms. Even so, conversion efficiencies are not very good and starting, say, with 200 mW of power at a frequency of 24 GHz the following power levels are typically found in the harmonics: 48 GHz (20 mW), 72 GHz (2 mW), 96 GHz (500 μW), 120 GHz (100 μW), 144 GHz (50 μW), 168 GHz (12 μW), 192 GHz (5 μW), 216 GHz (2 μW), 240 GHz (0·8 μW), 288 GHz (0·2 μW), 360 GHz (0·05 μW). Nevertheless, submillimetre spectroscopy is perfectly feasible with these devices. In difficult cases it might be necessary to go over to a more sensitive video detector such as the indium antimonide detector developed by Putley or else to use superheterodyne methods, but the majority of cases investigated have involved very sharp lines with a more or less transparent continuum between. In this regimen power levels of the order 10^{-8} W can lead to perfectly interpretable (even if rather noisy) spectra. The highest frequency at which spectroscopic results have been reported[17] using these methods is 806 GHz (27 cm^{-1}), but non-linear mixing experiments with a view to determining the absolute frequency of laser lines (see Chapter 6) have involved the generation of harmonics at over 2000 GHz. This type of experiment has also been carried out using the harmonics of lower frequency lasers and, although this radiation is not yet available at useful power levels, it is not too fanciful to imagine that microwave techniques will eventually be available throughout the infrared. This is especially indicated by the recent discovery[58] of the metal–metal rectifying junction which has been used to detect the CO_2 laser radiation near 10 μm.

    The results which have so far been obtained in the frequency range up to 27 cm^{-1} have been copious and elegant and a few examples will now be detailed to illustrate the power of the method. Observations on the pure rotation spectra of light hydrogenic molecules such as HCl can give very accurate B_0 values. However, only one or two lines occur in the accessible region and since the effects of centrifugal distortion are large and a reasonable account requires several coefficients in the expansion of $\bar{v}(J'')$ as a function of J''—see equation (6.62), p. 309—microwave observations are not going to make infrared measurements redundant. In fact, in one sense, the two are complementary, for microwave measurements are always based via a long chain of harmonic multiplication on a fundamental time standard of frequency. In the infrared, on the other hand, the measured quantity is a length so that quoted frequencies in cm^{-1} are related to the ultimate standard of length. It follows that if a rotational constant such as B_0 for a molecule is known in both systems, the velocity of light can be deduced from the ratio. As an example Gordy[17] gives B_0 for H^{35}Cl as $312 \cdot 9913 \pm 0 \cdot 00026$ GHz and, quoting the very accurate infrared value of Rank,[59] namely $10 \cdot 440254 \pm 0 \cdot 000010$ cm^{-1}, he deduces that

$$c = [2 \cdot 997928 \pm 0 \cdot 000004] \times 10^{10} \text{ cm s}^{-1}.$$

The topic of c determinations will be taken up again in Chapter 6.

The resolving power available in this type of spectroscopy is so high that hyperfine multiplets are commonly observed. The $J = 0 \rightarrow J = 1$ line of H^{35}Cl which should occur at $625 \cdot 9192$ GHz is in fact found[17] as a triplet with none of the components actually occurring exactly at this frequency. The separations from the expected frequency are $-13 \cdot 60$, $+3 \cdot 40$ and $17 \cdot 00$ MHz respectively. This splitting arises from interaction of the rotational angular momentum with the spin momentum of the ^{35}Cl nucleus via its quadrupole moment. The total angular momentum is the vector sum of $\boldsymbol{J}$ and $\boldsymbol{I}$, the nuclear spin, and is usually called $\boldsymbol{F}$, though strictly it should be called $\boldsymbol{J}$, and the mechanical angular momentum should be called N. The splittings of the multiplet components away from the unperturbed position are given by[15]

$$W_Q = -eqQ \left[\frac{3/4 \, C(C+1) - I(I+1) \, J(J+1)}{2I(2I-1)(2J-1)(2J+3)} \right] \qquad (2.9)$$

where $C = F(F+1) - I(I+1) - J(J+1)$. The quantities e, q and Q are respectively the electronic charge, the second derivative of the electric potential at the nucleus in question and the quadrupole moment of that nucleus. The quantity in brackets is sometimes called Casimir's function, $f(I, J, F)$, and for H^{35}Cl for which the spin of the ^{35}Cl nucleus is 3/2 it has the values[15]

$$f(3/2, 0, 3/2) = 0 \qquad\qquad W_Q = 0$$
$$f(3/2, 1, 5/2) = 0 \cdot 05 \qquad\quad W_Q = 3 \cdot 40 \text{ MHz}$$
$$f(3/2, 1, 3/2) = -0 \cdot 20 \qquad W_Q = -13 \cdot 60 \text{ MHz}$$
$$(f3/2, 1, 1/2) = 0 \cdot 25 \qquad\quad W_Q = +17 \cdot 00 \text{ MHz}$$

From this data, the quantity eqQ is found to be -68 MHz. The value of Q can sometimes be inferred from nuclear magnetic resonance experiments and taking this together with the submillimetre spectrum provides a method for the determination of q. This quantity can also be calculated if a molecular wave function is available and, in fact, it is a quite sensitive function of the exact form of this. The submillimetre observation of hyperfine splittings can therefore be used either to obtain a value of Q or else to check on the validity of a molecular wave function depending on the situation.

When we come to heavier molecules for which several pure rotation lines will lie in the accessible region, the ability of microwave methods to determine as many rotational parameters as there are observable lines implies in general that the remaining submillimetre spectrum can be predicted to much higher accuracy than it can be observed with the limited resolution delay-type spectrometers which have of necessity to be used there. As an example Gordy[17] quotes the following frequencies for the first few lines of CO.

$J'' \to J'$	ν GHz	$\bar{\nu}$ cm^{-1}
$0 \to 1$	115·2712	3·845
$1 \to 2$	230·5380	7·690
$2 \to 3$	345·7959	11·534
$3 \to 4$	461·0407	15·379
$4 \to 5$	576·2678	19·222
$5 \to 6$	691·4726	23·065
$6 \to 7$	806·6517	26·907

These frequencies can be fitted to within the experimental error (varying from 15 to 600 kHz) with $B_0 = 57 \cdot 63597$ GHz and $D_0 = 0 \cdot 1839$ MHz. No higher centrifugal distortion constants are necessary and it follows that all of the submillimetre lines which can reasonably be observed can be predicted to better than $0 \cdot 01$ cm^{-1} using these parameters. Interferometric observation for lines with $J'' > 6$ are unlikely, therefore, to yield any fresh information, but it follows that such observations should provide a splendid means of frequency calibration for the instrument. In Chapters 3 and 4 it will be pointed out that the frequency scale of a spectrum derived from the Fourier transformation of an interferogram has to be corrected to give the true values. The correction is a consequence of finite radiation solid angle effects in the interferometer. In general it is not possible to calculate the correction to any particularly good accuracy and the best method is to set up a calibration curve derived from plots of apparent versus real frequencies for the CO pure rotation spectrum.

The spectra of symmetric top molecules (see Chapter 5) obtained with moderate resolution instruments consist of a series of more or less regularly spaced lines. Each line is in reality the unresolved profile of a set of K components, and the frequency of maximum absorption will be determined by the intensity distribution amongst the K components, their splittings and their widths.[60] Clearly no simple relationship between the frequency of maximum absorption and the frequency of the $K = 0$ components can be expected. This is especially true for oblate symmetric tops. It follows that if a plot of line frequency divided by $(J+1)$ versus $(J+1)$ is constructed, this may lead to erroneous values of B_0 and D_0 even if the data is well observed to reasonably high resolution. The splitting of K components arises from the term $D_{JK}J(J+1)K^2$ in the expression for the energy levels of a symmetric rotor (equation 5.1) and in many cases D_{JK} is large enough for the lines accessible to microwave methods to be resolved. Taking methyl-acetylene as an example, the $J = 5 \rightarrow J = 6$ transition at $102 \cdot 5477$ GHz is comfortably resolved[61] into six components, i.e. $K = 0$ to $K = 5$. For this particular molecule none of the nuclei has a quadrupole moment but this is far from typical and when we come to consider molecules such as $^{14}NF_3$ the fine structure of lines becomes quite complex. The $J = 1 \rightarrow J = 2$ line of this molecule is expected to have ten hyperfine components corresponding to the selection rule

$$\Delta K = 0, \qquad \Delta F = 0 \pm 1. \tag{2.10}$$

Seven are observed[62] spanning the range $42 \cdot 727$ 39 GHz to $42 \cdot 721$ 73 GHz. The transitions involving higher J values have much smaller hyperfine splittings because of the reciprocal dependence of W_Q on J in equation (2.9), but the K components of the $J = 4 \rightarrow J = 5$ line can be resolved.[63] The observed frequencies are $(K = 0)$ $106 \cdot 805$ 93 GHz, $(K = 2)$ $106 \cdot 804$ 54 GHz and $(K = 3)$ $106 \cdot 803$ 62 GHz. From this data and the observations on the $J = 1 \rightarrow J = 2$ line the rotational parameters can be derived: they are $B_0 = 10 \cdot 681$ 072 GHz, $D_J = 14 \cdot 2$ kHz and $D_{JK} = -25 \cdot 7$ kHz. The hyper-fine splitting parameter eqQ has the value $-7 \cdot 07$ MHz from which Gordy, with the aid of a plausible wave function, deduces[62] that $Q = 0 \cdot 01 \times 10^{-24}$ cm^2. From the rotational parameters and the known intensity functions, together with an assumed line-width, all of the submillimetre spectrum shown in Fig. 5.2 can be calculated.

The pure rotation spectrum of HCN has proved a fruitful source of spectroscopic information. The $J = 0 \rightarrow J = 1$ line of HC^{14}N was first observed in 1948 by Gordy.[64] This line is a triplet with a strong component at $88 \cdot 631$ GHz and two weaker satellites shifted by $+2 \cdot 07$ and $-1 \cdot 38$ MHz from the strong component. The splitting arises from the nuclear quadrupole moment of the ^{14}N atom and from the observed[65, 66] values eqQ can be deduced to be $4 \cdot 58$ MHz. The strong component is thus some $+0 \cdot 229$ MHz away from the unperturbed position and corresponds to the transition $F = 1 \rightarrow F = 2$. Very much later the observation of this triplet in absorption by the plasma inside a 337 μm laser was one of the experi-mental steps which identified HCN as the emitting species in this laser (see Chapter 6). This is another illustration of the great power of microwave methods to detect very tiny concentrations of polar gases. As will be shown

c

later in Chapter 5, the peak absorption coefficient α_{max} is sensibly independent of pressure down to very low pressures—only the line-width alters. When the resolving power is sufficiently high—as it is in radio methods—so that the measurement is more or less confined to the line centre, it is possible to detect strong absorption when lower resolution methods could report none. The only parallel that occurs in optical regions lies in the resonance absorption of radiation by atoms. It is well known for example that measurement of absorption by the D lines of sodium at low pressure is next to impossible with a scanning spectrophotometer. The smallest available spectral slit-width is still many thousands of times wider than the lines. However, if radiation from a specially constructed (to avoid self reversal) sodium lamp is available this will be strongly absorbed by the low-pressure vapour. The reason is once more the same: the radiant power is concentrated in the narrow spectral region where α is large.

The $J = 0 \rightarrow J = 1$ line has now been observed[65] with high precision for all the isotopic varieties of $HC^{14}N$, i.e. $D^{12}C^{14}N$, $D^{13}C^{14}N$, $H^{12}C^{14}N$ and $H^{13}C^{14}N$. The isotopic form $H^{12}C^{15}N$ has also been studied[67] and here, as expected, the triplet structure disappears since all the nuclei have zero quadrupole moment: just a single line at $86 \cdot 055$ GHz is observed. Higher lines in the pure rotation spectrum of any particular species are readily observed in the orthodox far infrared region (see, for example, Fig. 5.3) and from these, or else from vibration rotation studies, fairly accurate values of B_0 and D_0 can be obtained. Taking this value of D_0 and combining it with the microwave ν_0 (i.e. the frequency of maximum absorption in the absence of hyperfine splitting), a very accurate value of B_0 can be derived. Taking $H^{12}C^{14}N$ as an example, B_0 has the value $1 \cdot 478\ 22$ which is to be compared with the best infrared measurement, namely $1 \cdot 4784$. When one has B_0 values for more than one isotopic moiety it is possible to deduce internuclear separations, i.e. r_0 values, since there are only two unknown parameters, r_{CH} and r_{CN}. For HCN the calculated[65] values are $r_{CH} = 1 \cdot 0637 \pm 0 \cdot 004$ Å and $r_{CN} = 1 \cdot 1563 \pm 0 \cdot 001$ Å. These numbers differ from the hypothetical equilibrium distances, i.e. r_e values, due to the effects of anharmonicity and will be expected to differ from determinations using non-spectroscopic methods (such as electron diffraction) since different averaging procedures over the atomic motion are involved. In principle a different r_0 value should be found for CH and CD since only the r_e values are theoretically identical. However, even microwave methods are unable to reveal this difference with certainty.

Stimulated emission at $88 \cdot 63$ GHz has been obtained by Marcuse,[68] Barnes[69] and by De Lucia and Gordy[70] from the transition $J = 1 \rightarrow J = 0$ of $H^{12}C^{14}N$. The topic of masers will be discussed at length in Chapter 6 but here we will note that this device is a maser in the original sense of that word, i.e. it produces a population inversion by physically separating the $J = 1$ molecules from the $J = 0$ molecules. Unfortunately, molecular separation means molecular beams and that implies very low molecular densities. As a result the power levels available are rather low (10^{-9} W). Saturation of a submillimetre transition (see Chapter 6) was first obtained with HCN and both these phenomena depend really on the large dipole moment of HCN ($2 \cdot 986$ D) which makes the pure rotation lines inherently intense. Dipole moments are readily measured by radio techniques involving the Stark effect. When an electric field is applied to a polar gas this has the effect of removing the degeneracy of the M components of J. The M components are the projections of J on particular directions in space and under ordinary circumstances (i.e. no fields) space is quite isotropic and the effect of a projection in one direction is necessarily the same as in any other. The ($2J+1$) components arising from the obvious restriction $| M | \leqslant J$ are therefore necessarily degenerate. In the presence of a field this is no longer true and for a linear molecule a second-order splitting (so called because of the E^2 dependence) of the line into a number of components is observed. The splitting is given by[15]

$$\Delta\nu = [A+BM^2]\mu^2E^2 \tag{2.11}$$

where A and B are rather complicated functions of J and the rotational constants, E is the electric field strength, M the magnetic quantum number and μ the dipole moment. From a record of $\Delta\nu$ versus E^2 the dipole moment may be deduced. The method is capable of giving great accuracy and differences in dipole moment between isotopic forms of a molecule and between various excited states of the same molecule can readily be picked up. The above discussion applies strictly to transitions for which $\Delta M = 0$ and this happens when the static field and the radiation field are parallel. Experimentally this is quite easy to bring about by means of the so-called "strip in the waveguide" method.[15] A thin metal plate is inserted parallel to the long edge of the waveguide and insulated from it. A d.c. voltage can be applied between the waveguide and the strip and, since the microwave field in a rectangular waveguide operating in its lowest frequency mode is perpendicular to the long edge, the condition is satisfied. $\Delta M = \pm 1$ transitions for which the two fields have to be perpendicular are not observable by this method and Gordy and his co-workers[55] have introduced what they call a free-space absorption cell, especially for submillimetre work. This is really a reversion to optical techniques in which the submillimetre waves are radiated into free space (i.e. space not enclosed by waveguide walls) from a horn, whereupon they traverse a conventional absorption cell with two parallel electrodes and finally are collected by another horn and detected. This arrangement permits of any angle between the d.c. field and the r.f. field. The Stark effect not only permits the measurement of dipole moments but from the pattern of lines the value of the lowest J in the transition can usually be inferred. This can be invaluable in identifying lines in a complex spectrum. In practical work the Stark effect is commonly used as a method of modulating the microwave absorption at an audio frequency. Such modulation is usually desirable in order that narrow-band amplifiers may be employed in the detector chain to improve the signal-to-noise ratio. All that is required to bring this about is to apply an audio frequency high voltage to the Stark electrodes: as the microwave frequency approaches the absorption line, the split components will oscillate over the probing frequency and will generate an oscillating absorption which will lead to an audio frequency output from the detector. The amplitude of the oscillation can be set by adjusting the voltage on the plates and the whole arrangement is a most powerful means of spectrum analysis.

The lowest frequency transition in HCN in its ground state and, in the absence of fields, is just the $J = 0 \to J = 1$ line at $88 \cdot 63$ GHz. Excited states can absorb at lower frequencies. The state with the bending vibration excited by one quantum (i.e. $01^1 0$—see Chapter 6) exhibits l-type doubling, a phenomenon illustrated for the similar state $11^1 0$ in Fig. 6.1. The level $01^1 0$ lies some 712 cm^{-1} above the ground state and so will be significantly populated (Boltzmann factor $0 \cdot 03$) at room temperature. Transitions between the two components of the l-type doublets have been observed[71] between $0 \cdot 4$ and 94 GHz. The actual frequencies can be well represented by the formula (Maki and Lide[71])

$$\nu(\text{MHz}) = 224 \cdot 477\, J(J+1) - 0 \cdot 0027\, J^2(J+1)^2 + \text{smaller terms} \qquad (2.12)$$

which is the usual expansion of a rotational property in terms of $J(J+1)$ The l-type doubling can also be inferred from very careful measurement of the infrared spectrum. The Q branch lines (i.e. $\Delta J = 0$) as compared with the $P(\Delta J = -1)$ and $R(\Delta J = +1)$ branch lines of a Π to Σ band, such as the ν_2 fundamental, involve different upper state levels. This is because the parity of the lower state alternates with J, whereas each J level of the upper state has one component of even and the other of odd parity, the pair making up the l-type doublet. This is sometimes indicated by calling one set of l-components c and the other d. As will be seen from inspection of an energy level diagram, the l-type splitting in the upper state with $J' = J'' + 1$ is given by

$$\Delta = \bar{\nu}_{\text{rot}}(J'') + Q(J'' + 1) - R(J'') \qquad (2.13)$$

where $\bar{\nu}_{\text{rot}}(J'')$ is the frequency of the pure rotation transition starting at the level J'' of the ground state. Whenever it is possible to resolve the individual lines of the Q branch it is feasible to determine Δ using this relation. For

HCN the l-type splitting is very large and is easily detectable in the infrared spectrum. Nevertheless, the microwave methods are much more accurate and it is easier to analyse the spectrum knowing the l-type doubling rather than to have to infer it. This is illustrated by the work of Maki and Blaine[72] on perturbations in HCN where they used the microwave observations of Törring[73] to assist them in understanding the interactions which later on were shown to be responsible for the laser action in HCN at 337 μm.

The power of microwave methods to detect extremely low concentrations of polar molecules is, apart from line-shape investigations and a few rare analytical applications, only of moderate value in the study of stable molecules. When we come, however, to consider free radicals this facility is invaluable. The whole essence of most interesting free radicals is that they instantly combine with one another on contact. It is therefore axiomatic that they can only be produced at very low concentrations. Attempts to detect free radicals in the gas phase using conventional infrared methods have been disappointing and only the technique of matrix isolation has proved really useful. Ultraviolet and visible spectra of electronic transitions can give a great deal of information, especially about excited states, but the resolution is limited, and the spectra of polyatomic molecules sometimes so complex that clear-cut analyses are not always possible. Radicals which have been investigated by microwave methods include SO, SH, CS, CN, whilst some unstable molecules such as H_2S_2 have also been studied. The spectra of radicals are complicated by the presence of electronic orbital and spin angular momentum and the way these two combine with the mechanical angular momentum N to give the resultant J determines the position of the energy levels and dictates the selection rules. SO is rather like O_2 which is discussed in Chapter 6. The ground state is $^3\Sigma$, that is the molecule is a diradical with $S = 1$. The splitting of the three states $J = N-1$, N and $N+1$ is large, so that pure rotation transitions of the type

$$N \to N+1, \qquad J \to J+1$$

can occur in the same spectral region as electron spin transitions of the type

$$N \to N, \qquad J \to J+1.$$

As an example[55] of this the $N = 2 \to N = 3$, $J = 1 \to J = 2$ pure rotation transition occurs at 109·252 22 GHz, whilst the $N = 4$, $J = 3 \to J = 4$ electron spin transition occurs at 109·138 57 GHz. The former is, however, electric-dipole-allowed and is very strong whereas the latter owes its intensity to a magnetic dipole and is very much weaker. The spectrum of CN was first observed by Evenson, Dunn and Broida[74] in connection with the perturbations between close-lying states of this radical. These perturbations were formerly thought[75] to be the origin of the laser action at 337 μm in pulsed discharges through organic mixtures and they are discussed in Appendix 5. The levels $B^2\Sigma^+$, $V = 0$, $N = 4$, $J = 3\frac{1}{2}$, parity plus, interacts very strongly with the nearly coincident $A^2\Pi_{3/2}$, $V = 10$, $J = 3\frac{1}{2}$, parity plus, level and as a result quantum mechanical mixing occurs leading to a displacement of the levels. Evenson, Dunn and Broida[74] have observed microwave transitions between the unperturbed level of $A^2\Pi$ and both the perturbed and the unperturbed (i.e. $J = 4\frac{1}{2}$) level of $B^2\Sigma^+$. The levels are split by hyperfine interaction with the ^{14}N nucleus so quite a complex spectrum stretching between $8\cdot8$ and $9\cdot9$ GHz results. The energy levels and a schematic spectrum are shown in Fig. 2.5.

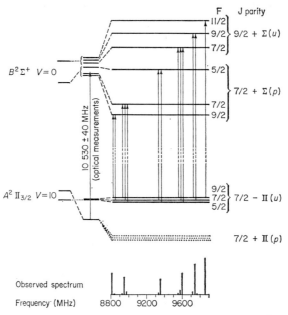

FIG. 2.5. Energy-level diagram of CN in the vicinity of the $B^2\Sigma^+$, $A^2\Pi_{3/2}$ resonance—reproduced by courtesy of the authors and the editor of the *Physical Review* from "Optical detection of microwave transitions between excited electronic states of CN etc.", by K. M. Evenson, J. L. Dunn and H. P. Broida.

The $\Pi(p) \to \Sigma(p)$ and $\Pi(p) \to \Sigma(u)$ lines where the p signifies perturbation are forbidden for electric dipole transitions because the two levels have the same parity, but they are allowed for magnetic dipole transitions. Very surprisingly these transitions occur, with only about one order of magnitude reduction in intensity, as a set of lines between $10\cdot4$ and $11\cdot5$ GHz and, correspondingly, the $\Pi(p) \to \Pi(u)$ lines are observed between $1\cdot58$ and $1\cdot65$ GHz. There is, of course, nothing particularly surprising about this latter since these arise from the perfectly allowed transitions between the split components of the Λ doublet. What is most remarkable about the whole experiment is that for this electronic transition in the microwave region the positions of all the lines are known to high accuracy. This permits not only a refinement of the spectroscopic parameters but also a rigorous test for the quantum mechanical treatments of the perturbation. The large (≈ 300 MHz) hyperfine splittings in $B^2\Sigma^+$ have been discussed by Radford[76] in terms of valence-bond pictures of the electronic structure of the radical. He favours a structure $:C\doteq N$ for $B^2\Sigma^+$ in contrast with the ground-state structure $.C\equiv N$. This latter is expected to have a small dipole moment and Evenson et al.[74] deduce this to be about $0\cdot 2$ D from pressure-broadening studies. Stark measurements are not usually possible on gaseous free radicals since they are normally produced in a plasma which would conduct. Nevertheless, from what has been mentioned above, it will be realized that microwave studies of free radicals can prove a most valuable tool in understanding the structure and bonding of molecules.

Alkali halide vapours have been extensively investigated by microwave methods.[55] The bonding in a molecule such as NaCl is most interesting for presumably it is not an ion pair whereas the crystal is entirely made up of ions. Fairly high temperatures are necessary to get significant vapour pressures of these materials and, since the vibration frequencies are low ($Na^{35}Cl$ 364 cm^{-1}), highly excited states will be significantly populated. This greatly complicates the spectra since the B values are functions of degree of vibrational excitation. However the B values themselves are so small that transitions occurring in the millimetre and submillimetre regions necessarily involve high J numbers and, because of this, hyperfine splitting is usually negligible. So many transitions are usually observable that equilibrium spectroscopic parameters—that is parameters referring to the hypothetical position at the lowest point of the potential well—can be derived. For $Na^{35}Cl$, r_e has the value $2\cdot 360\ 898$ Å and the equilibrium vibration frequency ω_e is $364\cdot 6$ cm^{-1}. It is interesting to observe that this frequency is derived with more precision from the temperature dependence of microwave pure rotation lines than it can be measured by direct observation in the far infrared. Another reason for preferring millimetric observations over centimetric techniques is the rapid rise of line intensity with frequency (equation 5.27). This combined with the "free space" techniques and the consequent availability of molecular beam methods has led to a branch of spectroscopy in which fabulously high resolution occurs. In a molecular beam apparatus a stream of molecules traverses a series of slits into a high-vacuum chamber. They emerge travelling along parallel trajectories and if observation is confined to a direction perpendicular to the line of flight the effects of both pressure (i.e. collisional) and Doppler broadening can be eliminated. An account of these fascinating techniques has been given by Strauch, Cupp, Derr and Gallagher[77] who describe an electric resonance millimetre wave spectrometer capable of operating up to 216 GHz. The term electric resonance is used because the separation of molecules into distinct energy states is accomplished by the use of inhomogeneous electric fields which, acting on the molecular dipole moments, alter the flight path. The ultra-high resolution comes from combining the conventional microwave techniques with the use of a Fabry–Perot resonator. This latter is fed by, and delivers its output power to, a horn-lens combination. The first studies with this apparatus were on the two pure rotation lines of H_2S, $1_{01} \to 1_{10}$ at $168 \cdot 7$ GHz and $2_{02} \to 2_{11}$ at 216 GHz. These are the analogues of the well-known lines $18 \cdot 58$ and $25 \cdot 08$ cm^{-1} in the pure rotation spectrum of water (see Fig. 5.1). The observed line-widths were as narrow as 350 Hz and this meant that not only were Stark measurements easy but that the complete hyperfine pattern could be readily resolved. With low electric fields applied to give Stark splittings each level of 1_{01} and 1_{10} splits into two components, $M_J = 0$ and $M_J = \pm 1$. Since $\Delta J = 0$ the transition $\Delta M = 0$ is forbidden for $M = 0$, because the intensity is proportional to M^2. Initial observations used the interferometer plates as electrodes and only $\Delta M = \pm 1$ transitions could therefore be seen, but this restriction was removed in later versions of the apparatus described by Cupp, Kempf and Gallagher[78] who added additional electrodes to permit the observation of $\Delta M = 0$ transitions. It might be thought that there would be no hyperfine structure since no nucleus in $H_2{}^{32}S$ has a quadrupole moment, but the protons have half integral spin and this leads to a splitting, but one so small that it could not be observed without the ultra-high resolution techniques. The quantum number F can range from $J+I$, that is 2 to $J-I$, i.e. 0, and combining this with the selection rule $\Delta F = 0, \pm 1$, but

$$F' = 0 \leftarrow | \to F'' = 0$$

leads to the expectation of six hyperfine components which are, in fact, observed between $168 \cdot 762\ 734\ 310$ GHz and $168 \cdot 762\ 796\ 986$ GHz. These numbers are believed accurate to ± 36 Hz and represent a staggering feat of spectroscopic accuracy. The hyperfine splittings of the upper state are 3667 Hz ($F' = 0 \to 1$) and 37 506 Hz ($F' = 1 \to 2$). Such small splittings imply that the coupling between J and I is very weak and can easily be undone. In fact, when the Stark modulation field approaches 1000 V cm^{-1} the hyperfine structure collapses. Because of this and the ultra-high precision of measurement, care has to be taken to prevent stray fields affecting the system and even the Zeeman effect of the Earth's magnetic field can be significant. Measurements have now been extended to the $4_{22} \to 4_{31}$ line of H_2S at $369 \cdot 126\ 91$ GHz and even as far as the $4_{31} \to 4_{40}$ line at $424 \cdot 315\ 47$ GHz, but the latter has not so far been measured by electric resonance methods. These techniques promise to yield a whole range of interesting molecular parameters such as spin-rotation coupling constants which, because of their small size, should provide really rigorous tests for quantum mechanical theories of molecular structure. The use of a Fabry–Perot interferometer as the absorption cell of a millimetre-wave spectrometer permits the observation of the Zeeman effect in free radicals. Interesting results on several isotopic variations of CS have been obtained using this technique.[79] In technological applications, the ability to determine submillimetre absorption frequencies, on the time scale, to ten significant figures opens up new metrological possibilities. The prospect of locking a laser onto an absorption line only a few kiloHertz wide may provide a means of determining the velocity of light to better than 1 part in 10^8.

These spectacular results which are flowing from the extension of microwave methods into the submillimetre region should not blind us to the obvious fact that there is little merit in using ultra-high resolution methods if there is nothing to resolve. Submillimetre spectroscopy divides rather neatly into the very high resolution work on gases and the very much lower resolution work on liquids and solids. For the former radio techniques are superior, although a great deal of work has been done by other methods, but for the latter, where resolutions up to $0 \cdot 01$ cm^{-1} are perfectly adequate, interferometric delay-type spectroscopy reigns supreme. This has been neatly summarized by Gordy[55] who remarked, "It seems inefficient, if not downright wasteful, to use a high-resolution source for the study of very broad resonances". The topic of interferometric spectroscopy will be developed in the next two chapters.

CHAPTER 3

Theory of the Michelson Interferometer

3.1. General Theory

A full account of the operation of two-beam interferometers is very complicated and is best developed within the concepts of coherence theory.[80]
Nevertheless, by making certain simplifying assumptions, it is possible to
develop most of the results of practical significance within a very much
simpler mathematical framework. This approach will be developed in the
sections which follow.

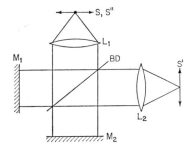

Fig. 3.1. Schematic layout of a two-beam interferometer.

The optical arrangement of the interferometer is shown in Fig. 3.1.
The radiation from an extended source S is made quasi parallel by a lens
L_1. The quasi-parallel radiation is split into two beams by a beam divider
BD which, ideally, is 50 per cent reflecting and 50 per cent transmitting.
These two beams are reflected from the two mirrors, M_1 and M_2, recombined
at the beam divider where again division of intensity occurs, and finally
brought to focus at S′ and also at S″ which is coincident with S. The
behaviour of real beam dividers will be discussed in detail later but for the
moment we will imagine the beam divider to be an extremely thin metallic
film. When the two beams are recombined at the beam divider interference
occurs for each wavelet making up the total wavefront and the problem
is to compute the intensity distribution across S′ and S″ as functions of
wavelength and the difference in path length of the two arms. The equivalent
optical system is shown in Fig. 3.2.

43

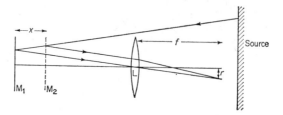

Fɪɢ. 3.2. Equivalent optical system of a two-beam interferometer.

To simplify the discussion we will assume the source to be monochromatic, of frequency v, and consider the radiation incident on the mirrors in the angle range θ to $\theta+d\theta$. Such a beam will be imaged to a small region at a distance r from the optical axis where

$$r = f\tan\theta \tag{3.1}$$

The electric field strength of the radiation in this small region will then be the sum of that from the two arms of the interferometer. We thus have

$$S', E(r) = \tfrac{1}{2}E_0 \sin 2\pi vt + \tfrac{1}{2}E_0 \sin [2\pi vt + 4\pi\bar{v}x \cos\theta]$$

$$S'', E(r) = \tfrac{1}{2}E_0 \cos 2\pi vt - \tfrac{1}{2}E_0 \cos [2\pi vt + 4\pi\bar{v}x \cos\theta] \tag{3.2}$$

where $\bar{v} = v/c$. The phase angle $4\pi\bar{v}x \cos\theta$ arises because of the difference in path length $2x \cos\theta$ between the two beams and the difference in sign arises from the phase shifts in reflection and transmission (π and $-\pi/2$ respectively) at a metallic surface: the beams reaching S' have undergone two such reflections whilst those reaching S'' have undergone three and one reflections respectively. The sums in equation (3.2) are vector sums but, assuming no rotation of the plane of polarization in the instrument, they can just as well be regarded as scalar sums—the general point being that for incoherent sources interference is only possible between a wavelet and itself. Thus, since we have from classical electromagnetic theory[81] that

$$I = (cn/4\pi)\,\bar{E}^2 \tag{3.3}$$

where c is the velocity of light and n is the refractive index of the medium, it follows by integration with respect to time that

$$S', I(r) = \tfrac{1}{2}I_0[1 + \cos 4\pi\bar{v}x(1 + r^2/f^2)^{-1/2}]$$

$$S'', I(r) = \tfrac{1}{2}I_0[1 - \cos 4\pi\bar{v}x(1 + r^2/f^2)^{-1/2}] \tag{3.4}$$

since $n = 1$ for the vacuum or air spacing in the instrument.

I is the intensity in watts per square centimetre. It will be seen that the sum of the intensities at corresponding points in S' and S'' is a constant, and this illustrates the conservation of energy that must of course apply in a non-absorbing system. It also illustrates a general principle of interferometry that one can only have dark fringes in a field if there is somewhere else for the intensity to be redistributed.

Figure 3.2 has cylindrical symmetry, so the operation of the interferometer leads to the formation of a ring pattern in the image planes. The radii of the circles of maximum intensity in, say, the S′ plane are given by

$$r_{\max} = [f/(2\bar{\nu}x)][(2\nu x - m)(2\bar{\nu}x + m)]^{1/2} \qquad (3.5)$$

where m is an integer $\leqslant 2\bar{\nu}x$. If x is zero then $r_{\max}$ becomes indeterminate, that is the field is bright everywhere in S′ and dark everywhere in S″. If $2\bar{\nu}x \gg 1$ then $r_{\max}$ can be approximated as

$$r_{\max} = 2\bar{\nu}xf/m \qquad \text{for } m \ll 2\bar{\nu}x; \qquad (3.6)$$

that is the pattern is one of rings whose radii are inversely proportional to the natural integers for small integral values. The interferometer can therefore be used to measure the wavenumber of monochromatic radiation. A suitable detector with a very small aperture or "window", is moved so that its window moves in the image plane radially over the interference pattern. The output of the detector as a function of r is the interferogram and from the positions of the maxima and the known value of x the wavenumber follows by applying equation (3.5). Conversely, if $\bar{\nu}$ is known, then the separation of the mirrors, i.e. x, can be inferred. This latter procedure has some promising metrological aspects since situations can be envisaged in which the two "mirrors" are metallic surfaces which are either inaccessible to or unsuitable for normal contact gauges. As a general spectroscopic tool, however, this method is not very promising. If the interferometer is irradiated with broad-band (so-called "white") radiation then the output pattern becomes

$$I(r) = \int_{0}^{\infty} S(\bar{\nu})[1 + \cos 4\pi\bar{\nu}x(1 + r^2/f^2)^{-1/2}] \, d\bar{\nu} \qquad (3.7)$$

where $S(\bar{\nu}) \, d\bar{\nu}$ is the spectroscopic intensity between $\bar{\nu}$ and $\bar{\nu} + d\bar{\nu}$. There is no simple way of extracting $S(\bar{\nu}) \, d\bar{\nu}$ from $I(r)$ using equation (3.7) because of the non-linear form for the argument of the cosine function. Hence another method of using the interferometer is almost universal in practice.

In this alternative method the detector is fixed, so that its circular window is at the centre of the interference pattern and one of the mirrors is moved from negative values of x, through the zero-path position, to positive values of x. To find what happens now, it is necessary to calculate the total power through the detector window as a function of x. Again, for monochromatic radiation we have

$$W = \int_0^a 2\pi r I(r)\, dr \qquad (3.8)$$

where a is the radius of the circular aperture. Thus

$$W(x) = \tfrac{1}{2}I_0 \int_0^a 2\pi r[1 + \cos 4\pi\bar{v}x(1 + r^2/f^2)^{-1/2}]\, dr. \qquad (3.9)$$

This integral is formidable, in general, but if, as is always the case, the range of r (i.e. $0 \to a$) is such that $r^2/f^2 \ll 1$ for all r it becomes handleable. In fact by a familiar approximation

$$W(x) = \tfrac{1}{2}I_0 \int_0^a 2\pi r[1 + \cos 4\pi\bar{v}x(1 - \tfrac{1}{2}r^2/f^2)]\, dr \qquad (3.10)$$

and thus

$$W(x) = \tfrac{1}{2}I_0\pi a^2 + [I_0 f^2/(4\bar{v}x)][\sin 4\pi\bar{v}x(1 - \tfrac{1}{2}a^2/f^2) - \sin 4\pi\bar{v}x]. \qquad (3.11)$$

This can be rewritten as

$$W(x) = \tfrac{1}{2}I_0\pi a^2 + [I_0 f^2/(2\bar{v}x)] \cos 4\pi\bar{v}x(1 - \tfrac{1}{4}a^2/f^2) \sin \pi\bar{v}xa^2/f^2. \qquad (3.12)$$

If we restrict the range of observation to values of x such that

$$\pi\bar{v}xa^2/f^2 \text{ is very small} \qquad (3.13)$$

a further approximation leads to

$$W(x) = \tfrac{1}{2}I_0\pi a^2[1 + \cos 4\pi\bar{v}x(1 - \tfrac{1}{4}a^2/f^2)],$$

that is

$$W(x) = \tfrac{1}{2}W_0[1 + \cos 4\pi\bar{v}x(1 - \tfrac{1}{4}a^2/f^2)] \qquad (3.14)$$

with a complementary expression for the power through a similar detector in S''. This expression has a linear argument for the cosine function and is therefore very amenable for spectroscopic purposes. Again, if irradiation is carried out with broad-band radiation, then

$$W(x) = \tfrac{1}{2}\pi a^2 \int_0^\infty S(\bar{v})[1 + \cos 4\pi\bar{v}x(1 - \tfrac{1}{4}a^2/f^2)]\, d\bar{v} \qquad (3.15)$$

and this is a Fourier integral. Applying Fourier's integral theorem to this, one has

$$S(\bar{v}) \propto \int_{-\infty}^{+\infty} \left[W(x) - \tfrac{1}{2}\pi a^2 \int_0^\infty S(\bar{v})\, d\bar{v} \right] \cos 4\pi\bar{v}x(1 - \tfrac{1}{4}a^2/f^2)\, dx. \qquad (3.16)$$

Since

$$\tfrac{1}{2}\pi a^2 \int_0^\infty S(\bar{\nu})\, d\bar{\nu}$$

is one half the total power over the whole spectral range, this is merely the average value of $W(x)$ which means that the spectrum function can be recovered by the Fourier transformation of $[W(x) - \overline{W(x)}]$. Fourier transformation is nowadays a very simple operation in a high-speed computer and because of this Fourier transform spectroscopy has become very attractive, bearing in mind the advantages briefly mentioned earlier. Of course, since $W(x)$ is an experimental quantity the transformation has to be effected numerically, that is, a number of values of $W(x)$ are observed for equally spaced intervals of x and the calculation can only be done over a finite range of values of x. These approximations lead to some complications which are not experimentally onerous, but which must always be in the experimentalist's mind, and these will be discussed later. For the moment, some further results of importance can be obtained by considering analytical functions and their transforms.

Firstly we will consider "monochromatic" radiation. Truly monochromatic radiation is physically impossible since it would correspond to an infinite coherence length; what is meant, when the term monochromatic radiation is used, is radiation restricted to a very narrow spectral region. As a model for such radiation we will assume a rectangular line-shape of peak height $1/u$ and lying between $\nu_0 - u$ and $\nu_0 + u$. Such a model will always have a finite area (corresponding to the transmission of a finite power) no matter how small u becomes. Substituting this rectangular form for $S(\bar{\nu})$ in equation (3.15) leads to

$$W(x) \propto 1 + \cos 4\pi\bar{\nu}_0 x(1 - \tfrac{1}{4}a^2/f^2) \qquad \text{for } x \ll \frac{1}{4\pi u} \qquad (3.17)$$

so that the output of the interferometer as the mirror moves will be a cosine wave. The first thing to notice about equation (3.17) is that in a real experiment the distance the mirror moves will be determined (in a way to be discussed later) relative to some absolute scale of distance. It follows therefore that the wavenumber of the cosine oscillation deduced from these scale readings will *not* be the true wavenumber of the radiation; in fact

$$\bar{\nu}_{\text{obs}} = \bar{\nu}_0(1 - \tfrac{1}{4}a^2/f^2). \qquad (3.18)$$

If we define the solid angle subtended by the detector window (if this is the limiting stop in the system) as

$$\Omega = \pi\theta_{\text{extremal}}, \qquad (3.19)$$

then by equation (3.1) for θ_{extremal} very small

$$\Omega = \pi a^2/f^2$$

and thus

$$\bar{\nu}_{\text{obs}} = \bar{\nu}_0(1 - \Omega/4\pi). \qquad (3.20)$$

Wavenumbers observed with a Michelson interferometer will therefore always be too low by the factor $(1 - \Omega/4\pi)$ and hence should be corrected by the inverse of this factor to give true values. This complication does not turn out to be serious in practice, since the frequency shift $(\bar{\nu}_{\text{obs}} - \bar{\nu}_{\text{true}})$ is small for small $\bar{\nu}_{\text{true}}$ and it is only in this case that small values of f would be used in order to gain the maximum luminance with a given size of instrument. In fact at any frequency the dimensions of the instrument can always be chosen to make the correcting factor negligible. For simplicity the factor $(1 - \Omega/4\pi)$ will be omitted from the equations in the remainder of this chapter.

3.2. Resolution in a Michelson Spectrometer

The resolution obtainable in the transformed interferogram, i.e. the spectrum, can easily be deduced by continuing the discussion of the previous section. We have shown that the interferogram obtained from "monochromatic" radiation is a cosine wave. The question to be asked now is what spectrum is obtained by the Fourier transformation of a cosine wave. The condition that makes this question less than obvious is that in the practical world the range of integration is restricted. In fact, if the interferogram has been recorded from $x = -x_{\text{max}}$ to $x = +x_{\text{max}}$ then the transform will be

$$S(\bar{\nu}) \propto W_0 \int_{-x_{\text{max}}}^{+x_{\text{max}}} \cos 4\pi\bar{\nu}_0 x \cos 4\pi\bar{\nu}x \, dx. \qquad (3.21)$$

On evaluation this integral gives two terms but in the region near $\bar{\nu}_0$ one is much larger than the other, so $S(\bar{\nu})$ may be written

$$S(\bar{\nu}) \propto W_0 x_{\text{max}}\{\sin 4\pi(\bar{\nu}_0 - \bar{\nu})x_{\text{max}}/[4\pi(\bar{\nu}_0 - \bar{\nu})x_{\text{max}}]\}. \qquad (3.22)$$

The form of this well-known function is shown in Fig. 3.3.

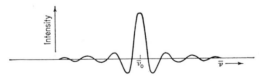

FIG. 3.3. Fourier transform of a truncated cosine wave.

The subsidiary maxima in this transform are very irksome and methods for eliminating them, using the principle of apodization, will be discussed later, but in the present context the problem is how near to $\bar{\nu}_0$ can we have another line of equal intensity so that in the transformed spectrum the two grand maxima will be resolved. Clearly one good criterion of this would be if the second grand maximum lay on the first subsidiary maximum of the first line. This first subsidiary maximum occurs at

$$\bar{\nu}_0 - \bar{\nu} = 1 \cdot 2/2x_{\text{max}} = \Delta\bar{\nu}. \tag{3.23}$$

Thus, we arrive at the very simple definition of the resolution available with a Michelson interferometer—that it is approximately the reciprocal of twice the maximum mirror movement from the zero-path difference position. This is a most felicitous feature of these instruments and one which has attracted many workers to them, for high resolution spectra can be obtained merely by ensuring that one is able to move a mirror parallel to its original position over a fairly long distance, and this is readily achievable in practice. However, at this point the approximations made in deriving the operating equation have again to be considered. Strictly the approximation made in going from equation (3.12) to (3.14) is given by (3.13), but because of the factor x in the denominator this can be relaxed considerably—and somewhat arbitrarily depending on the viewpoint adopted. A reasonable restriction on the range of x would be that the maximum value of x corresponds to the first zero of the function

$$\sin \pi\bar{\nu}x(a^2/f^2)/(2\bar{\nu}x),$$

namely

$$\bar{\nu}x(a^2/f^2) = 1$$

leading to the relation (via equation 3.23)

$$\Delta\bar{\nu}/\bar{\nu} = 0 \cdot 6 \, \Omega/\pi. \tag{3.24}$$

We have thus modified the simpler definition given above by restricting the maximum range of mirror travel, but of course within this range equation (3.23) holds fully. It is worthwhile pausing now to consider how limiting this restriction is. A very luminous interferometer for the 50 cm^{-1} region can be constructed with $a^2/f^2 \approx 10^{-3}$. It therefore follows that the limiting resolution available with such an interferometer will be 0·03 cm^{-1} giving an order of magnitude better than that available with a good grating instrument. The interferometer has a very high intrinsic energy throughput so still higher resolution can be achieved—with a given size of instrument—by going to longer focal lengths and thus sacrificing some intensity. This point emphasizes a profound relationship which applies to all spectroscopic systems, namely that increased resolution is always accompanied by a loss in energy throughput—closing the slits of a prism spectrometer is a familiar example. The Michelson interferometer, because of its cylindrical symmetry, has the highest product of energy throughput and resolving power of any system. The actual configuration of condensing optics to be used should always be chosen to give the optimum combination of these two quantities. It is clearly poor practice to suffer the indifferent signal-to-noise quality of a very high resolution instrument if accurate photometry at low resolution is the object of the experiment.

3.3. Apodization

As we have seen above, the spectra obtained from truncated interferograms possess undesirable features. Sharp lines are accompanied symmetrically by subsidiary maxima and in a real experiment, where the full nature of the expected spectrum is not known, these subsidiary maxima could easily be mistaken for real spectral features. The situation can be very considerably improved by mathematical procedures inside the computer if a slight loss of resolution can be tolerated. These mathematical procedures are known as "apodization" from the Greek words meaning "removal of the feet", i.e. the subsidiary maxima. In a full mathematical analysis it can be shown[82] that the "feet" arise from the sharp cut-off at x_{max} where x_{max} is the last value of x supplied to the computer. If it can be arranged that the ordinates are smoothly and progressively reduced to zero at x_{max} then, by the concepts of information theory, a much better spectral profile will be obtained from the Fourier transform. The procedure is quite simple and is usually built into the programme for Fourier transformation. Various functions are available, three such being

$$f(x) = 1 - |x/x_{max}|,$$
$$f(x) = 1 - (x/x_{max})^2,$$
$$f(x) = \cos(\pi x/2x_{max}). \tag{3.25}$$

The computer then produces the apodized spectrum, as

$$S(\bar{\nu}) \propto \int_{-x_{max}}^{+x_{max}} f(x) \, W'(x) \cos 4\pi\bar{\nu}x \, dx. \tag{3.26}$$

To show how this improves the line-shape we will consider the last of these and compare the calculated transform with that of an unapodized spectrum, i.e. with $f(x) = 1 \cdot 0$. When the instrument is irradiated by "monochromatic" radiation of wavenumber $\bar{\nu}_0$ then we have

$$W'(x) = [W(x) - \overline{W(x)}] = \tfrac{1}{2}W_0 \cos 4\pi\bar{\nu}_0 x \tag{3.27}$$

and

$$S(\bar{v}) \propto W_0 x_{max} \left[\frac{\sin 4\pi(\bar{v}_0 + \bar{v}) x_{max}}{4\pi(\bar{v}_0 + \bar{v}) x_{max}} + \frac{\sin 4\pi(\bar{v}_0 - \bar{v}) x_{max}}{4\pi(\bar{v}_0 - \bar{v}) x_{max}} \right] \quad (3.28)$$

for $f(x) = 1 \cdot 0$

and

$$S(\bar{v}) \propto \frac{2}{\pi} W_0 x_{max} \left[\frac{\cos 4\pi(\bar{v}_0 + \bar{v}) x_{max}}{1 - 64(\bar{v}_0 + \bar{v})^2 x_{max}} + \frac{\cos 4\pi(\bar{v}_0 - \bar{v}) x_{max}}{1 - 64(\bar{v}_0 - \bar{v})^2 x_{max}} \right] \quad (3.29)$$

for $f(x) = \cos(\pi x / 2 x_{max})$.

In each case the second term becomes large for $\bar{v} \approx \bar{v}_0$ so we need only consider these terms in the neighbourhood of $\bar{v}_0$. The normalized functions are plotted in Fig. 3.4. The effective suppression of the subsidiary maxima

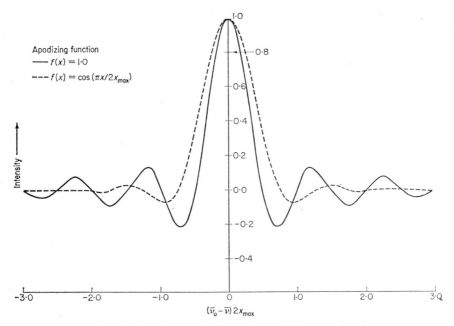

FIG. 3.4. Apodized and unapodized transforms of a truncated cosine wave.

in the apodized spectrum is very clearly demonstrated in this Figure as is also the unavoidable broadening of the line. It was remarked earlier that definitions of resolution are somewhat arbitrary and most authors would regard the definition used previously as somewhat too strict. An alternative definition frequently used is that two lines are resolved if the combined profile shows a distinct minimum between the two maxima, this distinct minimum being ≈ 80 per cent of each maximum. Using this more permissive definition we would have (from Fig. 3.4)

$$\text{Unapodized} \quad \Delta\bar{\nu} = 0\cdot6/2x_{\max}, \tag{3.30}$$

$$\text{Apodized} \quad \Delta\bar{\nu} = 0\cdot9/2x_{\max}. \tag{3.31}$$

So we have a 50 per cent loss in resolution as a consequence of the gain in acceptability of the line-shape profile. It should be noted that $4x_{\max}$ is the total optical path length introduced, so this particular definition leads to the simple rule that the resolution is approximately the reciprocal of the total optical path difference. In terms of the solid angle subtended by the limiting stop, the maximum resolving power of a Michelson interferometer is

$$\Delta\bar{\nu}/\bar{\nu} = \Omega/2\pi \tag{3.32}$$

for the unapodized case.

The discussion so far, although it has enabled us to demonstrate several important results, has had a strong element of unreality about it because in essence we have a perfectly behaved cosine wave over the range of x available to us and we are pretending that we have no idea what happens in the inaccessible region. The use of equation (3.26) implies that we introduce a sharp discontinuity at $x = x_{\max}$ forcing the function $W'(x)$ to suddenly drop to zero for all values greater than this. Clearly it would not be un-justifiable to assume that the cosine wave just continues on past $x_{\max}$ to arbitrarily large values of x. If this is the case the integration can be carried through over a larger and larger range of x and ultimately it will approach the so-called delta (δ) function

$$\delta(\bar{\nu}_0) = \int_{-\infty}^{+\infty} \cos 4\pi\bar{\nu}_0 x \cos 4\pi\bar{\nu}x \, \mathrm{d}x \tag{3.33}$$

as the spectral function. This function is infinite at $\bar{\nu} = \bar{\nu}_0$ and zero everywhere else and clearly there are no subsidiary maxima to worry about. Equation (3.33) is the most clear-cut demonstration of a general principle which applies to pairs of functions which are Fourier "mates" of each other. This principle states that any feature localized in one will lead to a feature extended in the other and vice versa; thus, "monochromatic" radiation in a spectrum leads to an interferogram which is an endless cosine wave and the arbitrary introduction of a discontinuity in an interferogram (by limiting the range of computation) leads to disturbances in the transformed spectrum over a considerable frequency range.

The reality of the discussion is, of course, at once restored when one reflects that for sources of radiation other than lasers the procedure of analytical continuation outlined above is either impossible or potentially misleading. Nevertheless, it is necessary to take a close look at the apodization procedure to make sure that it is being used in such a manner as to be of the maximum benefit whilst being of the minimum nuisance. At this point we must introduce the important practical consideration that the system recording the interferogram must always have a lower limit of detectivity such that any change in the interferogram level less than this will not be recorded. Imagine now that an interferometer is irradiated with radiation made up of a number of "lines" of finite width. The resulting interferogram can readily be visualized by recalling the complete reciprocity of Fourier transform; hence, if the line-shape were to be given by equation (3.29) then the mth line would give a component in the interferogram

$$W(x) = \tfrac{1}{2}W_m[1 + \cos(\pi x/2x_{\mathrm{max}}) \cos 4\pi\bar{\nu}_m x] \quad \text{for } x < x_{\mathrm{max}} \quad (3.34)$$

$$= \tfrac{1}{2}W_m \quad \text{for } x > x_{\mathrm{max}}.$$

Thus each component becomes a "damped" cosine wave and x_{max} is now determined by the intrinsic width of the line. It follows that there will always be a value of x such that the fringe oscillations of even the sharpest line will drop below the discrimination of the system. Supposing that this value of x is close to the limit of mirror travel available, we need to find the best way of handling the data. If we apply equation (3.26) directly then the effect of the apodizing function will be to reduce the fringe oscillation information near x_{max} fed to the computer and this will lead to a loss of information in the resulting spectrum. An alternative approach would be to add to the digitized record supplied to the computer an extra section made up of constant numbers equal to the average value of $W(x)$ over the observed range. The apodizing function will then be finite at all values of x where there is real information and the spectral quality will be improved. This procedure is a form of analytical continuation and carries with it the hazards of all such procedures, but for many experimental situations it can be recommended since it leads to optimum resolution with optimum suppression of computational artefacts.

3.4. Tilt Adjustments in Michelson Interferometers

In general discussions of the operation of the interferometer, such as that previously outlined, it is assumed that the image of one mirror in the beam divider is perfectly parallel to the surface of the other. In practice it will not be possible to achieve this, so it is necessary to discuss the effect on the performance of the instrument of small departures from parallelism. This discussion proceeds quite naturally when it is remembered that for an incoherent source, such as a black body, interference is only possible between beams which arise from the division of the same wavelet; that is to say that the radiation from a given atom can interfere with itself but not with that from any other atom. Therefore we need only consider an interferometer irradiated by a wavelet from a single atom. Due to the phenomena of diffraction, the image of the atom formed on the detector window will not be a point but will be a system of rings which can be thought of as mostly contained within a circle of radius λ, where λ is the wavelength. If the two mirrors are not parallel then two such circular pools of light will be formed on the detector window and, whilst the detector signal will be twice as great as with one mirror alone, no interference will occur unless the two pools of light overlap. Thus, the condition for interference to occur is that

$$\tfrac{1}{2}d < \lambda. \tag{3.35}$$

where d is the separation of centres of the two pools of light. Maximum fringe contrast occurs when d is zero. The relationship between d and the angle of mirror tilt is shown in the Fig. 3.5. It will be seen that

$$d = f \tan \theta, \tag{3.36}$$

so that for interference to occur

$$\theta \approx \tan \theta = 2\lambda/f = 2/(f\bar{\nu}). \tag{3.37}$$

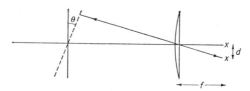

FIG. 3.5. Displacements of images in the focal plane due to mirror tilts.

As an illustration, for $f = 5$ cm and $\bar{\nu} = 200$ cm^{-1} the angle of tilt has to be less than $0 \cdot 1°$. The reciprocal dependence of θ on $\bar{\nu}$ is of considerable practical importance for it means that the adjustments become more and more critical as $\bar{\nu}$ rises and in the near infrared, for example, rather sophisticated mirror adjustments are needed to meet the highly stringent requirements on angular adjustment. In the millimetre wave region, on the other hand, simple arrangements of pushing and pulling screws with relatively coarse threads are quite adequate. With a given instrument therefore, adjusted to the best degree of parallelism possible, there will be an unavoidable degradation of fringe contrast as the frequency rises. Very similar effects arise from lack of flatness of the beam divider or of the mirror surfaces. The result of these phenomena is that when high-frequency radiation is being studied, the amplitude of the zero-path fringe will only be a small fraction of the asymptotic value, and the oscillations beyond the zero path difference position will rapidly fall to values less than the discrimination limit of the digitizing system. The transform of such an interferogram will be a low-quality spectrum. This effect can be mitigated in practice by increasing the gain of the amplifier and employing a large degree of d.c. subtraction, so that once again the zero-path fringe amplitude just fills the dynamic range of the digitizing system. Great care, however, must be taken to ensure that the signal power is not sufficient to drive the detector into a non-linear portion of its characteristic. This is always a hazard at frequencies above 500 cm^{-1}, due to the form of the black-body emission curve, but fortunately all that is required to ensure linear performance is a suitable attenuator such as an iris diaphragm. The procedure outlined above will not be possible if the band of radiation being studied includes low as well as high frequencies, for with the low-frequency radiation the full dynamic range for the zero-path fringe is achieved with the minimum necessary gain and d.c. subtraction. Therefore, to study such a broad band effectively, it is advisable to record spectra for the low-frequency region first and then to record the high-frequency region separately using appropriate low- and high-pass filters. What can be achieved with this method with only push-and-pull mirror adjustments is shown in Fig. 3.6. This is the interferogram obtained with a narrow band of radiation near 1100 cm^{-1}.

The adjustments of the tilt in practice are quite easily optimized. The coarse adjustment is nearly always done visually. In some interferometers, the condensing unit and detector can be removed and the visible radiation from the source can be examined by the eye (through suitable safety glasses); in others a white card can be placed in an image position after the beam divider. In both cases generally two source images will be observed, one from each mirror. The fixed mirror tilt adjustments are then altered until the two images are as coincident as possible. This procedure is greatly facilitated if there is some sharply delineated object such as a chopper blade in the source plane. After this adjustment has been made, the detector unit is restored or the white card removed and the moving mirror allowed to scan over the zero path difference position. A low contrast zero-path fringe system will be observed and the moving mirror is then set on the maximum of this pattern and the adjustments further altered until this bright fringe reaches a maximum intensity. The interferometer is then in optimum adjustment and ready for operation.

It is often observed that the low contrast zero-path fringe pattern obtained in the first stage of alignment is unsymmetrical. This does not arise from a symmetrical tilt of the fixed mirror about the optical axis of the system but from a shear or lateral displacement. It is difficult to construct an instrument so that the fixed mirror is perfectly centrally aligned on the optical

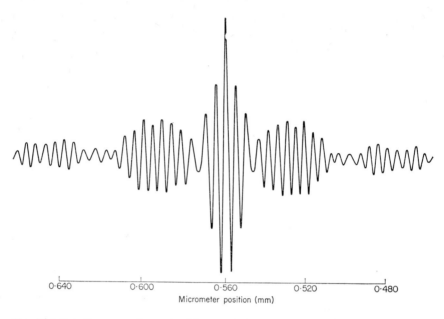

0·640   0·600   0·560   0·520   0·480

Micrometer position (mm)

Fig. 3.6. Interferogram observed with a modular Michelson interferometer irradiated by a narrow band of radiation near 1100 cm^{-1}. The "beat" pattern arises from the presence of a strong absorption band in the polypropylene specimen which essentially divides the spectral range into two regions. (From unpublished observations of J. W. Fleming.)

axis, and its tilt adjustments are, likewise, perfectly symmetrically disposed about this axis. If the lateral shear is Δ and the angle of tilt θ, then the variable part of the interferogram function is given by

$$W'(x) = A(\bar{\nu}, \theta)[\cos 4\pi\bar{\nu}x - 4\pi\bar{\nu}\theta\Delta \sin 4\pi\bar{\nu}x] \qquad (3.38)$$

where A is a function describing the imperfect overlap of the two pools of light and is unity for $\theta = $ zero. The presence of the sine component in this function, for which $\sin 4\pi\bar{\nu}x = -\sin 4\pi\bar{\nu}(-x)$, will make the interferogram function no longer absolutely symmetrical about $x = $ zero. Again, the degree of asymmetry will depend on the frequencies present in the incident radiation. It will also be seen that when $A(\bar{\nu}, \theta)$ has been made as close to unity as possible by careful maximizing of the zero-path fringe, then the asymmetry will reach a minimum since θ has the smallest value possible. The difficulties mentioned here can be largely bypassed by the use of cube-corner or cat's-eye reflectors in place of plane mirrors. This development is of most value in the near infrared but is beginning to appear in far infrared interferometers.[83]

3.5. Sampling Theory and the Phenomenon of Aliasing

As shown earlier (equations 3.15 and 3.16) the spectral distribution function $S(\bar{\nu})$ and the interferogram function $W'(x) = W(x) - \frac{1}{2}W_0$ are Fourier "mates" of each other and therefore each can be obtained from the other by Fourier transformation. The practical problem is, of course, to obtain $S(\bar{\nu})$ knowing $W'(x)$ which means determining the integral

$$S(\bar{\nu}) \propto \int_{-\infty}^{+\infty} W'(x) \cos 4\pi\bar{\nu}x \, \mathrm{d}x. \tag{3.39}$$

$W'(x)$ being an experimental quantity cannot be represented analytically and therefore the integration has to be performed in a computer. The experimental details of this operation will be discussed in the next chapter and here we will merely sketch these out so that the theoretical consequences can be clearly developed. In essence, as the mirror moves, a sensing device attached to it sends a signal to the detecting system each time the mirror travel equals an integral multiple of some fundamental distance x_0. This signal operates the recording system (paper or magnetic tape or punched card) and the final record of the interferogram is a sampled version consisting of $2n+1$ observations $W'(mx_0)$, where $m = -n \ldots 0 \ldots +n$. The sampled interferogram is then fed into the computer which carries through the calculation for each frequency of interest,

$$S(\bar{\nu}) \propto x_0 \sum_{-n}^{+n} W'(mx_0) \cos 4\pi\bar{\nu}mx_0. \tag{3.40}$$

The essential points are that a continuous function has been replaced by its ordinates at regularly spaced values of the abscissa and an integration over the whole range of path difference has been replaced by a summation over a limited range. As may be expected, the latter restriction merely leads (as discussed earlier) to a finite resolution in the spectrum obtained from the computer, the resolution being

$$\Delta\bar{\nu} = 0 \cdot 6/(2nx_0). \tag{3.41}$$

The replacement of a continuous function by a sampled one, followed by the replacement of an integration by a summation, leads, however, to new phenomena. It might be thought that the deliberate throwing away of a great deal of information would lead to a serious loss of quality in the final spectrum. The fact that this is not necessarily the case can be seen from a close examination of equation (3.40). Basically this equation enables us to find a number of cosine waves whose sum passes through all the observed points. Supposing, as the simplest example, that the original interferogram $W'(x)$ had been a pure cosine wave of frequency $\bar{\nu}_0$, then clearly there could be no other wave of frequency close to ν_0 which would pass through all the points. This means that equation (3.40) will recover the spectral function near ν_0 just as well as equation (3.39). However, it is also clear that an infinite number of higher frequency waves will pass through all the points in the range of observation if their frequencies are

$$\nu_l = \nu_0 + l/2x_0, \qquad l = 1, 2 \ldots \tag{3.42}$$

Equation (3.40) will therefore only give the true spectral information in the frequency range $0 - l/2x_0$ and the record given by this equation will endlessly repeat in succeeding regions. A further complication can be deduced by noting that the sum in equation (3.40) is the same for $\nu = l/4x_0 \pm \Delta\nu$. Hence the function reflects about $\bar{\nu} = l/4x_0$ and therefore the true information is restricted to the range

$$\bar{\nu} = 0 \rightarrow \bar{K}_0 \tag{3.43}$$

where $\bar{K}_0$, the so-called "folding" frequency, is given by

$$\bar{K}_0 = 1/4x_0. \tag{3.44}$$

The existence of spurious spectral information above the folding frequency is known as "aliasing". The enormously important practical consideration is that if the spectrum is broad band with components at frequencies higher than $\bar{K}_0$ these too will be reflected about $\bar{K}_0$ and appear spuriously in the fundamental region $0 \rightarrow \bar{K}_0$. The phenomenon is reminiscent of the "ghosts" due to higher orders of a grating and like these can be eliminated by the use of suitable filters to restrict the band pass to the range $0 \rightarrow \bar{K}_0$. Unlike the grating problem, however, in the absence of suitable filters the "aliasing" can be simply removed by sampling more frequently, i.e. reducing x_0. The spectral effects of aliasing for well-behaved broad-band radiation are illustrated in Fig. 3.7.

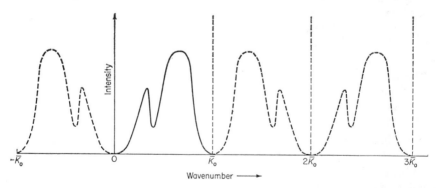

FIG. 3.7. The production of spurious spectral features by "aliasing" due to the use of a finite sampling interval.

Several workers have proposed that the phenomenon of aliasing should be turned to useful purpose to overcome a drawback to the use of Fourier transform spectroscopy in the higher frequency regions. This drawback is the increasing number of input data that must be supplied to the computer as the frequency rises to obtain spectra of a given resolution. If the highest frequency component in the incident radiation is $\bar{K}_0$, then the interferogram has to be sampled at intervals $x_0 = 1/4\bar{K}_0$. If the required resolution is $\Delta\bar{\nu}$, then the total number of observations required is

$$N = 2\bar{K}_0/(\Delta\bar{\nu}). \tag{3.45}$$

As illustrations, with $\bar{K}_0 = 50 \text{ cm}^{-1}$ and $\Delta\bar{\nu} = 0\cdot1 \text{ cm}^{-1}$, only 500 input observations will be required, whereas with $\bar{K}_0 = 2000 \text{ cm}^{-1}$ 20 000 input observations must be obtained. The time taken by the computer will thus rise rapidly and the cost of the computing likewise. Some alleviation is possible since the interferogram of a well-adjusted interferometer is symmetrical about the zero path difference and so in principle it is only necessary to observe points on one side—the so-called "single-sided operation"; but this merely reduces N by a factor of 2. To overcome this irksome dilemma it has been proposed to sample very much less finely and to use filters to remove all radiation in the fundamental region. Spectral intensity will then be observed in the fundamental region due to aliasing of the genuine intensity in the repeat regions. As an example, suppose we wish to study a band near 1300 cm^{-1} at high resolution. If, by means of suitable filters, the band pass can be restricted to the range $1200–1400 \text{ cm}^{-1}$ and $\bar{K}_0$ chosen to be 200 cm^{-1}, then the calculated spectrum in the region $0–200 \text{ cm}^{-1}$ will be the aliased true spectrum in the region $1200–1400 \text{ cm}^{-1}$. The number of points required to give $0\cdot1 \text{ cm}^{-1}$ resolution will therefore be reduced by seven times.

So far the discussion has been restricted to the noise-free ideal case, but in real spectroscopy the problem of noise has to be faced. The effect of noise on the analogue record (i.e. the interferogram function) is to make its ordinates uncertain. It therefore follows that there will be some uncertainty as to the cosine waves which pass through the chosen ordinates; in other words, we will obtain a noisy spectrum. If the interferogram is sampled at finer intervals than the minimum indicated by the sampling theorem (equation 3.44), the uncertainty in the cosine waves will be reduced, since they have to pass through more ordinates. Then, by a familiar theorem of Information Theory, the noise in the spectrum will be inversely proportional to the square root of the number of ordinates. This turns out to be rather a convenient state of affairs because the noise problem is most acute in the low-frequency region (due to the source characteristic) where one can most readily afford to make additional observations (see equation 3.45). In the high-frequency region noise is seldom a serious handicap and therefore the reduction in the number of ordinates to take advantage of the aliasing method does not lead to an unacceptably noisy spectrum. Another interesting aspect of the presence of noise in the analogue record is that the noise power spectrum may have components above $\bar{K}_0$ and these will appear in the fundamental region—again due to aliasing. It therefore follows that the recording system should be arranged to have a suitable time constant so that no noise fluctuations are present in the interferogram of wavenumber greater than $\bar{K}_0$. In the context of discussions of noise it is most important to realize that spectra should not be computed to higher resolution than the finest detail present. The reason for this is that after the corresponding point in the interferogram all oscillations are random noise and will transform to random noise distributed everywhere in the spectrum.

3.6. Discrimination and Bandwidth Restrictions

We will now take up in more detail the matter first raised in the discussion of apodization, namely the finite discrimination of real systems. We have a Michelson interferometer irradiated by broad-band radiation and the resulting interferogram is to be recorded by a digital system which can indicate M values; that is, each ordinate will be recorded as one of the integers between 0 and M. The question to be answered is: how does this discrete "quantization" of sampled ordinate affect the spectral quality in the transformed spectrum? Two possibilities arise: firstly that the incident radiation has a smooth profile devoid of sharp regions, and secondly that sharp regions are present. The effects can well be discussed using hypothetical model spectra, since the theory covers any form for $S(\bar{v})$ and it turns out in practice that the behaviour observed with real spectral functions resembles quite closely that calculated with hypothetical analytical forms for $S(\bar{v})$. We can consider "white" radiation as such a model—this metaphorical phrase is used loosely amongst spectroscopists to mean radiation whose smooth spectral profile changes slowly with frequency, the analogy being with white light. Such "white" radiation can be represented by the condition that $S(\bar{v}) = 1/u$ for $\bar{v} = 0 \rightarrow u$ and is zero elsewhere. The interferogram obtained with this model radiation as the hypothetical input will be

$$W(x) = 1 + (4\pi ux)^{-1} \sin(4\pi ux) \tag{3.46}$$

which is similar to the function discussed previously and illustrated in Figs 3.3 and 3.4. As u gets larger and larger, the oscillations become confined sensibly more and more to small values of x and in the limit we have the δ function mentioned earlier. If we arrange the digital system so that the ordinate at $x = $ zero is associated with the number M, then it is clear that for large u the oscillations of this function will become less than unity for some small value of x, and beyond this value the digital record will contain no information other than that the oscillations are less than one unit. However, when it is recalled that by the sampling theorem it will be necessary to sample the interferogram more and more finely as u increases, it will be seen that no information is lost on this count, the only loss being the inability of the system to detect the very small oscillations at large x. As these contribute only marginally if M is reasonably large, the interferometer will reproduce the spectrum quite well, although the resolving power will be low, but this will scarcely matter since there is nothing to resolve. If there is a sharp region present very different conclusions apply. Such a sharp region will give a relatively un-damped cosine wave whose amplitude relative to the zero-path fringe (due mostly to the "white" radiation) will be the ratio of the power in the sharp region to the total power in the "white" regions. If u is large this ratio can easily approach $1/M$ and the undamped cosine wave be poorly observed. Of course, if the ratio is less than $1/M$ it will not be observed at all, apart from some additional complications due to noise.

There are three ways which have been suggested to overcome this difficulty. Firstly, M can be increased, but there are limitations to this set by the nature of available digital systems and a value of M equal to 10 000 seems to be the present limit. Secondly, the gain of the recording system can be increased after the zero-path fringe has been recorded at a lower gain, and hence the oscillations of the sharp component will be increased in size. This possibility is difficult to achieve satisfactorily in practice and additionally there are fresh problems due to the linearity requirements introduced. These problems arise because the mean signal level will be high because of the presence of the now unvarying component due to the "white" radiation, and, if the gain is increased to make the much weaker (but oscillating) sharp component detectable, high input voltages will be supplied to the detecting system and this system will be required to give an output linearly proportional to the input over an enormous range of input. As may be imagined equipment with this degree of performance is difficult to construct and the whole method has been jocularly compared with determining the weight of the captain of an ocean liner by weighing the liner with and without him on board. The point of the joke arises because a large and constant d.c. voltage must be subtracted from the final output to bring the voltage supplied to the digital system within its range. Another point concerned with linearity is that the broader the spectral band pass of the incident radiation becomes the larger will be the power incident on the detector, and this too has a limiting power input beyond which its response becomes non-linear. Bearing these difficulties in mind, the solution adopted generally is the third, namely to restrict the spectral bandwidth of the incident radiation by means of suitable optical filters. By a reasonable choice of these both the zero-path signal and the oscillating signals remote from zero path can be brought within the dynamic range of the recording system.

The situation can be looked at quite fruitfully within the concepts of information theory. The interferometer and its recording system can be regarded as an information channel and, if unwanted and ultimately to be rejected "messages" are to be transmitted in addition to the information of value, this will lead to degradation in information content in the message of interest. It is interesting in this context to consider two alternative experiments, namely observing a given structured spectral band in absorption and in emission. In the former a great deal of the information reaching the detector is unwanted, telling us much irrelevant information about the source characteristic each side of the band and between the sharp lines making up the band. In the latter only relevant information reaches the detector and optimum performance is produced. In the far infrared spectral region emission methods cannot in general be used because of the dependence of intensity inversely on the cube of the wavelength, but for very high resolution measurements in the near infrared these methods should be considered if it is possible to heat up the specimen to a sufficiently high temperature to populate the upper level of the transition. When, as is generally the case, absorption methods have to be used, suitable filters should be employed with the best compromise of overall absorption in the pass band relative to the resolution required in the final spectrum.

Finally we must consider what is the best value to choose for M. The smaller this is, the simpler and less expensive becomes the digital system and the ease of computing increases. The larger it becomes the more the spectral quality improves. As might be expected, the optimum value for M is set by the noise level on the analogue record. If the noise fluctuations are less than one unit on the scale then the approximations involved in forcing each ordinate to have an integral value on this scale lead to indeterminacy in the computed spectrum, these indeterminacies being known—somewhat fancifully—as "quantization noise". If the noise fluctuations are larger than one unit the "quantization noise" in the final spectrum becomes negligible in comparison with the genuine noise. The answer to the question therefore is that the dynamic range of the recording system should be divided into M parts where 1 part equals the mean noise fluctuation on the record. The noise fluctuations can be arbitrarily reduced at the expense of overall recording time by the use of sufficiently long time constants in the recording system, and hence M can be increased with some gain. This is an illustration of another aspect of information theory that the longer one is prepared to receive a constantly repeated message in the presence of noise the more certain does one become of the information content.

3.7. Beam Divider Operation

In the discussion of the instrument given earlier the beam divider was assumed to be an infinitely thin film which was 50 per cent reflecting and 50 per cent transmitting. Of course it is not possible to make such beam dividers, so we must now consider in detail the operation of the real dividers used in practical interferometers. For the visible and near infrared regions these are made by evaporating a thin film of a metal or a semiconductor onto a thick block of a suitably transparent material which has been polished so that its surfaces are parallel to each other and flat compared with the wavelength to be measured. Metals such as aluminium or gold have very high reflectivities and very high absorption coefficients in these regions, so the film has to be very thin. In general, the absorption coefficient decreases with frequency so that suitably thin metallic films can be achieved for operation in the visible region, but for the infrared semiconductors are preferable. If the frequency of operation is lower than the band edge these materials no longer behave optically as metals and their reflectivities at normal incidence are given by the relation

$$R = [(n-1)/(n+1)]^2 \qquad (3.47)$$

where n is the refractive index. At such frequencies the semiconductor film acts as a dielectric beam divider. The principal complication introduced by the necessity to mount the thin film on a thick substrate is the phenomenon of dispersion in the substrate material. In all that has gone before in this chapter the quantity $2x$ has really meant the optical path difference between the two arms, and we have been able to identify this uniquely with twice the separation of the mirror images in the beam divider. If a dispersive plate is introduced into the interferometer asymmetrically then this is no longer the case and the optical path difference becomes frequency dependent. The situation is shown in Fig. 3.8(a) where it will be seen that the radiation reaching the detector from one arm has traversed the plate three times whilst that from the other has only passed through the plate once. The

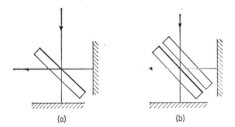

(a) (b)

FIG. 3.8. Uncompensated (a) and compensated (b) beam dividers in a two-beam interferometer. The deviation due to refraction is ignored in this schematic representation.

varying part of the interferogram function for each monochromatic spectral element will therefore be

$$W'(x) = W'(\bar{\nu}) \cos 4\pi\bar{\nu}\{x + d[(n^2 - \sin^2 \theta)^{1/2} - \cos \theta]\} \qquad (3.48)$$

where d is the thickness of the plate and θ is the angle of incidence on the medium. Since the medium has been chosen to be transparent over the spectral range of interest, it follows by very fundamental arguments (Kramers–Kronig dispersion law) that the refractive index n varies only slowly over this range. We can therefore divide the range up into narrow areas over which n is sensibly constant, and thus the pth narrow area will give a fringe system with its maximum located at

$$x = -d[(n_p^2 - \sin^2 \theta)^{1/2} - \cos \theta]. \qquad (3.49)$$

The total interferogram will be the sum of the contributions from all the narrow areas and will be characterized by having its brightest fringe displaced an amount

$$\bar{x} = -d[(\bar{n}^2 - \sin^2 \theta)^{1/2} - \cos \theta] \qquad (3.50)$$

from the physical zero-path position, where $\bar{n}$ is an average refractive index defined by this relation, and by having a distorted profile (because of the frequency dependence of n_p) no longer symmetrical about the grand maximum. This state of affairs is not very satisfactory and is nearly always circumvented in practice by introducing another plate (as nearly identical as possible) into the instrument. The operation of this compensating plate is shown in Fig. 3.8(b). With the compensating plate in position the optical path difference between the beams is once again exactly $2x$ and is therefore no longer frequency dependent. Symmetrical interferograms with their grand maxima located at $x =$ zero are thus obtained.

Beam dividers for use in the far infrared region (< 1000 cm^{-1}) are not usually constructed in this fashion because of the difficulty of finding suitably stable and transparent substrates from which to make the optical flats. As examples of this the alkali halides, of which CsI is transparent down to 200 cm^{-1}, are very hygroscopic and attack by water vapour, which occurs when the instrument is at atmospheric pressure, leads to a deterioration in performance. Instead, the beam dividers are made in a very simple fashion by stretching a thin film of a dielectric material, such as polyethylene terephthalate, in a metal frame. The stretching, sometimes further aided by heat treatment, makes the surfaces flat and the film is used, without any coating, directly as a beam divider. This type of beam divider is crucial to the operation of modern Michelson interferometers in the far infrared and it is necessary to discuss the manner of operation rather fully.

3.8. Thin-film Interference in the Beam Divider

The principal phenomenon displayed by transparent dielectric beam dividers is that of multiple beam interference. The multiple beams arise from reflections inside the film in the manner shown in Fig. 3.9.

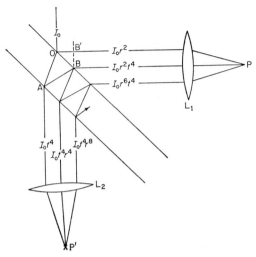

FIG. 3.9. Generation of multiple beams in a thin film.

A narrow pencil of radiation is incident at an angle θ and is partly reflected (OB′) and partly refracted (OA) at an angle θ'. The beam is partly transmitted at A and partly reflected (AB) and so on. The result is that a series of beams emerges on each side of the narrow film with the intensities given in the Figure, where r^2 is the reflectivity and t^2 the transmissivity of the film at each of its surfaces. The total reflected intensity is therefore

$$I_r = 2I_0r^2/(1+r^2) = I_0R \qquad (3.51)$$

and the total transmitted intensity is

$$I_t = I_0(1-r^2)/(1+r^2) = I_0T \qquad (3.52)$$

since $r^2+t^2 = 1$ for a non-absorbing film. As will be seen on inspection, these two quantities add up to the total incident power. All these beams, however, arise from the division of one incident beam so they are all coherent with each other and interference can occur. In the diagram, two lenses bring the beams to foci at P and P′, and we will now calculate the intensities at these two points. The various rays arriving at P or P′ have undergone varying delays which appear as phase angles in the expressions for the electric field strength. If we take the phase of the incident ray at O to be the

D

phase origin, the phase of the beam reflected at O is π. This arises because of the Fresnel equations[84] governing reflection and refraction at the interface of two media of refractive indices n_1 and n_2 which are

$$r_\parallel = \frac{n_2 \cos \theta - n_1 \cos \theta'}{n_2 \cos \theta + n_1 \cos \theta'} \qquad t_\parallel = \frac{2n_1 \cos \theta}{n_2 \cos \theta + n_1 \cos \theta'}$$

$$r_\perp = \frac{n_1 \cos \theta - n_2 \cos \theta'}{n_1 \cos \theta + n_2 \cos \theta'} \qquad t_\perp = \frac{2n_1 \cos \theta}{n_1 \cos \theta + n_2 \cos \theta'}. \qquad (3.53)$$

Since, for dielectric transparent media, n_1, n_2, θ and θ' are all real, it follows that the Fresnel coefficients are also real and, depending on whether they are positive or negative, the ray is reflected (or refracted) with a phase change of zero or π. In fact, examination of the above relationship shows that the actual situation is very simple and that the phase changes are zero, except for a reflection from and into a less dense medium at its interface with a dense medium. The phases of the remaining rays therefore only differ from the phase of the incident ray by virtue of the distance travelled; for example, the phase at B will be

$$\delta = 2\pi\bar{\nu} \, (2nd/\cos \theta - \mathrm{OB}')$$

$$= 4\pi nd\bar{\nu} \cos \theta'. \qquad (3.54)$$

The reader will recall that the expression used in equation (3.2) for the path difference introduced by the mirror separation in a Michelson interferometer was just this with n equal to unity. In fact, the physical situation of Fig. 3.9 is closely similar to that of Figs 3.1 and 3.2. This is especially true if r^2 is small so that only the first two beams each side of the film have appreciable intensity—a situation where again two-beam interference will be observed. There is, however, one very important difference in that the Michelson fringes have cylindrical symmetry and therefore the interference pattern is a series of rings. The thin-film interference fringes will be a series of straight lines parallel to the perpendicular to the plane of Fig. 3.9.

We now have all the information necessary to write down the electric field strength at P; thus, ignoring constant geometrical factors, we obtain

$$E(\mathrm{P}) = r\sqrt{I_0} \left[-\cos 2\pi\nu t + t^2 \cos (2\pi\nu t + \delta) + t^2 r^2 \cos (2\pi\nu t + 2\delta) \right]$$

$$+ t^2 r^4 \cos (2\pi\nu t + 3\delta) + \ldots \qquad (3.55)$$

The intensity at P is given by the time average of the square of $E(\mathrm{P})$ which is

$$I(\mathrm{P}) = \frac{2I_0 r^2}{1+r^2} \left[1 - (1 - r^2) \left(\frac{\cos \delta - r^2}{1 + r^4 - 2r^2 \cos \delta} \right) \right]$$

$$= \frac{2r^2(1 - \cos \delta)I_0}{1 + r^4 - 2r^2 \cos \delta}. \qquad (3.56)$$

It will be noted that when $\cos \delta = 1$, $I(P)$ is zero; in other words the fringes are of perfect contrast. Many treatments of this subject are in terms of the first two beams only and give the approximate form

$$I(P) \approx 2I_0 r^2 [\tfrac{1}{2}(1+t^4) - t^2 \cos \delta] \qquad (3.57)$$

and this is not zero, in fact $I_0 r^6$ when $\cos \delta = 1$.

A similar treatment of the transmitted beam gives

$$I(P') = \frac{I_0(1-r^2)}{1+r^2} \left[1 + 2r^2 \left(\frac{\cos \delta - r^2}{1 - 2r^2 \cos \delta + r^4} \right) \right]$$

$$= \frac{I_0(1-r^2)^2}{(1 - 2r^2 \cos \delta + r^4)} \qquad (3.58)$$

with the corresponding approximate expression when only two beams are involved:

$$I(P') = I_0 t^4 (1 + r^4 + 2r^2 \cos \delta). \qquad (3.59)$$

It will be noted that the sum of the intensities at P and P' is constant independent of δ when the correct expressions are used and thus, once again, energy is shown to be conserved in interference phenomena. All the amusing "paradoxes" of energy non-conservation in interference can usually be traced either to the use of approximate mathematical methods or to non-physical assumptions such as no phase shifts by π *anywhere* in a system containing beam dividers.

There are several additional points of interest about the mathematical analysis outlined above. Firstly the amplitude of the interference pattern in, say, the transmitted beam is

$$P_{\max} - P_{\min} = 4I_0 r^2 / (1+r^2)^2 \qquad (3.60)$$

whereas the power of the "weak" beam which is interfering with the strong beam is merely $I_0 r^4 (1 - r^2)^2$. This illustrates a general theorem which applies to power detectors (also called square-law detectors) that if two signals coherent with each other are brought to the detector and the weaker of the two is labelled by suitable modulation (in this case the phase shift δ), then the output of the detector gives a modulated component whose amplitude is proportional to $\sqrt{(P_1 P_2)}$ where P_1 and P_2 are the powers in the two signals. If $P_1 \gg P_2$ this leads to considerable amplification of the desired modulated signal. In practice this has applications where a beam of radiation is to be sent over and to return over a large distance, for all that is necessary is to abstract some of the initial beam and send this unmodulated direct to the receiver where it is mixed with the returning, and greatly enfeebled, modulated beam. Of course, the coherence length of the radiation has to be long enough for interference still to be possible. In the present case if $r^2 = 0 \cdot 1$ (which it might well be for dielectric films) then the "weak" transmitted beam is only 1 per cent of the strong transmitted beam; nevertheless, the interference fringes are 10 per cent of the mean transmitted energy. The second point follows on from this and applies generally to all spectrometers in the infrared region. It will be observed that if a completely transparent dielectric film is placed in the beam of a spectrometer, the spectrometer will show a varying transmission whose general quality will be determined by equation (3.58) modified by the nature of the condensing optics and the detector aperture size. Nevertheless the transmission will be minimal when

$$4\pi n d\bar{v} \cos \theta' = (2l+1)\pi, \qquad l = 0, 1, 2, \text{ etc.} \qquad (3.61)$$

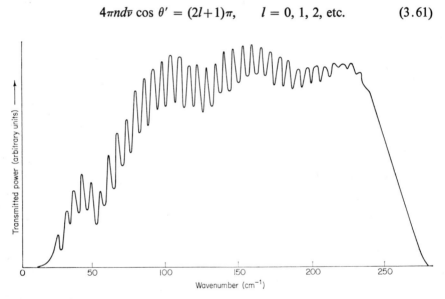

FIG. 3.10. Spectral transmission function of an interferometer containing a thin plane parallel silicon disc in the beam. High-frequency cut-off due to a quartz filter.

These minima can easily be mistaken for genuine spectral absorption bands. This is a real danger because plane parallel films tend to occur only too frequently in far infrared instruments. In Fig. 3.10 are shown such so-called "channel" fringes obtained with a thin film of silicon. Fringes of this type are recognizable by their repetitive nature, but this may not be a sure touchstone if only a limited spectral range is available for study. A better procedure is to ensure that all samples, windows or filters in the system are "wedged", so that they have two surfaces inclined at an angle to one another.

3.9. Thin Dielectric Films as Beam Dividers for Michelson Interferometers

In the Michelson interferometer, the lenses of Fig. 3.9 are replaced by two plane mirrors and the wavefronts return to the beam divider where each again suffers division. Clearly phase changes at each of the plane mirrors can be ignored as these are the same for all beams and for the moment we will have the mirrors equidistant from the beam divider. The problem is to calculate the intensity distribution in S' and S" (see Fig. 3.1). Ignoring interference for the moment, we observe that each of the infinite number of returning beams when it arrives at the beam divider itself generates an infinite number of beams in an analogous fashion to those generated by the original incident beam. By adding up the doubly infinite number of terms for each side of the beam divider it is found that the intensities in the four returning beams are

$$M_1 \rightarrow \text{detector} = M_2 \rightarrow \text{detector} = 2I_0 r^2 (1-r^2)/(1+r^2)^2 = I_0 RT$$

$$M_1 \rightarrow \text{source} = I_0 R^2 \qquad M_2 \rightarrow \text{source} = I_0 T^2. \qquad (3.62)$$

Therefore the total power in the four beams is

$$I_0(R^2 + 2RT + T^2) = I_0. \qquad (3.63)$$

Now we will consider the effects of interference between the beams arriving at the image planes (S' and S''). By means of the cumbersome methods given earlier, or in terms of the more elegant approach given in Appendix 1, it can readily be shown that the resulting intensities in these image planes are

$$S', \qquad I = \frac{8I_0 r^2 (1-r^2)^2 (1-\cos \delta)}{(1+r^4 - 2r^2 \cos \delta)^2} \qquad (3.64)$$

$$S'', \qquad I = I_0 \left[\frac{2r^2(1-\cos \delta) - (1-r^2)^2}{1 - 2r^2 \cos \delta + r^4} \right]^2 \qquad (3.65)$$

when the mirrors are equidistant from the beam divider.

These equations merit close study. Firstly, they demonstrate the asymmetry in the two image planes which is especially pronounced if r^2 is small when most of the incident power is returned to the source. The dielectric films used in the construction of beam dividers have relatively low refractive indices ($\approx 1 \cdot 7$) so this is always the case. Secondly, the fringe contrast in the detector plane is perfect, i.e. the intensity falls to zero when $\cos \delta = 1$; but when $\cos \delta = -1$, the power to the detector rises rapidly, and with $r^2 = 0 \cdot 07$ the power to the detector becomes 75 per cent of the incident power and that reflected back to the source only 25 per cent. Since, for a given $\bar{v}$ and angle of incidence set by the instrument, δ is proportional to

d (the thickness of the film), it follows that the thickness of the film should be carefully chosen so that $\bar{\nu}$ coincides with one of the frequencies of maximum transmission given by

$$d = (2l+1)/(4n\bar{\nu} \cos \theta') \qquad l = 0, 1, 2, 3, \text{ etc.} \qquad (3.66)$$

The performance of various thicknesses of polyethylene terephthalate (mylar or melinex) when used as a beam divider is shown in Fig. 3.11. These curves are somewhat idealized since the real material is not perfectly transparent

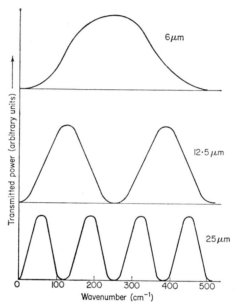

Fig. 3.11. Transmission minima of interferometers equipped with different thicknesses of dielectric film beam divider. The diagrams apply for a hypothetical material of refractive index 1·7 and without any spectral variation of absorption coefficient.

and in fact shows an absorption coefficient which increases with frequency. The effect of this is to reduce the second and subsequent maxima relative to the first and, this being the case, the thickness of the beam divider is usually chosen so that its first maximum coincides with the frequency of interest. Since the absorption is proportional to the thickness of the film, the two effects tend to cancel to a certain extent because when working at high frequencies, where the intrinsic absorption coefficient is high, the thickness of the film will be small so that the actual energy loss is more or less constant regardless of frequency.

The principal experimental difficulty introduced by the multiple beam fringes arises when it is desired to cover a wide spectral range, especially one including the low frequencies. From Fig. 3.11 it will be seen that the thinnest film (6 μm) permits an effective coverage of over 300 cm^{-1} for each transmission region, but its performance at the lower frequencies (< 70 cm^{-1}) is no good at all. If the thickness of the film is increased so as to improve the low-frequency performance, the spectral range per transmission region falls. In fact, to get adequate coverage of the lower frequency region it is usually necessary to carry out several experiments with differing thicknesses of beam divider. In this connection, the development of interferometers which feature rapid and reproducible interchange of beam dividers has been an enormous step forward.

Before leaving the question of multiple beam interference in the beam divider we must once again consider the question of the finite area of the detector window. It has been shown that the effect of the interference is the formation of a set of linear fringes in the two image planes and we have calculated the intensity at points in the patterns corresponding to refraction angles θ' in the plate. The total signal given by the detector will therefore be the integral of the intensity function over the detector aperture. Fortunately, this difficult calculation does not need to be made since the fringes are widely spaced relative to the detector aperture if, as is always the case, r/f is small. The power through the detector window can therefore be found to a very good approximation by simply multiplying equation (3.64) by the area of the detector window. Combining equation (3.64) interpreted in this manner with equation (3.14) leads to the following expression for the output of the detector of a Michelson interferometer irradiated with broad-band radiation

$$V(x) = G \int_{0}^{\infty} \frac{S(\bar{\nu})4r^2(1-r^2)^2}{(1-2r^2 \cos \delta+r^4)^2} (1-\cos \delta)[1+\cos 4\pi\bar{\nu}x]\,d\bar{\nu}. \quad (3.67)$$

This means that the detector "sees" the source spectral function modified by the multiple-beam interference function. G is a constant which takes account of the various geometrical factors in the instrument which affect the energy transfer and G also includes the detector sensitivity. It is assumed in this that the detector is a "black" detector, i.e. not frequency dependent, but any departures from this are taken up in $S(\bar{\nu})$ which is really the spectral source function modified by any absorption processes (such as filters) which occur between the lamp and the detector.

The radiation does, however, traverse the beam divider film, and so questions of dispersion and compensation should be considered. It might be thought that since the various multiply reflected beams reaching the detector have travelled different distances inside the film, an uncompensated interferogram would be obtained. However, it can be shown (see Appendix 1) that the system can be thought of in terms of the two complex waves once reflected and once transmitted which arrive at the detector and, since these are identical, perfect compensation ensues. This is reflected in the fact that the transmission function involves only cos δ and not cos 2δ etc. The interferogram will therefore be perfectly symmetrical (for optimum mirror tilts of course) about the zero path difference position. However, the minima in the transmission function may not be regularly spaced if dispersion occurs since δ is a function of n. Measurements of these minima with a thick beam divider can be used to gauge the extent of the dispersion in the beam divider material, but since this has been chosen to be transparent in the region of interest such dispersion will be very small.

3.10. Polarization Effects in Michelson Interferometers

The Fresnel amplitude reflection and transmission coefficients given earlier (equation 3.55) depend on the angle of incidence θ. It follows that if a beam of unpolarized radiation is incident on a beam divider the reflected and transmitted radiation will be partly polarized. Consider a unit area of beam divider surface irradiated by radiation of intensity I_0 polarized in the perpendicular direction and incident at an angle θ. In nearly all practical cases the first medium is either air or vacuum so we can set $n_1 = $ unity. The total power incident on the unit area will be

$$P = I_0 \cos \theta \qquad (3.68)$$

by Lambert's cosine law, and, combining this with equation (3.3), the amplitude of the incident electric field will be given by

$$P_i = (c/4\pi)E_\perp^2 \cos \theta. \qquad (3.69)$$

The reflected power will therefore be

$$P_r^\perp = \frac{c}{4\pi} \left[\frac{\cos \theta - n \cos \theta'}{\cos \theta + n \cos \theta'} \right]^2 E_\perp^2 \cos \theta \qquad (3.70)$$

and the transmitted power will be

$$P_t^\perp = \frac{cn}{4\pi} \left[\frac{2 \cos \theta}{\cos \theta + n \cos \theta'} \right]^2 E_\perp^2 \cos \theta' \qquad (3.71)$$

and, satisfying the law of conservation of energy,

$$P_r^\perp + P_t^\perp = P_i. \qquad (3.72)$$

A completely analogous treatment applies to the radiation polarized in the parallel direction, the results being

$$P_r^{\parallel} = \frac{c}{4\pi} \left[\frac{n \cos \theta - \cos \theta'}{n \cos \theta + \cos \theta'} \right]^2 E_{\parallel}^2 \cos \theta, \qquad (3.73)$$

$$P_t^{\parallel} = \frac{cn}{4\pi} \left[\frac{2 \cos \theta}{n \cos \theta + \cos \theta'} \right]^2 E_{\parallel}^2 \cos \theta'. \qquad (3.74)$$

The equations are very interesting for, whilst $P_r^{\perp}$ is always finite, $P_r^{\parallel}$ falls to zero when

$$\tan \theta = n. \qquad (3.75)$$

This particular value of angle of incidence is known as the Brewster angle and, if unpolarized radiation is incident on a dielectric film at this angle, the reflected radiation is 100 per cent polarized in the perpendicular sense. Conversely, if radiation polarized in the parallel sense is incident on such a film none will be reflected and if the film is transparent 100 per cent will be transmitted. This latter feature has attracted a very great deal of attention since the development of lasers for, whereas the few per cent losses introduced by windows in ordinary equipment are perfectly tolerable, they may be sufficient to stop a laser working altogether. If, however, the windows inside a laser cavity are inclined at the Brewster angle, then those modes of the cavity which are polarized in the parallel sense will be transmitted without loss.

Polyethylene terephthalate, which is widely used as a beam divider in far infrared equipment, has a refractive index of ≈ 1.69, so the Brewster angle for this material is $59°$. Beam dividers are commonly used, principally for ease of construction, at an angle of $45°$ to the incident beam and consequently a considerable degree of polarization is expected in the emergent beam. In fact a polarization ratio of approximately $5 : 1$ is expected in the image aperture of Fig. 1.1 with the component perpendicular to the plane of the Figure the more intense. Experimentally values closer to $3 : 1$ are found, but, if the mean angle of incidence were chosen to be the Brewster angle, much more highly polarized radiation would leave the exit aperture. This is a very attractive feature of interferometers for many spectroscopic experiments require polarized radiation and an interferometer constructed with this angle of incidence would provide this very easily and, quite importantly, without the additional losses that conventional polarizers introduce. If, however, alteration of the angle of incidence is inconvenient and polarizers are to be used, the optimum operational mode is to set the polarizer with its transmission in the vertical direction and then to rotate the sample.

We must now go on to consider how the treatment given earlier to the multiple beam effects in the beam divider is modified by the fact that the reflectivities and transmissivities of the beam divider are different in the vertical and horizontal directions. The incident unpolarized radiation can be imagined as split up into two components, one polarized vertically and the other horizontally. Equation (3.64) then applies separately to each component and we have

$$I(\text{detector}) = 4I_0 \left[\left(\frac{r^2(1-r^2)^2(1-\cos \delta)}{(1-2r^2 \cos \delta + r^4)^2} \right)_{\text{perpendicular}} \right.$$

$$\left. + \left(\frac{r^2(1-r^2)^2(1-\cos \delta)}{(1-2r^2 \cos \delta + r^4)^2} \right)_{\text{parallel}} \right] \quad (3.76)$$

This function is plotted for angles of incidence of 45° and 70° on a 100 μm thick beam divider of polyethylene terephthalate ($n = 1 \cdot 69$) in Fig. 3.12.

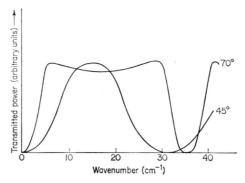

Fig. 3.12. Transmission of an interferometer with two different angles of incidence on the beam divider.

It will be seen that the transmission function is much more acceptable for the 70° incidence than for the 45° angle of incidence.[85] The performance is very much better at low wavenumbers and the range which can be covered with one beam divider is wider. Interferometers continue to be made with the mean angle of incidence 45° for mechanical and design considerations, but it would seem eminently worth-while to investigate the possibility of manufacturing instruments with a larger angle of incidence.

3.11. Spectral Performance of Michelson Interferometers

We now consider how the overall transmission of a Michelson interferometer varies with frequency of the incident radiation. This can be readily derived merely by looking at equation (3.67) in a different way. This equation is derived by dividing the spectral range of $S(\nu)$ into narrow "monochromatic" regions and adding up the cosine waves from each at each value of x. Another way of looking at it is to say that the detector merely integrates at each value of x the spectral transmission function of the interferometer multiplied by the source spectral characteristic. The spectral characteristic in the small region containing the detector window is thus given by

$$S'(\bar{v}) = \frac{S(\bar{v})4r^2(1-r^2)^2}{(1-2r^2\cos\delta+r^4)^2}(1-\cos\delta)(1+\cos 4\pi\bar{v}x) \qquad (3.77)$$

and the interferogram function is merely

$$V(x) = \text{constant}\int_0^\infty S'(\bar{v})\,d\bar{v}. \qquad (3.78)$$

It follows therefore that if a spectrometer is placed to examine the radiation emerging from this region when the detector has been removed, the record obtained will be $S(\bar{v})$ multiplied by a cosine function due to the mirror offset x. The operation of the instrument and the generation of the characteristic "white light" fringes, looked at from this point of view, is shown in Fig. 3.13. The broken line curve is chosen to be $S(\bar{v})$ modified by filters and also including the effect of the $(1-\cos\delta)$ term. The filters have been chosen to limit the spectral band pass to the first transmission region of the beam divider. The dotted curve is the true interferometer function $(1+\cos 4\pi\bar{v}x)$ and the solid line curve is the product of these two. The first four inserts show these functions for various values of x and the integral under the solid curve for these four (and all values of x in the range covered) is plotted in the fifth insert which is the interferogram. The origin of the damped oscillations characteristic of broad-band interferograms is clearly brought out in this Figure. At values of x beyond D in the Figure the "pitch" of the offset cosine wave becomes very fine and eventually just as much of the original integrated power is eliminated by it as is let through by it, independent of the particular value of x. In other words, the interferogram becomes a featureless straight line parallel to the x-axis. It is commonly thought by people inspecting such an interferogram that interference has "ceased" in some way, but all that is happening is that there are as many frequencies where constructive interference is occurring as there are where destructive interference is occurring. This is illustrated in Fig. 3.14 which shows the spectrum of the radiation transmitted through an interferometer with a relatively large mirror offset.[86] The high frequencies have been eliminated by the use of a quartz filter.

In the light of this approach, several interferometric phenomena are readily understood. Thus, imagine that the input spectral function has a narrow absorption region; every time the mirror displacement is such as to produce a minimum of $S'(\bar{v})$ coincident with the absorption band, a maximum of

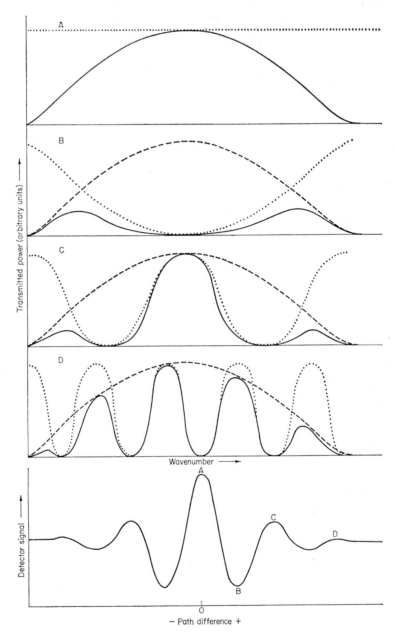

FIG. 3.13. Spectral transmission of an interferometer as a function of mirror displacement and the resulting generation of the interferogram. See text for detailed explanation.

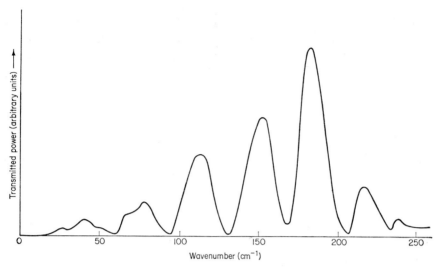

FIG. 3.14. Spectrum of the radiation transmitted through a Michelson interferometer with a mirror offset of 0·135 mm. The modular interferometer (see Chapter 4) featured a 12·5 μm beam divider and a quartz filter to eliminate the higher frequencies.

effective transmission will occur, since the absorption band will have little effect. Conversely, whenever a maximum of $S'(\bar{\nu})$ coincides with the absorption band a minimum transmission effect will be shown. The net effect is that the interferogram will show a ripple extending to large values of x. Now the width of the "offset fringes", as can be seen from Fig. 3.11, decreases as x increases: eventually the width of the obscuring fringe must become less than the width of the absorption band and the amplitude of the ripple will steadily decrease. This is just what is observed in practice—the sharper the line the further out in the interferogram does the ripple extend. Another phenomenon[87] readily interpretable in this picture is that of "signatures". The pure rotation spectrum of a polar gas—such as HF—occurs in the far infrared region and for linear molecules of this type the spectrum is particularly simple, consisting of a series of more or less equispaced lines. In the case of HF these occur at 40, 80, 120 etc. cm^{-1}. The interferogram obtained when a sample of HF gas is placed in the emerging beam shows localized features called "signatures" at values of x which are integral multiples of 0·125 mm. This is shown in Fig. 3.15 which displays the interferograms obtained with and without the gas sample in the beam. The reason for this is that at values other than these integral multiples the regularly spaced absorption lines and the regularly spaced Michelson "offset fringes" are out of phase with each other and only an average sort of absorption is observed; however, when the path difference is an integral multiple each

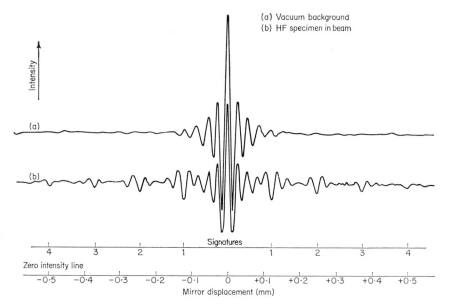

FIG. 3.15. Interferograms obtained with (b) and without (a) hydrogen fluoride (10 mm +760 mm of dry nitrogen) in the beam. The spectral band pass is approximately 60–240 cm^{-1}. The drop of the asymptotic value and the reduction of the zero-path amplitude are both due to absorption by the pressure-broadened pure rotational lines of HF near 80, 120, 160 and 200 cm^{-1}.

absorption line coincides exactly with an instrumental maximum throughput and a much enhanced effective absorption is observed. It is interesting to observe that interferograms of this sort can be interpreted directly without recourse to a computer and measurements of the positions of the signatures give directly the spacing of the lines in the spectrum. The rate of fall-off of signature contrast can also be directly interpreted in terms of the width of the pure rotation lines. In a similar sort of fashion, "channel spectra" of the type discussed earlier lead to interferograms displaying signatures. From the position of the signatures, the thickness of the offending plane parallel component can be inferred, often providing an unambiguous identification. When the component has been identified it can be optically treated to eliminate the "channel" fringes. If this is not possible, the punched paper tape version of the interferogram can be "edited"—that is, the signatures removed by replacing the sampled ordinates in the vicinity of the signature by a constant value equal to the average value in that region. This is a particularly felicitous feature of Fourier transform spectroscopy and the recovery of good quality spectra from a record completely obscured by "channel" fringes is very satisfying.

We have seen, therefore, that by a suitable choice of beam divider thickness and mirror offset it is possible to have two different sets of cosine waves marching across the spectral input function. If, additionally, suitable optical filters are introduced it is possible to isolate narrow spectral regions or, in other words, to turn a Michelson interferometer into a monochromator. The importance of this feature is that such a monochromator will have a higher energy throughput than any comparable system. It will be recalled that even with relatively low reflectivities the throughput at zero path difference of the interferometer approached 70 per cent. Now entirely analogous reasoning shows that at any value of x this figure will apply to those particular frequencies which are maximally transmitted, provided that the beam splitter function also peaks at these frequencies. What this means is that a monochromator can be constructed using realistic materials which has 70 per cent of the ideal throughput of a Michelson interferometer. The possibilities of such devices for gas analysis are very attractive, for the spectral transmission of the instrument can be "tailored" in the manner outlined above to fit a given absorption band of a gas whose concentration is to be measured. In Fig. 3.16 is shown such a spectral transmission arranged for measuring the concentration of UF_6 in the gas phase. This gas absorbs[88] very strongly at 186 cm⁻¹, the band having a half-width of 20 cm⁻¹. The

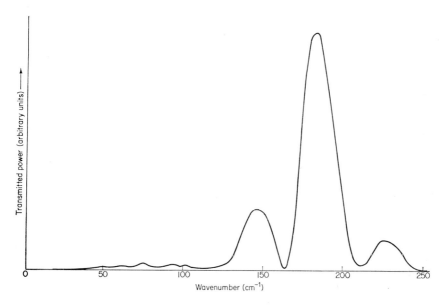

FIG. 3.16. Spectrum of the radiation transmitted through the experimental arrangement of Fig. 3.14 but with additionally a caesium iodide filter to suppress the low (< 140 cm⁻¹) frequency component.[86]

perfect fit obtained is obvious as is also the zero transmission at 164 and 205 cm^{-1} where two pure rotational lines of HF (an unavoidable impurity) occur. An instrument made with such a monochromator coupled to a long path cell will be very sensitive to low concentrations of UF_6 and quite insensitive to any conceivable impurity.

We have seen, therefore, that the operation of Michelson interferometers in the far infrared introduces new features and concepts when compared with orthodox spectroscopy. The need to develop new ways of thinking has tended to put workers trained in the older methods off the new. Additionally, a good grasp of what is going on is essential if the many pitfalls are to be avoided. However, the interesting feature is that when such pitfalls are avoided and the optimum mode of operation achieved everything works in the operator's favour. Experimental methods and results will be discussed in the next chapter, but here it is only necessary to remark that present-day interferometric observations completely outclass those from any other delay-type technique and yet there is little doubt that these interferometric methods are nowhere near the limit of their exploitation.

CHAPTER 4

The Practice of Interferometric Spectroscopy in the Submillimetre Region

As described in the preceding chapters, there are occasional submillimetre observations best done by the use of grating or prism spectrometers; in situations requiring ultra-high resolution harmonic generators are indispensable, but for the vast majority of submillimetre experiments interferometric techniques are far superior. In the frequency range above 50 cm^{-1} the Michelson interferometer is the preferred form, but for lower frequencies it encounters competition from the lamellar grating which does not suffer from the disadvantage of transmission minima arising from multiple-beam interference in the beam divider. In this chapter commercially available Michelson interferometers and lamellar gratings will be discussed and the various optical and electronic components in them will be analysed. The scope and range of modern interferometric spectroscopy will be illustrated by suitable spectra but discussion of the physical interpretation of the observations will be postponed until the next chapter.

4.1. Commercial Michelson Interferometers

Early forms of Michelson interferometric spectrometers began to come on the market about 1962 from the English companies, Sir Howard Grubb Parsons and Co. Ltd and the Research and Industrial Instrument Co. Ltd. The instruments were quite large in physical size and were adapted from laboratory prototypes developed[89] at the National Physical Laboratory at Teddington. The basic engineering concept was that all the optical components were rigidly mounted on a steel baseplate and that the baseplate itself was contained inside a large steel vessel which could be evacuated to obviate absorption by water vapour. Not surprisingly, these instruments were not only large and cumbersome but also very heavy. From 1965 onwards a radically new design was developed[90] at the National Physical Laboratory based on the modular principle and instruments constructed using this principle were small and light with no sacrifice of luminosity. The instrument is illustrated in Fig. 4.1 and some idea of its physical size can be gained by

Fig. 4.1. NPL–Grubb Parsons modular Michelson interferometer.

observing that its maximum dimension is 50 cm. Basically the baseplate and vacuum tank of the old design have been amalgamated into a single entity which is "wrapped round" and supports all the optical components. The overall instrument is made up of a number of modules which can be readily removed or restored, thus ensuring maximum accessibility and maximum flexibility of experimental disposition.

The layout of the various modules and components is shown in Fig. 4.2. The heart of the system is a "cube" C made from aluminium alloy which is bored through between opposite pairs of vertical faces, the resulting holes being finished in each face with a 45° chamfer to provide vacuum sealing against the O-ring carried on the male flange of the component to be mounted on that face. From the top to the bottom of the cube is cut a diagonal slot to carry the beam divider B which is a stretched film of a polymer held in a metal frame. Vacuum sealing of the top and bottom faces of the cube is effected by means of flat plates carrying an O-ring in a recess. Four components are attached to the cube:

1. a source unit S containing a Philips 125 HPK medium-pressure mercury lamp with a concentric perforated aluminium cylinder A serving as a chopper;

2. a moving mirror unit M which features a 6 cm diameter plane mirror P attached directly to the non-rotating shaft of a micrometer R. The spindle

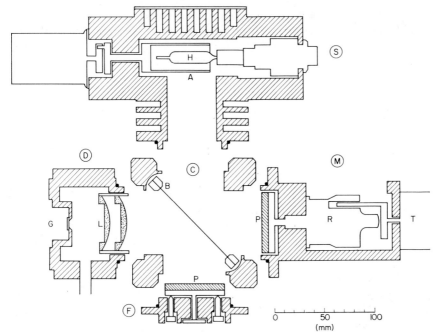

FIG. 4.2. Plan section of the NPL–Grubb Parsons modular Michelson interferometer. See text for explanation of symbols.

passes through a vacuum seal and the micrometer is driven by a stepping motor T;

3. a fixed-mirror unit F which has a 6 cm diameter plane mirror P mounted on a backing plate which is held under tension by a spring against three screws mounted on a fixed plate. Manipulation of these screws enables tilt adjustments to be made;

4. a specimen chamber unit D which also carries the condensing lens L and the Golay detector G.

The mercury lamp generates broad-band submillimetre radiation by thermal emission from its quartz envelope and also from the plasma contained in the envelope (see Chapter 5). The lamp also gives out radiation near 1 μm which is detected by three photodiodes (after being modulated by the chopper) and the voltage output from these serves as a reference signal for the phase-synchronous amplifier (see Fig. 4.7) which also receives the output signal from the Golay cell. The chopper frequency used is $16\frac{2}{3}$ Hz which is perhaps rather high for the Golay cell to respond to optimally, but this frequency is easy to achieve using synchronous motors operating off 50 Hz mains. It is also desirable to work at as high a frequency as possible to minimize the effects of noise in the subsequent electronic chain for, as is well known, the noise power is inversely proportional to the frequency for low frequencies. No collimating arrangements are normally used and the interferometer therefore works in divergent radiation; the optical paths through the instrument are illustrated in Fig. 4.3. It would be rather difficult to have any lenses

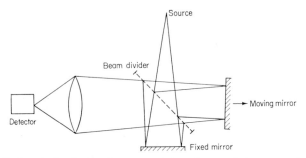

FIG. 4.3. Optical paths in the interferometer; it is to be noted that no collimating optics are employed, so the instrument is truly a Michelson (rather than a Twyman–Green) interferometer.

near to the very hot lamp, and mirror collimating systems are rather awkward, but (and rather fortunately) collimating optics are unnecessary in the normal mode of operation since the image of the extended source (≈ 200 mm^2) is a fair match for the entrance aperture of the Golay cell (≈ 9 mm^2) using just the one condensing lens (i.e. $\times 7$ demagnification). No extra efficiency in radiation transfer would therefore accrue from the presence of a collimating lens; all that would happen is that more radiation would be collected from the smaller area of the lamp "seen" by the detector. Sometimes long-path cells are required and these are customarily inserted between the cube and module D. Under these circumstances it now becomes advantageous to introduce an extra lens to provide more efficient energy transfer and this is inserted in the exit plane of the cube C. The beam divider is nearly always made from polyethylene terephthalate which has the advantage of a high refractive index (1·69) and is also transparent to visible radiation. It is therefore possible to align the interferometer by removing module D and adjusting the fixed mirror until the two images of the source (one from each mirror) seen through the exit path of C are coincident. When doing this it is essential to wear dark spectacles to prevent damage to the eyes from the intense visible and ultraviolet radiation from the lamp. Polyethylene terephthalate film (known under the trade name of Melinex in England and Mylar in the United States) is available in a range of thicknesses. The most commonly used thickness is 6 μm which has a first minimum of transmission (see equation 3.61) near 500 cm^{-1} and is therefore very valuable for broad-band observations over the range 70–430 cm^{-1}. Thicker beam dividers are used progressively to cover the lower frequency region, thicknesses of up to 240 μm having been employed at one time or another. The thicker beam dividers do, however, introduce a whole array of minima across the observed spectrum and this implies that meaningful observations can only be made in narrow spectral regions. As an example of this, Fig. 4.4 shows the observation of the

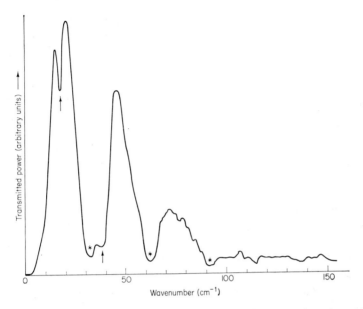

FIG. 4.4. Lattice spectrum of CCl₄ observed with an interferometer, featuring a 100 μm polyethylene terephthalate beam divider. True absorption features are indicated by arrows (↑) and instrumental transmission minima by stars (★).

19 cm⁻¹ band of crystalline carbon tetrachloride using a 100 μm beam divider. This beam divider produces minima at approximately 31, 62, 93 etc. cm⁻¹ (the actual values differing slightly from expected due to dispersion) and it will be seen that the very weak 19 cm⁻¹ band is clearly observed, whereas the strong 38 cm⁻¹ band is only observed as a hump on the side of the 31 cm⁻¹ transmission minimum. This figure also illustrates another drawback to the use of thick polyethylene terephthalate beam dividers, namely the heavy attenuation of far infrared radiation in this polar polymer. Polyethylene terephthalate is quite heavily absorbing in a very broad-band sort of fashion throughout the submillimetre region, the absorption coefficient increasing with frequency.[85] The net effect is that, despite the rapidly rising black-body characteristic, the energy transmitted through successive maxima first increases but then rapidly falls off. In Fig. 4.4 a good deal of this attenuation is ascribable to scatter from the polycrystalline specimen, but nevertheless

even in the spectrum observed without any specimen in the beam the power reaching the detector is largest at 45 cm^{-1} where the second transmission maximum occurs. Polyethylene and polypropylene films are occasionally used as beam dividers and they are certainly more transparent than poly-ethylene terephthalate; however, the effect of the lower reflectivities due to the lower ($n \approx 1\cdot45$) refractive indices is such that the transmission of energy to the detector is lower. This is not so serious a drawback in the region above 100 cm^{-1} where there is ample radiation from the source and the transmission minima observed with thick films can sometimes be used advantageously in conjunction with filters to isolate narrow bands for high-resolution studies. As an example, a 110 μm thick polyethylene beam divider used with quartz and caesium iodide as low- and high-pass filters respectively will give a total transmission band for the interferometer extending only from 170 to 190 cm^{-1}. It is of course worth pointing out that the demerits of polyethylene terephthal-ate only apply to attempts to use it for observations in the higher transmission regions of its characteristic. If, as is generally the case, the thickness has been chosen so that the region of interest coincides with the first transmission maximum, the losses here will be low and the attenuation at higher frequencies will be welcome as a further contribution to the experimental need to restrict the spectral pass band solely to the region of interest. In addition to the broad-band absorption, a few sharp absorption bands are observed in polyethylene terephthalate films; the strongest of these occurs at 380 cm^{-1} and there are weaker features at 26 and 12 cm^{-1}, but none is sufficiently intense with the thicknesses of film used in interferometers to cause any experimental incon-venience.

After partial reflection and partial transmission at the beam divider, the split beams encounter the two mirrors of the interferometer. The fixed mirror design has evolved considerably since the instrument was first constructed and now features adjusting screws passing through vacuum seals to the exterior. It is thus possible to correct any small misalignments which sometimes occur when the instrument is evacuated. The screw adjustments are amply fine enough to give high-quality interferograms over the whole range to which the instrument has been applied. This is illustrated in Fig. 3.6. The moving mirror design is the most controversial feature of the instrument. The require-ments on the moving mirror have been discussed in detail in Chapter 3 but may be summarized here as being (a) the mirror surface must move parallel to its original position accurately to better than $\frac{1}{4}\lambda$ where λ is the minimum wavelength to be studied, and (b) the increments of path difference should be very accurately equal in magnitude. To achieve these twin requirements earlier interferometers featured sophisticated drives using pistons in cylinders or carriages riding on optically polished glass blocks, together with moiré fringe crossed gratings to sense the amount of mirror movement. The modular interferometer features a mirror connected directly to the spindle of a micrometer and the movement sensing is achieved merely by noting (electronically of course) the amount of rotation of the micrometer thimble. In essence therefore we are relying on the accuracy of the micrometer lead screw to provide accurately spaced increments of path difference. Screw threads are subject to periodic pitch errors and it may be shown that if these are significant then the resulting spectrum will contain artefacts which are complicated Bessel functions of the frequency. This phenomenon has actually been demonstrated using an admittedly poor lead screw (from a small lathe) on an interferometer irradiated with the nearly perfectly monochromatic radiation from an HCN laser at $29 \cdot 712$ cm^{-1}, a technique which has promising applications for testing lead screws.[91] In common with most imperfections in interferometers, the effects of lead screw errors get progressively worse as the frequency rises. The modular interferometer was originally devised to cover the range below 200 cm^{-1}, and in this region no artefacts have ever been observed even to resolutions represented by spectra such as in Fig. 5.2. There is, however, no obvious reason why the instrument should not be used to much higher frequency; values up to 1000 cm^{-1} are suggested by the

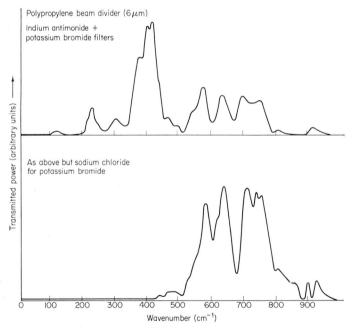

FIG. 4.5. High-frequency performance of the interferometer at moderate resolution. The ordinates of the two insets are not to scale. The discrete features arise from absorption in the beam divider.

flatness of stretched film beam dividers and the quality of the mirror adjustments, and it is therefore most important to know if the micrometer lead screw
is good enough to obtain high-quality spectra in this higher frequency region.
The moderate resolution results shown in Fig. 4.5 indicate no observable
artefacts. These spectra were obtained with alkali halide high-pass filters and
all the observed features can be assigned either to known absorption bands
in the materials in the beam—principally the polypropylene beam divider—
or to interference effects in the beam divider. Nevertheless, the artefacts might
only appear at higher resolutions; that this is not in fact the case is shown
in Fig. 4.6 which illustrates the ν_2 band of HCN near 720 cm^{-1} observed at

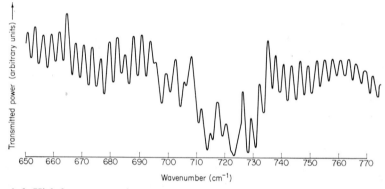

FIG. 4.6. High-frequency performance of the interferometer at 1 cm^{-1} resolution. The
Figure shows the P, Q, R branches of the ν_2 band of HCN. Gas pressure is 6 torr, temperature 293 K and path length 5 m. The interferometer featured has a 4 μm polyethylene
terephthalate beam divider and a 1600 μm polypropylene window. Spectral bandwidth
limitation is by means of indium antimonide and potassium bromide filters.

a resolution of 1 cm^{-1}. All the observed lines in this spectrum can be assigned
to the P, Q and R branches of the ν_2 band, together with some instrumental
absorption bands in the same region. The spectrum is also very interesting
in another connection since it illustrates the frequency contractions discussed
in Chapter 3. With the relatively high apertures used in far infrared interferometers this can become significant and values of approximately 1 cm^{-1} are
expected at 800 cm^{-1}. The average frequency contraction shown by the sharp
lines in Fig. 4.6 is 1·5 cm^{-1}. It will be seen therefore that, apart from the
need to apply corrections to observed frequencies, the mirror arrangements are satisfactory for use up to 1000 cm^{-1}. The micrometer is rotated
by a stepping motor which carries out 200 steps in one revolution and, since
this is 0·5 mm of micrometer travel, each step is 5×10^{-4} cm which corresponds
to a cut-off or aliasing frequency of 1000 cm^{-1}. The current pulse to the motor
causing it to step also activates a circuit which delivers a triggering pulse to
the paper tape recorder (see Fig. 4.7). If observations are being restricted to

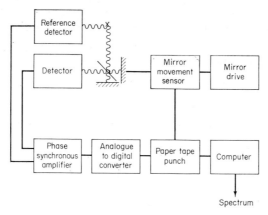

Fɪɢ. 4.7. Schematic diagram of the complete instrument.

low-frequency regions, it is unnecessary and expensive in computer time to sample the interferogram as frequently as even 5×10^{-4} cm. This can be obviated by trigger circuits which deliver a triggering pulse after every second, third, etc. driving pulse.

The returning beams from the mirrors are recombined by the beam divider and part of the radiation then travels to the condensing lens. The lens is a doublet usually made from low-density polyethylene but occasionally from polypropylene or TPX (poly-4-methylpentene-1). For high-frequency applications the lens is normally made from high-purity zone-refined silicon since the polymers start to absorb quite heavily above 500 cm^{-1}. Silicon lenses have low effective transmissions because of losses due to reflection, approximately 25 per cent of the incident radiation being reflected from each of the two surfaces, but the reflection loss is essentially independent of frequency and losses of this order can be tolerated in the 700 cm^{-1} region where there is ample radiation from the lamp. The spectral characteristics of lens materials will be discussed later in a general review of submillimetre materials. The convergent beam from the lens then reaches the detector after traversing a suitable thickness of black polyethylene (or for high-frequency applications indium antimonide) to eliminate near infrared radiation. The detector most commonly used is the Golay[22] cell which works by detecting the heating effect of the incoming radiation upon a gas contained in a heat absorbing cavity. As the gas heats up so it expands and dilates a diaphragm the movement of which is detected by a light beam and a photocell. Because of its mode of operation, the Golay cell cannot respond very quickly to changes in the intensity of the radiation and for this reason the chopper frequency has to be relatively low. The optimum frequency is between 1 and 2 Hz, but higher frequencies are preferred in practice to circumvent the electronic difficulties of working at such low frequencies. The Golay cell is perhaps the best purely thermal detector available and can detect an energy input of 4×10^{-9} W with unit signal-to-noise ratio in a bandwidth of 1·0 Hz. The total power arriving at the detector over the range 0–200 cm^{-1} in the conventional modular set-up is calculated to be approximately 1 μW in the absence of any absorbing specimen. The instrument will therefore be expected to produce interferograms with a signal-to-noise ratio of approximately 250 to 1 when the electronic amplifier and rectifier have a time constant of 1 second. Values in excess of 100 to 1 are found experimentally. The direct proportionality between input power and signal-to-noise ratio arises because, in the far infrared, the principal noise source is the thermal agitation of electrons in resistors—the so-called Johnson noise. Compared with this, the noise due to random fluctuation of photon arrival is negligible and the system is said to be detector-noise limited. In the visible region, of course, using photomultipliers, the situation is the other way round and such instruments are said to be photon-noise limited. Under these circumstances the signal-to-noise ratio is proportional to the square root of the input power. Other detectors are sometimes used in submillimetre work. The pyroelectric detector developed by Putley[23] using a triglycine sulphate crystal is inferior to the Golay cell in detectivity but has a very much shorter response time (1 μs). It is therefore quite valuable for work involving pulsed lasers (see Chapter 6) and is coming into common use in the metrological applications of submillimetre interferometers. In these instruments, which are used in industrial situations, the pyroelectric detector has the advantage of robustness as well as room-temperature operation. There are several detectors which operate at liquid helium temperatures and they are all superior to the Golay cell in detectivity but they are normally only used in special applications because of the need for cryogenic facilities. Of these, the two favoured varieties are the carbon resistance bolometer,[92] which is particularly simple to fabricate, and the indium antimonide photoconducting detector[23] which is virtually essential for high-quality photometry in the 2–20 cm^{-1} region. In this range, the indium antimonide detector has a noise equivalent power of 5×10^{-13} W into a bandwidth of 1 Hz and this detector has been used[93] in conjunction with the modular interferometer to give interferograms with a signal-to-noise ratio in excess of 100 to 1. With heavily absorbing samples, such as liquid water in the beam, transformed spectra have been obtained in which the scatter in the calculated optical density between runs is only a few per cent at frequencies less than 10 cm^{-1}. Performance of this quality is not possible with Golay cells. The response times of the solid-state detectors are quite short (≈ 1 μs) and much higher chopping frequencies may be used. This gives a further improvement in signal-to-noise quality because the noise power in the amplifying chain is not "white" but varies inversely with the frequency.

Chopping frequencies as high as 400 Hz have been used with the Putley detector.

The output from the detector is fed to a phase-synchronous amplifier together with the reference signal which comes either from the photodiodes mentioned earlier or, as in some variant instruments, from a generator mounted on the chopper shaft. The two signals are passed through high-gain narrow-bandwidth amplifiers and are then combined in a phase-synchronous detector. The reference signal acts as a switch determining the timing of a full wave rectifying circuit. The output of this rectifier can be a positive, negative, or zero d.c. voltage depending on the phase of the reference signal with respect to the detector signal. It is therefore necessary to have a phase-shifting circuit in the amplifier receiving the reference signal so that the d.c. output can be maximized. When this has been achieved, noise signals 180° out of phase with the desired signal will be completely excluded and noise signals of other phase angles more or less attenuated. The output of the rectifier is fed to a resistance-capacity (RC) smoothing network which improves the signal-to-noise ratio in the final interferogram by progressively attenuating the higher frequency noise whilst having little effect on the slowly varying signal.

The use of frequency selective amplifiers, phase-synchronous rectifiers and RC smoothing circuits is common practice in infrared instrumentation but their presence in a Fourier transform spectrometer introduces some novel complications. When using a grating instrument, it is merely necessary to ensure that the time taken to scan each spectral element is longer than the finite response time of the electronic system. The operator will set the response time of the instrument so that an acceptable signal-to-noise ratio prevails in the spectrum and, having determined the time constant in this way, the proper scan speed will follow. In the case of a two-beam interferometer illuminated by monochromatic radiation, the moving mirror is generating in the detector an a.c. signal whose frequency is set by the wavenumber of the radiation and the velocity of the mirror. If these two quantities are designated $\bar{\nu}$ and ν_m, it follows that the corresponding frequency will be given by $\nu = 2\bar{\nu}\nu_m$. If the radiation is modulated, the a.c. signal will appear as two side bands separated from the modulation frequency by the frequency interval ν. The highest wavenumber that should be present in the radiation (see Section 3.5) is the folding or Nyquist wavenumber $\bar{K}_0$. If in a practical example this were 1000 cm^{-1} and the mirror velocity 1/2000 cm s^{-1}, it would follow that ν would be 1 Hz. The tuned amplifier should therefore have a peak response at the modulation frequency and have a bandwidth of at least 2 Hz, so that the sidebands will be transmitted without attenuation. The output of the phase-synchronous rectifier will be a wave of frequency ν, and it follows that the time constant of the subsequent RC smoothing circuit should not be greater, in this instance, than 1 second. If longer time constants are required, the moving mirror velocity must be reduced.

So far this is fairly analogous to the grating case, but the multiplex operation of the instrument and the process of Fourier transformation which is to be applied to its output make us ask why we need noise suppression in the instrument at all. Basically, the cosine wave, which each wavenumber element produces, is observed by the detector for the whole time of the recording process, and the precision of determination of its amplitude will be set by this time quantity, which is the time available for averaging. The observing time is frequently of the order of many minutes and in a very real way this is the time constant which determines the signal-to-noise ratio of the final spectrum. It is a commonplace experience to feed a very noisy interferogram into the computer and receive back a quite acceptable spectrum. The reason why additional noise suppression is necessary in the recording electronics lies in the finite discrimination of the recording system. If the noise oscillations are large compared to the signal, they will fill the available dynamic range of the digitizer and the oscillations of the signal waveform may be less than the lower limit of discrimination. With noise suppression the signal may be amplified further without overloading the recording system and more true information passed to the computer. A corollary of this is that the noise suppression should not be taken too far and good practice is to set the noise oscillations so that they have an amplitude equal to one "bit" of the digital system. The presence of the noise voltage is capable of occasionally lifting a real oscillation to within the compass of the digital system and improved spectral quality results. The operation of the computer sorts out the various frequency components in the observed interferogram and assigns them to their proper place in the spectrum. Naturally it does this for the noise components as well as the signal and so the computer acts as an electronic smoothing network which separates the signal frequencies from the great bulk of the noise frequencies. This being the case, it might be thought that noise suppression is unnecessary, since the computer will filter off noise which does not lie in the signal channels, and that noise which does may not be preferentially attenuated by any process other than longer observation. This conclusion is also a fallacy, the reason this time being the finite sampling of the interferogram. We have said previously that wavenumbers in excess of $\bar{K}_0$ must not be present in the incident radiation because they will be aliased about $\bar{K}_0$ and appear spuriously in the fundamental interval. Noise frequencies in excess of $\bar{K}_0$ will also be aliased and the noise separated from the signal channels will promptly be returned therein. It follows that the observing system should have a time constant such that wavenumbers up to $\bar{K}_0$ are more or less unattenuated whilst those above $\bar{K}_0$ are severely attenuated. This is the same conclusion that was reached on other grounds above. In an experimental situation the numerical value of $\bar{K}_0$ may exceed the highest wavenumber actually present and in this case the time constant may be increased with profit.

The output voltage of the electronic system is, in common parlance, an analogue record of the interferogram. By this is meant that, presuming the detector and electronic chain to be perfectly linear in their response, the output voltage is directly proportional to the radiant power arriving at the detector. The interferogram in its analogue form has still to be transformed to give the spectrum and it is here that procedural divergence is first encountered. The traditional method is to send the analogue voltage to an analogue-to-digital converter (either a digital voltmeter or shaft encoder attached to a pen recorder) and to feed the digital output of this device (punched tape, punched cards or magnetic tape) to a digital computer which effects the Fourier transformation in the manner outlined in Chapter 3. An alternative method now available is to feed the analogue record directly to an analogue computer, a device, essentially a wave analyser, which finds a finite set of cosine waves which would add up to give the observed interferogram. The output of the analogue computer is a record of cosine wave amplitude versus frequency for a finite set of frequencies, that is, the spectrum. The analogue method has attractions for the routine analyst who will be running many spectra a day, always over the same range and with the same resolution. In operation the instrument is much akin to a single-beam dispersing instrument, since all the operations can be made fully automatic and all that is necessary is to put in the sample and switch the instrument on. At the end of the run the spectrum is drawn out quite automatically. If a sample-free background spectrum has been recorded beforehand, the instrument becomes comparable with a double-beam monochromator giving a record of percentage transmission versus frequency. Both methods are capable of doing all that is required of a spectroscopic system since they are merely alternative ways of effecting the essential Fourier transformation, but in practice for any given application one is generally superior to the other. The digital system is much better for applications involving experimental flexibility—i.e. those with varying spectral range and varying resolution—or in applications where the output data is to be further processed. This might occur, for example, when studying very heavily absorbing samples when it might be desirable to take the mean of several spectra to improve the photometric quality. The analogue system is at present cheaper and quicker, since there is no question of having to wait for time to become available on a big computer; furthermore, the system is suitable for operation by unskilled labour. The situation is rapidly changing, however, and the price and size of the small digital computers suitable for Fourier transformation are both decreasing. It may well be that in the next ten years the use of analogue methods may become obsolete.

At this point it is worth pointing out that the two methods outlined above are both aperiodic methods. The interferogram is observed only once, stored in some way and then broken up into its component cosine waves separately and in a time no way related to the observing time. Periodic methods, in which the mirror moves very rapidly back and forth across the zero path difference position and the detector output is simply analysed by a filter network, have been used only occasionally in the far infrared.[94] The basic difficulty is once more the shortage of radiant power. The interferogram is made up of cosine waves with path difference as the independent variable. When the moving mirror is oscillating periodically over the interferogram the effect, as shown earlier, is to transform to time as the independent variable and the interferogram is now made up of a number of audio-frequency signals. The contribution to the interferogram from signals in the audio-frequency range ν to $(\nu + \Delta\nu)$ is found by feeding the detector output to a narrow-band filter having this frequency range of response. The performance of narrow-band filters improves with frequency, so it will be necessary to oscillate the mirror quite quickly and the time constant of the rectifying circuit will have to be very short. The signal-to-noise ratio will therefore be poor unless each frequency band is studied for some time to allow effective integration. It will be seen on reflection that this is tantamount to throwing away the multiplex advantage which the aperiodic methods enjoy.[30] Periodic methods have been used in the near infrared region where the overabundance of radiant power permits this extravagance, but it is unlikely that they will have any application in the submillimetre region unless very much more intense sources become available. An interesting feature of periodic methods is that it is unnecessary to use amplitude modulation of the radiation from the lamp since the transformation from a d.c. to an a.c. signal is introduced by the oscillation of the mirror itself. This does imply a gain in radiant throughput since the detector is observing the lamp all the time instead of only half the time, there now being no chopper blades to interrupt the radiation. Nevertheless, this is not sufficient to compensate for the loss of the multiplex advantage, but there is a technique closely related to the periodic method called phase modulation (which will be discussed later in this chapter) which manages to combine both advantages.

The modular interferometer shown in Figs. 4.1 and 4.2, developed at NPL and now commercially available from Sir Howard Grubb Parsons and Co. Ltd, has proved a wonderfully flexible instrument for submillimetre spectroscopy. A rather similar modular instrument[95] which uses mirror optics and is larger has been developed by the Research and Industrial Instrument Co. Ltd. It has likewise enjoyed a great deal of success and popularity. The optical layout of this latter instrument is shown in Fig. 4.8. Interferometric methods were slow to win general acceptance because of essentially irrational objections to a computer based spectroscopic system. Basically spectroscopists

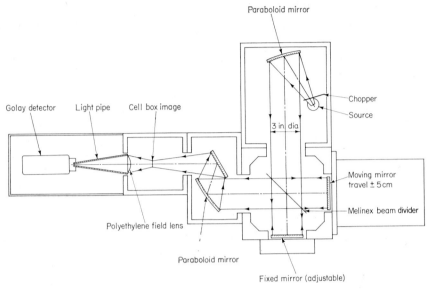

FIG. 4.8. Optical layout of the Research and Industrial Instrument Company's modular Michelson interferometer; this instrument operates in quasi-parallel radiation.

wanted submillimetre spectrometers that had the same comforting shape and type of operation as their familiar mid-infrared instruments. Emotional forces of this type met a response from the instrument manufacturers who produced wonderfully complex feats of engineering that enabled them to manufacture automatic double-beam grating spectrophotometers covering the far infrared to as low a frequency as 33 cm^{-1}. Not surprisingly, these instruments are extremely expensive. An astute awareness of these attitudes led the Research and Industrial Instrument Company to develop their analogue computer to go with a Michelson interferometer to give a system having much in common —externally that is—with a conventional instrument. Similar thinking by the Coderg Company led them to develop a non-modular interferometer working into a real time computer. With this instrument it is also possible to view the progress of the computation on an oscilloscope and thus once more have the comforting feeling of immediacy.† However, there is growing up a new generation of spectroscopists who do not have the built-in prejudice of their seniors. New types of problems are being encountered and in chemical spectroscopy highly reactive and insoluble compounds are being studied and

† This facility does have the very real advantage of telling the operator if anything has gone wrong with the registration of the interferogram. For very high resolution work, involving observation times of some hours, this could prevent a considerable waste of instrumental time.

the ease with which these may be tackled, using the highly flexible modular instruments, is gaining them general acceptance as the normal and proper spectrometers for the submillimetre region.

When homogeneous samples such as gases, liquids or single crystals are to be studied and the overall absorption is quite weak and low resolution adequate, grating instruments can compete with interferometers, but if any of these conditions is not satisfied the spectra from interferometers are superior. Grating instruments also suffer from three snags that are absent from interferometric instruments. Firstly, grating instruments are usually so large that it is not practical to evacuate them and the difficulty of water vapour absorption can be only partly obviated by flushing with dry nitrogen. The reader need only be reminded of the famous spectrum of water vapour, published[96] in Herzberg's "Infrared and Raman Spectra", recorded in an instrument carefully dried with phosphorus pentoxide, to realize that this is not very satisfactory. It has to be faced that there is always a great risk of misleading results when observations are being made in regions of heavy water vapour absorption. The second snag is the problem of stray radiation. In an interferometer, high frequency radiation may reach the detector but it will not be reported to the computer unless it modulates the interferogram. If it does this it will be assigned to its proper place in the computed spectrum (provided that its frequency does not exceed the Nyquist or Folding frequency), and if it does not modulate the interferogram it will be ignored. The only risk is if the high-frequency radiation drives the detector into a non-linear region of its characteristic, but this can always be readily avoided by the use of filters or attenuators. In monochromators, however, stray radiation cannot be distinguished from that properly emerging from the exit slit except by laborious tests on standard samples. There is no doubt that stray radiation is a serious hazard, especially at the low-frequency end of the spectral range of a grating instrument. Some workers have actually reported to the author their failure to observe the well-characterized band of crystalline carbon tetrachloride at 38 cm^{-1}, this failure being presumably due to the combined effects of the two hazards just mentioned. The third snag is not so serious since it can always be avoided in practice. It arises because long integrating times will be necessary, in the electronics following the detector of a dispersive instrument, to make up for the loss in luminous throughput. If the spectrum is scanned through quickly the absorption bands will be reported at erroneous frequencies because of the response lag. The remedy is to observe very slowly and preferably twice with different scanning speeds, but this can be irksome in practice. The problem does not arise in interferometers, for if the interferogram is scanned too quickly the only effect is to progressively attenuate the intensities of high-frequency components. Bands may therefore be reported of incorrect intensity but they will always occur at the correct frequency. In this it is assumed that the finite aperture corrections discussed in Chapter 3 have been made.

The desirability of modern interferometers for submillimetre experiments arises from two distinct features. Firstly, we have the high throughput and multiplex advantages which all forms of the instrument share, and secondly we have the advantages of the small size and modular construction. The former advantages are so well known and have anyway been so fully discussed earlier that we will here merely remark that spectra such as those in Figs. 5.6 and 5.4, which arise from polycrystalline (and hence heavily scattering) samples, could not be obtained in any other way. Similar remarks apply to the high-resolution results quoted in Chapter 5. The advantages that accrue from the small size and modular construction are less well known. Conventional spectrometers are usually so bulky and so integral in construction that it is necessary to take the specimen to the spectrometer and not vice versa. Normally this is not a handicap but situations can arise where it may be. Imagine that an extremely reactive solid compound has been made in a dry-box free of oxygen and water and that we require its submillimetre spectrum. It might be very awkward to enclose the sample in a suitable cell or prepare it in a mull form in a non-reacting dispersant. The small interfero-meter could be included inside the dry-box and mounted in the fashion shown in Fig. 4.9. In this configuration the specimen could be placed on a sheet of polyethylene or other suitable material just as a heap of powder immediately in front of the Golay window and be held in position by gravity. No cell or mulling agent would be required and the specimen need never leave the dry-box. Other applications where the small size is distinctly advantageous are in astrophysical measurements where the equipment has to be conveyed to high-altitude observing stations or flown in balloons or high-flying aircraft.

The modular construction is particularly advantageous in two types of experiment. Firstly when it is desired to introduce the specimen between the beam divider and one of the mirrors, as in Fourier refractometry which will be discussed in detail later in this chapter, and secondly when long-path cells or other special forms of specimen holder are being used. The commonest form of long-path cell for the study of gaseous samples is based on the design of White[97] and is commonly known as a White cell. It consists basically of three spherical mirrors all with the same radius of curvature (ensured in practice by cutting all three out of one much larger mirror) arranged as in Fig. 4.10. An image of the source is formed near the edge of the unique mirror and the cone of radiation diverges to fill one of the pair of mirrors at the other end of the cell. From here the radiation is brought to a focus on the surface of the unique mirror and then diverges to fill the second mirror of the pair. The returning beam from this mirror can either leave the system (as in Fig. 4.10) or again form an image on the surface of the unique mirror

FIG. 4.9. Configurational flexibility of the NPL modular interferometer; this position is convenient for reactive specimens or for those liquids and powders which cannot readily be studied in conventional cells.

and thus traverse the cell four more times. The total path through the system is always equal to $4nL$ where n is an integer and L is the separation of the mirrors. The value of n is determined by the tilt adjustments on the second mirror of the pair. This design is a particularly good one since it features a high luminous throughput (determined by L and the physical size of the mirror pair) whilst still permitting the use of very long effective paths. The only instrumental loss of radiant power arises from imperfect reflection at the mirrors, but in the far infrared region especially metals reflect extremely well (> 99 per cent) and very little loss is experienced in practice.

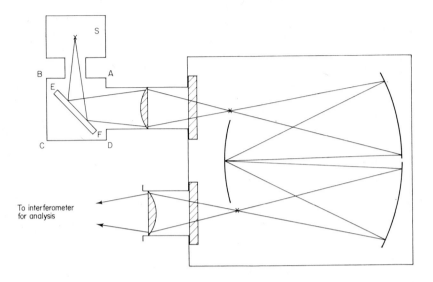

TPX lenses and windows

FIG. 4.10. Long-path cell for the observation of the far infrared spectra of gases; S is the source module, ABCD a cube module, E an alkali halide or metallic plane mirror, and the windows and lenses are constructed from TPX (poly-4-methylpentene-1) which is described later.

The modular construction of modern interferometers enables them to be attached very readily to White cells. The source module is removed and attached to another "cube" (ABCD in Fig. 4.10) which features a 45° reflecting plate of an alkali halide to act as a reflection reststrahlen filter. A cylindrical tube featuring the standard flanges then connects this "cube" to the White cell and also carries the lens to form an image of the source in the correct place. At the exit window of the cell another cylindrical tube connects the cell to the "cube" of the interferometer. The lenses and windows are constructed from the polymer TPX (poly-4-methylpentene-1) which is transparent both in the visible region and in the far infrared. It is thus possible to determine the total path being used by counting the number of source images on the front surface of the unique mirror. A photograph of the assembly is shown in Fig. 4.11.

In normal investigations, the specimen mounted in a suitable holder (the Research and Industrial Instrument Company's FH-01 cell is particularly convenient) is placed in the convergent beam of radiation in module D of

FIG. 4.11. Modular interferometer coupled to a long path cell for the study of gases. In this instance, the gas was the highly corrosive UF_6 so the cell and gas handling valves were all constructed from aluminium.

Fig. 4.2. However, if accurate photometry is required, it is better to work in quasi-parallel radiation and then an additional module[98] can be inserted between C and D. This is illustrated in Fig. 4.12. The additional lens makes the radiation quasi-parallel and after traversal of the specimen the beam can be focussed down on to the Golay cell by the normal lens, since this need only be moved a short distance from its conventional position. If it is desired to study the specimen at low temperature, it may be mounted on the cold finger of a Dewar vessel protruding into the module. This illustrates an auxiliary advantage of interferometers for, since they are evacuated, cryogenic techniques are quite straightforward and there are no additional windows to mist up and cause experimental difficulties. Other modules may readily be constructed. The tubes which connect one module to another can be sealed with suitable windows to make single-pass gas cells, and modules involving several lenses can be constructed to study small specimens or to study specimens by reflection.

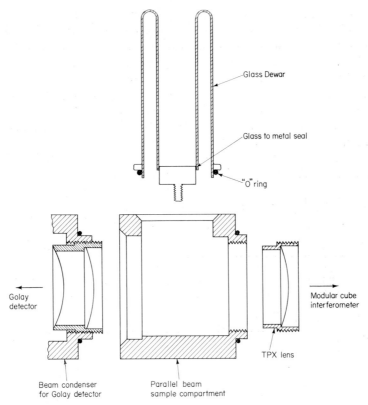

FIG. 4.12. Additional module for producing quasi-parallel radiation through the specimen. This module is inserted between the cube and the Golay cell condenser module D, and like the latter can accommodate a Dewar "finger" for varying the temperature of the specimen.

4.2. Performance of Submillimetre Interferometers

The discussion of commercially available interferometers has been illustrated by specific reference to the NPL modular interferometer developed at the National Physical Laboratory and manufactured by Sir Howard Grubb Parsons & Co. Ltd. This instrument is in common use at NPL but, as mentioned earlier, a similar instrument code-named FS-720 is manufactured by the Research and Industrial Instrument Company and is likewise widely used in many laboratories throughout the world. Both manufacturers supply complete electronic equipment to give digitized interferograms in input forms suitable for a wide range of computers and also supply programmes. In addition, RIIC can supply an analogue computer for immediate transformation of the interferogram. Electronic equipment is also available from other manufacturers for the experimentalist who wishes to assemble his own equipment. Lock-in amplifiers (i.e. narrow-band phase-sensitive amplifier detectors) are available from Princeton Applied Research in the United States and from AIM electronics and the Brookdeal Company in the United Kingdom. Digital voltmeters or shaft encoders can be obtained from a wide range of manufacturers.

The quality of the spectra produced by modern commercial interferometers will be evident from many of the illustrations in this book but, nevertheless, it is worth bringing together a few more examples to emphasize the power and range of the method. The commonest use of interferometers is to observe broad-band spectra at modest resolution of specimens of rather variable optical quality. An example of this is shown in Fig. 4.13 which illustrates the

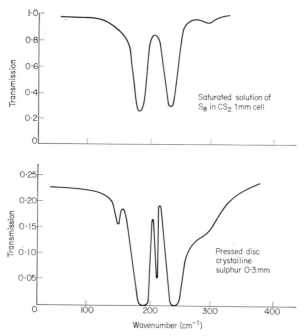

FIG. 4.13. Far infrared spectra of sulphur S_8 (A. Anderson[100] unpublished).

spectra of the octatomic (symmetry D_{4d}) sulphur molecule, both in solution where scattering losses are negligible and as a pressed disc where they are severe. The crystal spectrum is particularly interesting because of the presence of the two weak bands which arise from forbidden transitions made weakly active by the lowered site symmetry of the crystal.[99] The second example (Fig. 4.14) shows the high resolution which can be attained with gaseous samples even in the energy starved low-frequency region. The spectrum is the more remarkable because the path length required was 180 metres. The

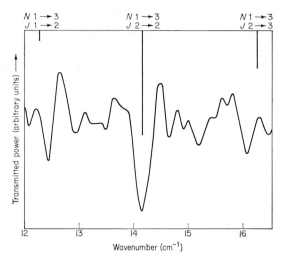

FIG. 4.14. Pure rotational absorption by oxygen[101] near 14 cm^{-1}. Path length is 180 m, pressure 3 atm, and resolution 0·2 cm^{-1}.

absorption lines arise from pure magnetic dipole transitions in the oxygen molecule and, since magnetic dipole transitions are of the order 10^{-5} of electric dipole transitions, pressures in the range of a few atmospheres and path lengths of the order of hundreds of metres are required in order that the lines may have observable intensity. Even with the advantages of interferometers, the spectra obtained under such extreme conditions will show large random fluctuations (in laboratory parlance "noise") which will obscure the detail. Fig. 4.14 is in fact obtained[101] by averaging several spectra in the computer, when, as is well known, the noise is suppressed relative to the real features by the factor $N^{1/2}$ where N is the number of spectra in the average. The fact that the spectra are available in digital forms makes averaging a very straightforward process.

The third example shown in Fig. 4.15 is a reflection spectrum of a potassium chlorate single crystal obtained using a Research and Industrial Instrument Company modular interferometer type FS720, together with a reflectance attachment manufactured by the same company. The spectra were obtained using polarized radiation with the electric vector parallel and perpendicular to the c-axis of the crystal. Ionic crystals absorb so heavily in the submillimetre region that it is normally quite impossible to obtain the absorption coefficient and refractive index spectra of the crystal by transmission methods. However, if the reflection spectra are known over a sufficiently wide range of frequency, the optical constants can be deduced by Kramers–Kronig methods. This method is quite powerful and, since the results can be compared with reasonably good theoretical treatments of lattice dynamics,

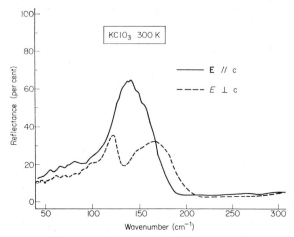

F_IG. 4.15. Reflection spectra of potassium chlorate in the reststrahlen region obtained with Research and Industrial Instrument Company instrumentation. (R. C. Milward, private communication.)

it is assuming considerable importance in solid-state physics. If the crystal has less than cubic symmetry, the optical constants will be anisotropic and reflection spectra will be required in polarized radiation and from several crystal orientations. All the advantages of interferometers detailed above commend them to the solid-state physicist faced with the problem of determining, in a reasonable time, a great deal of data which must be free from errors such as grating ghosts and stray radiation artefacts.

4.3. Computational Aspects

We will not concern ourselves with details of how digital computers are programmed to carry through the Fourier transformation of digitized interferograms (see equation 3.40), since the methods are standard and programmes are available from the manufacturers of interferometers. There are, however, some experimental points to be considered which are germane to the optimum use of interferometric spectrometers within the boundary conditions laid down by the computational processes. The first of these, and one which has attracted a good deal of attention, is the question of how best to use the necessarily finite length of mirror travel available with any given instrument.

It was implied in Chapter 3 that the zero-path position would be set in the middle of the total available mirror travel and the interferogram observed equally on either side of the zero-path position. Early in the development of the art it was pointed out that the available resolution could be doubled if

the zero path difference were set at one end of the mirror travel and as much
as possible of one half of the interferogram observed. The essential point is
that if the interferogram is perfectly symmetrical it is only necessary to observe
one half of it, for the other half can be obtained by reflecting the data about
the zero-path position. This procedure has been adopted for a great deal of
the high-resolution work done with interferometers, but there are two experimental difficulties. Firstly, the analogue record has to be very accurately
symmetrical, i.e. the interferometer has to be in very good alignment and,
secondly, the digital record has to begin with its first point coinciding exactly
with the grand maximum at zero path difference. The first point only calls
for careful experimental technique, but it is most difficult to ensure the second.
As this is the case we must consider what will happen when we transform in
a computer an interferogram, all the points of which are displaced a small
amount η from the positions which the computer assumes them to have.
This is equivalent to replacing equation (3.40) by

$$S'(\bar{\nu}) \propto x_0 \sum_{0}^{+n} W'(mx_0 + \eta) \cos 4\pi\bar{\nu}mx_0. \qquad (4.1)$$

It can be shown that the effect of this displacement is to multiply the true
spectrum function by a cosine function, thus

$$S'(\bar{\nu}) = S(\bar{\nu}) \cos 4\pi\eta\bar{\nu}. \qquad (4.2)$$

The quantity $\eta\bar{\nu}$ cannot exceed $\frac{1}{8}$ in practice, since the first ordinate must be
between $-\frac{1}{2}x_0$ and $+\frac{1}{2}x_0$ of the true position and $\bar{\nu}$, by the sampling theorem,
must be less than $\frac{1}{4}x_0$. We thus have an attenuating factor which reduces the
true intensity progressively with frequency, the degree of attenuation depending on the seriousness of the displacement. It was for this reason that the
standards of photometry in the early days of interferometric spectroscopy
were rather poor. The positions of sharp lines are not affected by the displacement, apart from the changes in line-shape introduced by the distortion of the
apodized spectral window consequent upon the displacement. High-resolution
spectroscopy, in which only the positions of lines and not their intensities are
required, was thus feasible and many successful investigations were carried
out. It has recently been shown[102] that the effect of the displacement can be
undone in the computer and reliable spectra once more obtained by including
the experimentally determined value of η as a parameter in the calculation.
All that is done is to replace x_0 by $x_0 + \eta$ in the arguments of both the Fourier
kernel (cos $4\pi\bar{\nu}mx_0$) and the apodizing function. Using this technique it is
possible to obtain reasonably good photometry with the maximum resolution
possible from a given mirror drive.

When the highest quality photometry is required, even at the expense of
sacrifice of resolution, the only recourse is to observe both sides of the inter-

ferogram and additionally to use a full complex transform; that is, a transform using both sine and cosine functions.[103] This approach was pioneered for dealing with the highly distorted and displaced interferograms resulting from dispersive Fourier refractometry which will be discussed later in the chapter. For the moment we will just remark that the result of this kind of transform is to eliminate all effects of residual lack of alignment or residual lack of perfect optical equality in the two mirror arms as well as coping with the displacement problem outlined above. This can most readily be shown by reverting to the integral form of transform in which we write

$$\hat{S}(\bar{\nu}) \propto \int_{-\infty}^{+\infty} W'(x) \exp(4\pi i \bar{\nu} x)\, dx \qquad (4.3)$$

for the complex case. The experimentally determined $W'(x)$ can always be resolved into two components $W'_+(x)$ of even parity with respect to change of sign of x and $W'_-(x)$ of odd parity. Of course, under normal circumstances $W'_-(x)$ will be very much smaller than $W'_+(x)$. Substituting these into equation (4.3) and noting that the integrals are zero unless both $W'(x)$ and the Fourier kernel have the same parity, we obtain

$$\hat{S}(\bar{\nu}) \propto \int_{-\infty}^{+\infty} W'_+(x) \cos 4\pi\bar{\nu}x\, dx + i \int_{-\infty}^{+\infty} W'_-(x) \sin 4\pi\bar{\nu}x\, dx = P(\bar{\nu}) + iQ(\bar{\nu}).$$
$$(4.4)$$

The true spectral function is then derived by taking the modulus of the complex spectral function, that is

$$S(\bar{\nu}) \propto [P^2(\bar{\nu}) + Q^2(\bar{\nu})]^{1/2}. \qquad (4.5)$$

This method has proved of great value in transform spectroscopy and is nearly always used, except when the limit of resolution is required. Photometric accuracy is now only limited by experimental considerations such as long-term stability of sources, detectors and digitizing systems. With only normal care, photometric precision of the order of 1 per cent is available throughout the submillimetre region.

After computation of the power spectra, with and without the specimen in the beam, the two digital outputs are re-fed into the computer which calculates their ratio, i.e.

$$T(\bar{\nu}) = \frac{S(\bar{\nu})\ \text{specimen}}{S(\bar{\nu})\ \text{background}} \qquad (4.6)$$

and $T(\bar{\nu})$ is therefore the transmission spectrum. If the specimen is heavily absorbing it is usual to increase the gain of the amplifier and to employ additional d.c. subtraction of the resulting interferogram so that its maximum and minimum ordinates just fill the dynamic range of the digitizing system. This will have also been arranged for the background interferogram. It is necessary therefore to insert, as a parameter to the computer, the exact increase of gain if true transmissions are to be calculated. The amount of d.c. subtraction is irrelevant in all the operations since the Fourier transform of a d.c. analogue signal, and by this we mean a constant output voltage independent of mirror position, is confined to the region of ultra-low frequencies which is quite outside the range that would ever be studied by these spectroscopic techniques. If the absorption coefficient is required, the transmission spectrum in digital form is read back into the computer which performs the operation†

$$-d^{-1}\ln T(\bar{\nu}) = \alpha(\bar{\nu}) \tag{4.7}$$

where d is the thickness of the specimen, to give the absorption coefficient in neper cm^{-1}. It is worth pointing out that a subsidiary advantage of Fourier spectroscopy is that all the data is in digital form and immediately ready for further processing. This is not the case with the conventional output from a dispersive instrument. A great deal of effort has been expended to find ways of transforming the output of these instruments to digital form, so that a vast amount of information can be made available by computer search techniques. This is undeniably a desirable end but fortunately, in the submillimetre region at least, no further instrumentation is required.

4.4. Lamellar Grating Interferometers

The history of lamellar grating interferometers has followed rather a similar path to that of Michelson interferometers. The original instruments were large and cumbersome, but modern forms are compact and modular in construction. A commercial instrument manufactured by the Research and Industrial Instrument Company gives good spectra over the range 3–70 cm^{-1} with a limiting resolution of 0·1 cm^{-1}. A photograph of this instrument (type LR-100) is shown in Fig. 4.16 and an optical diagram in Fig. 4.17.

Lamellar grating interferometers have much in common with Michelson interferometers, since both are two-beam multiplex instruments of high luminous throughput and both give an interferogram which has to be Fourier transformed to give the spectrum. They can be regarded as two ways of realizing in practice the physically impossible system shown in Fig. 3.2. In this Figure the radiation has to pass through mirror M$_2$ to reach mirror M$_1$. Michelson achieved this by placing the two mirrors in arms at 90° to each other and using a half reflecting and half transmitting beam divider so that

---

† Better practice (see Section 4.5) is to record two transmission spectra of two different thicknesses when, from their ratio, true absorption coefficients, corrected for reflection losses, may be computed,

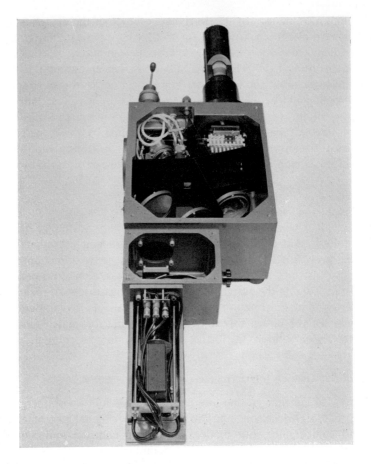

Fig. 4.16. Research and Industrial Instrument Company's Lamellar grating interferometer.

the radiation had to traverse the image of a mirror and not the physical mirror itself. His interferometer therefore features amplitude division of the incident wavefront. In the lamellar grating interferometer, mirror M_2 is made up of strips of totally reflecting mirror (perpendicular to the plane of Fig. 3.2), separated by strips of the same size which are completely transparent. Half the wavefront is therefore reflected from the strips making up M_2 and the other half continues on through the transparent strips to reach mirror M_1, there also to suffer total reflection. This interferometer therefore features division of wavefront. The system of split mirrors is realized in practice by making each from solid blocks of metal. Mirror M_2 then has a number of rectangular section grooves cut right through it, whereas mirror M_1 is cut to the form of a number of tongues which just fit the grooves and can slide smoothly up

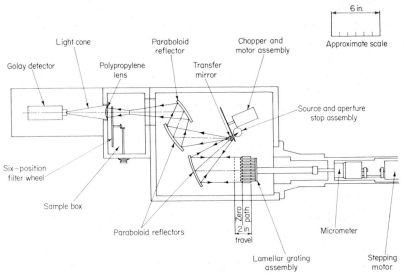

FIG. 4.17. Optical layout of Research and Industrial Instrument Company's lamellar grating interferometer LR-100.

them. The arrangement is shown in Fig. 1.4. The tongues are longer than the grooves so that, by progressively moving mirror M_1, the path difference can go from positive, through zero, to negative values.

The theory of the lamellar grating has been developed in an elegant paper by Strong and Vanasse.[104] The system is simultaneously a two-beam interferometer and a diffraction grating, and the mathematical analysis is strongly reminiscent both of equations (1.10) and (1.13). Consider a lamellar grating of groove width $\frac{1}{2}w$ and groove depth x illuminated by monochromatic plane parallel radiation of wavelength λ incident normally to the reflecting surfaces. The total power reflected at an angle α to the normal is given by

$$W = K^2 w^2 \left\{ \frac{\sin\left[(\pi w/2\lambda)\sin\alpha\right]}{(\pi w/2\lambda)\sin\alpha} \right\}^2 \left\{ \frac{\sin\left[(N\pi w/x)\sin\alpha\right]}{\sin\left[(\pi w/\lambda)\sin\alpha\right]} \right\}^2$$
$$\left\{ \cos\left[(\pi w/2\lambda)\sin\alpha + (\pi x/\lambda)(1+\cos\alpha)\right] \right\}^2,$$

$$(4.8)$$

where K is a constant and N is the number of mirror strips. The first of the three factors in square brackets gives the effect of illumination by just one strip alone, the second gives the effect of illumination by the composite of N strips, and the third gives the effect of interference between the two wavefronts which are emerging with a path difference of $2x$. The second term has maxima when

$$\sin\alpha = k\lambda w^{-1}, \qquad k = 0, \pm 1, \pm 2, \text{ etc.} \qquad (4.9)$$

and the angles which satisfy this equation define the orders of the grating. The first term is zero for all even values of k other than zero, which means that the only orders in which there is reflected intensity are the zero order and the odd orders. The lamellar grating will be constructed in practice so that the width of the strips will be much larger than the longest wavelength under investigation, i.e. $w \gg \lambda_{max}$, and therefore the values of α for the first few orders will be very small. We can therefore use the familiar trigonometrical approximations and write the third factor as

$$C^2 = \cos^2 [2\pi x/\lambda + k\pi/2]. \qquad (4.10)$$

As x varies, the relative power in the various orders also changes; when x is zero all the reflected intensity is in the zero order, whereas when x is $\frac{1}{4}\lambda$ no power is reflected in the zero order and we have the fractions $(2/\pi)^2$, $(2/3\pi)^2$, etc. of the incident power reflected in the first, third, etc. orders. If a detector, with a window sufficiently small to receive only the zero order, is placed at the focus of a lens or mirror receiving the reflected radiation, then the output of the detector will vary cosinusoidally with grating groove depth which illustrates once more the general principle of interferometry that destructive interference can only occur at a given point in space if constructive interference is also occurring at other points in space. In the present instance, when no power is arriving in the zero order, all that has happened is that the total reflected power is now distributed in the higher odd orders of the grating. It has occasionally been remarked that the lamellar grating interferometer is twice as efficient as an ideal Michelson interferometer because no power is reflected back to the source. Even if it is assumed that the awkward problems of collecting the reflected radiation from the lamellar grating (for after all in the simplest configuration the detector and source would have to be coincident!) have been completely solved, this view is still incorrect. In an ideal Michelson interferometer, irradiated by monochromatic radiation, the power arriving at the detector as a function of mirror displacement varies from zero to 100 per cent of the incident power. It therefore exhibits a modulation depth of 100 per cent and clearly one can never do better than this. The lamellar grating does have some real advantages over the Michelson interferometer for very long wavelengths in that it is easy to achieve 100 per cent reflecting metal surfaces, whereas it is almost impossible at present to make ideal 50 per cent transmitting and 50 per cent reflecting beam dividers, and one does not have the problem of transmission minima due to multiple-beam interference in the divider itself. It is precisely the absence of perfect beam dividers which is responsible for the factors of two or more, quoted by some authors, for the under-performance of real Michelson interferometers as compared with real lamellar gratings in the region below 70 cm^{-1}.

We must now consider the distribution of intensity in the image plane which contains the detector window. The orders of the lamellar grating will lead to a system of straight-line fringes in this plane, and the calculation of power through the detector window and efficiency of modulation as a function of path difference is very similar to that described in Chapter 3 for the Michelson interferometer. Again it is found that there is a frequency contraction and a resolution limit, determined by the solid angle subtended by the limiting stop in the system, at its appropriate condensing surface. These arise as in the Michelson case because it is impossible, with finite size of detector window and source, to have the collimated beam striking the lamellar grating strictly normal to the surfaces. But there is one interesting feature of the lamellar grating interferometer which permits substantially higher energy throughput than one might at first imagine. So far we have assumed that the detector window is sufficiently small to receive only the first order of the highest frequency radiation present. If a is the radius of the detector window (assumed as before to be the limiting stop) and f the focal length of the condensing optics, then the maximum frequency which can be investigated, having a first-order fringe which just fails to enter the detector, can be found from equations (3.1) and (4.9); the result for α small is

$$\bar{\nu} = \tfrac{1}{2} f a^{-1} w^{-1}. \tag{4.11}$$

Thus, with $f = 18$ cm, $a = 0.25$ cm and $w = 1.0$ cm, $\bar{\nu}_{max}$ would be 36 cm^{-1}. In the commercial instrument,[105] a light pipe is used to increase the solid angle over which radiation is collected. With this refinement, the limiting stop is determined by the size of the source ($a = 0.5$ cm) and therefore $\bar{\nu}_{max} = 18$ cm^{-1}. It would thus seem necessary to introduce filtering to restrict the range of observation to $\bar{\nu} < 18$ cm^{-1} since the higher frequencies would not be modulated and would merely give a continuous signal. This might overload the detector and even if it did not, it would have to be subtracted electronically if an interferogram spanning the dynamic range of the recording system is to be obtained. In principle, the operation of the interferometer could be extended to higher frequencies by reducing the source aperture, but, since this would reduce the signal drastically, this proposal is not very practical. Fortunately, as first pointed out by Richards,[106] the power in the first, third, etc. orders is much less than in the zero order; the first order is only 40 per cent and the third order only 4 per cent as intense as the zero order, which means that the interferometer will still modulate frequencies greater than $\bar{\nu}_{max}$ but with decreasing efficiency. The fall off in modulation efficiency is countered somewhat by the increasing power from the source and in practice it is found that the commercial instrument can be used as far as 70 cm^{-1}. This is a convenient frequency for overlap with the broad-band Michelson interferometer equipped with a 6 μm beam divider.

The low-frequency performance of the lamellar grating is limited by another phenomenon. All the treatments of interference and diffraction in this book are based on what is known as the scalar wave approximation; that is, we do not attempt to treat any problem by an exact solution of Maxwell's equations. Normally, this is an excellent approximation but it fails when we start to discuss the interaction of an electromagnetic field with bodies of the same order of size as the wavelength. Thus, for example, this approximation is worthless when discussing microwave devices. The channels in a lamellar grating interferometer begin to behave more and more like waveguides as the frequency falls. The phase velocity of waves in a waveguide exceeds that in free space by the factor $[1-(\lambda/w)^2]^{-1/2}$ and thus, when w equals λ, the phase velocity becomes infinite, i.e. the wave is no longer propagating and the waveguide is said to be cut off. The increase in phase velocity also affects the resolving power and it turns out that resolutions better than $0\cdot1$ cm^{-1} at 3 cm^{-1} are impossible unless grating constants greater than $1\cdot0$ cm are used and, as remarked above, this is undesirable in terms of the high-frequency performance.[105] The situation is somewhat improved if polarized radiation can be employed but, since spectroscopy below 3 cm^{-1} is readily achieved with standard microwave methods, the choice of operating conditions so that the instrument performs well over the range 3–70 cm^{-1} is quite apt.

The output of the detector as a function of path length, bearing in mind all the limitations mentioned above, is given by equation (4.10) with $k = $ zero, that is

$$\mathcal{I}(x) \propto W(x) \propto \int_0^\infty S(\bar{v})\,[1 + \cos 4\pi\bar{v}x]\,d\bar{v}. \tag{4.12}$$

As in the Michelson case, the spectrum can be obtained by Fourier transformation of

$$\mathcal{I}'(x) = \mathcal{I}(x) - \overline{\mathcal{I}(x)} \propto W(x) - \overline{W(x)}.$$

As an example of the performance of the commercial instrument the spectrum of water vapour is shown in Fig. 4.18. Assignments of some of the lines in

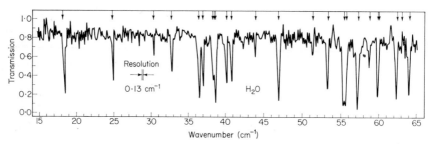

Fig. 4.18. Submillimetre spectrum of water vapour obtained with a lamellar grating interferometer (from R. C. Milward[105]).

this spectrum are given in Chapter 5. Improved signal-to-noise in the spectra can be obtained if detectors working at liquid helium temperature can be employed and Richards[107] has reported a similar spectrum with improved noise qualities, obtained using such a detector.

4.5. Refractive Index Determinations Using Michelson Interferometers

The optical properties of any isotropic dielectric material at any frequency $\bar{\nu}$ are completely defined if we know the complex refractive index[108]

$$\hat{n}(\bar{\nu}) = n(\bar{\nu}) - i\alpha(\bar{\nu})/(4\pi\bar{\nu}) \tag{4.13}$$

at that frequency. The absorption coefficient $\alpha(\bar{\nu})$ can be determined in any of the instrumental ways so far discussed, the only experimental difficulty being that some of the energy failing to reach the detector is lost by reflection rather than by true absorption. If $R(\bar{\nu})$ is the reflectivity of the front and back surfaces combined, and if the sample is sufficiently thick so that multiple beam effects can be neglected, it follows that

$$T(\bar{\nu}) = [1 - R(\bar{\nu})] \exp(-\alpha(\bar{\nu}) d) \tag{4.14}$$

where d is the thickness of the sample. The problem can be overcome in practice by observing transmission spectra of two identical specimens differing only in thickness when it follows that

$$\alpha(\bar{\nu}) = (d_2 - d_1)^{-1} \ln T_1(\bar{\nu})/T_2(\bar{\nu}) \tag{4.15}$$

The real part of $\hat{n}(\bar{\nu})$, i.e. the refractive index $n(\bar{\nu})$, can be determined in several ways, but before going on to describe these it is important to point out that the real and imaginary parts of $\hat{n}(\bar{\nu})$ are not independent quantities. Very fundamental arguments connected with the principle of causality indicate that if either is known for all frequencies then the other may be derived via an integral transform. This connection is reflected, for example, in equation (5.14) which shows essentially $n(\bar{\nu})$ and $\alpha(\bar{\nu})$ as the real and imaginary parts of a single complex function. Thus, in principle, we need only observe the absorption spectrum over a sufficiently wide range of frequency to be in a position to calculate the refraction spectrum and from this the reflection spectrum. In practice, this is seldom done because of the severe difficulties of observing a true absorption profile (see Chapter 5) but the corresponding transformation, of observing a wide range of $n(\bar{\nu})$ and from this data deducing integrated line intensities, is commonplace. To a lesser extent the deduction of $\alpha(\bar{\nu})$ and $n(\bar{\nu})$ from observed values of $R(\bar{\nu})$ is also carried out, especially for very heavily absorbing materials such as alkali-halides in the far infrared. The actual numerical transform (Kramers–Kronig relation) connecting $\alpha(\bar{\nu})$ and $n(\bar{\nu})$ takes on the form[109]

$$n(\bar{\nu}_0) - n(\infty) = 1/(2\pi^2) \int_0^\infty [\alpha(\bar{\nu})/(\bar{\nu}^2 - \bar{\nu}_0^2)] \, d\bar{\nu} \tag{4.16}$$

F

where $\bar{\nu}_0$ is the frequency of interest; it is understood that we calculate the principal value of the integral in the vicinity of the singularity at $\bar{\nu} = \bar{\nu}_0$.

Consider now that we have an isolated narrow absorption band with its centre frequency located at $\bar{\nu}_i$. There have been several line-shape functions suggested at one time or another and observed profiles do more or less agree with theory; they all lead to the characteristic bell-shaped or resonant type of curve indicated schematically in Fig. 4.19. Associated with such an absorp-

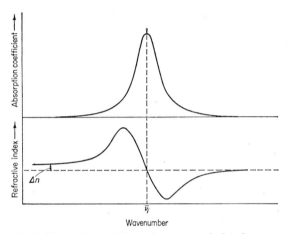

FIG. 4.19. Absorption and dispersion near an isolated resonance.

tion band will be an anomalous dispersion also indicated in the Figure. The refractive index at frequencies much less than $\bar{\nu}_i$ is higher than at frequencies much greater than $\bar{\nu}_i$ and this "step" in the refraction is a measure of the intensity of the band. There will be such a step for each absorption band of a material and the sum of all these steps accounts for the drop in refractive index in going from very low (radio) frequencies where $n \approx \sqrt{\epsilon_0}$ to very high (optical) frequencies where $n \approx \sqrt{\epsilon_\infty}$. In this connection it is interesting to observe that equation (4.16) is analogous to the well-known relation

$$\epsilon_0 - \epsilon_\infty = (2/\pi) \int_0^\infty [\epsilon''(\bar{\nu})/\bar{\nu}] \, d\bar{\nu} = (2/\pi) \int_{-\infty}^{+\infty} \epsilon''(\bar{\nu}) \, d(\ln_e \bar{\nu}) \qquad (4.17)$$

used in dielectric investigations. If an analytic function is being used for the absorption profile, the exact form of the dispersion curve can be worked out, but in general this procedure is not very justifiable and the approach to the determination of integrated band strengths starts with equation (4.16) which is completely general. If we suppose that the line under investigation is narrow, by which we mean that its half-width $\Delta\bar{\nu}$ is much less than its centre frequency $\bar{\nu}_i$, it follows that $\alpha(\bar{\nu})$ will only be significantly different from zero in the immediate vicinity of $\bar{\nu}_i$ and we can replace the integration over infinite limits with one over a small region of frequency near $\bar{\nu}_i$. The step in refractive index between a frequency $\bar{\nu}_-$ less than $\bar{\nu}_i$ and a frequency $\bar{\nu}_+$ greater than $\bar{\nu}_i$ will then be given by

$$n(\bar{\nu}_-)-n(\bar{\nu}_+)=(1/2\pi^2)\int_i \alpha(\bar{\nu})f_i \, d\bar{\nu} \qquad (4.18)$$

where

$$f_i = (\bar{\nu}^2 - \bar{\nu}_-^2)^{-1}+(\bar{\nu}_+^2 - \bar{\nu}^2)^{-1}.$$

If $\bar{\nu}_+$ and $\bar{\nu}_-$ are chosen so that they are a few times the band half-width away from $\bar{\nu}_i$, and we restrict the range of integration as above, f_i becomes essentially constant over this restricted range and can be approximated as

$$f_i' = (\bar{\nu}_i^2 - \bar{\nu}_-^2)^{-1}+(\bar{\nu}_+^2 - \bar{\nu}_i^2)^{-1}. \qquad (4.19)$$

It follows therefore that

$$n(\bar{\nu}_-)-n(\bar{\nu}_+) = (1/2\pi^2)f_i'\int_i \alpha(\bar{\nu}) \, d\bar{\nu}, \qquad (4.20)$$

that is, the step in refraction is proportional to the integrated strength of the band. It is to be noted that f_i is insensitive to small errors in the determination of $\bar{\nu}_i$; in other words we can still expect good intensity measurements even if the spectral resolving power is insufficient to completely resolve the feature. The permissible values of $\bar{\nu}_-$ and $\bar{\nu}_+$ are set by the approximations used in deriving equation (4.20), i.e. they must be sufficiently remote from $\bar{\nu}_i$ to essentially define the spectral extent of the band but not so remote that the assumption that f_i is constant over the region is violated. In practice $|\bar{\nu}_\pm - \bar{\nu}_i|$ is chosen to be approximately $2\Delta\bar{\nu}$. As an example of the method, $GeCl_4$ in the gas phase at one atmosphere presure has a moderately intense band centred near 460 cm^{-1} which arises from the ν_3 fundamental of this tetrahedral molecule. Taking $\bar{\nu}_- = 400 \text{ cm}^{-1}$ and $\bar{\nu}_+ = 520 \text{ cm}^{-1}$, the step in refractive index is found to be approximately 2×10^{-3}. With this choice of bounding frequencies f_i' is $3 \cdot 64 \times 10^{-5} \text{ cm}^2$ from which the integrated intensity is calculated to be $1 \cdot 1 \times 10^3 \text{ cm}^{-2}$ or 25×10^3 darks.[90] The dark is a unit in common use in the chemical literature and is introduced to cope with the concentration dependence (Beer's law) of absorption. The unit of concentration employed is mmol cm^{-3}, from which it follows that absorption coefficients in cm^{-2} can be converted to this unit in terms of darks by multiplying by $M\rho^{-1} 10^{-3}$ where M is the molecular weight and ρ the density. For the present case of a gas at atmospheric pressure the multiplying factor is simply $22\cdot4$.

For most practical cases, the assumption of narrow isolated absorption bands is not fulfilled and therefore the treatment becomes more complex.[110] The bands now have finite widths and we have contributions to the dispersion near $\bar{\nu}_i$ from neighbouring absorption bands. Normally such additional dispersions are assumed to vary slowly over the region of interest, and in favourable cases it is possible to assess their effects and subtract these from the observed refraction spectrum to obtain the dispersion due to the feature at $\bar{\nu}_i$. In more complicated cases it is necessary to disentangle the overall spectrum and this often involves an iterative process by which, starting with a guessed set of molecular constants, we converge to a set which best fits the observed refraction spectrum. Details of this procedure have been given by Chamberlain.[110] The effects of the finite bandwidth can be accommodated by introducing a damping term into the denominators of f_i (cf. equation 29 of Appendix 3). With both these refinements, integrated intensities of absorption bands are readily obtained from observations of the refraction spectrum over a wide frequency range. We must now go on to see how such refraction spectra are obtained in practice.

Basically there are two principal methods which have been used to obtain refractive index spectra. Firstly one can study the transmission of a plane parallel sample irradiated with parallel monochromatic radiation. Such a sample will show "channel" or Edser–Butler fringes in much the same way as does a Michelson thin-film beam divider. If the thickness of the specimen is d then the observed transmission for normal incidence will (see equation (3.58)) be

$$T = (1-r^2)^2/(1-2r^2 \cos \delta + r^4) \tag{4.21}$$

where

$$\delta = 4\pi n \bar{\nu} d.$$

The transmission will therefore show minima whenever $\cos \delta = -1$, i.e. when

$$d = (2m+1)/(4n\bar{\nu}), \qquad m = 0, 1, 2, \text{etc.} \tag{4.22}$$

and maxima when

$$d = m/(2n\bar{\nu}), \qquad m = 0, 1, 2, \text{etc.} \tag{4.23}$$

It therefore follows that if we plot the transmission as a function of sample thickness and locate the maxima and minima, the refractive index can be deduced. In this connection it is interesting to observe that the regularly spaced transmission minima of Michelson interferometers with polyethylene terephthalate beam dividers imply that the refractive index of this material does not vary much over the far infrared region. The channel fringe method cannot be used for frequencies which lie in heavy absorption regions of the specimen—near band centres for example. This is a general criticism of all methods and it is only occasionally that the full dispersion curve can be followed right through the anomalous region. It does not affect the validity of the method for determining integrated band strengths, since the measurements required in this connection have to be performed in the clear regions on each side of the absorption feature. The principal difficulties encountered in using the channel fringe method are poor fringe contrast and lack of intense tunable monochromatic sources. The fringe contrast can be increased by enclosing the gas or liquid sample with windows of high (and constant) dielectric constant. High resistance silicon is a suitable material for much of the infrared because its refractive index only varies from 3·57 to 3·40 for wavelengths of from 1 μm to 20 μm. As a result of this high index, the reflectivity is approximately 25 per cent per surface and the fringe contrast is much improved. As for sources, there are now a series of devices, principally gas lasers, which can be used for measurement at spot frequencies[111] throughout the infrared as far as 337 μm. These devices are not easily scanned over a range of frequencies so that to obtain a continuous refraction spectrum there is at present no recourse but a black-body source and a monochromator. The drawbacks of such a system from the point of view of energy throughput have been exhaustively spelled out in earlier chapters; here it will suffice to point out that, whereas several successful determinations of refraction spectra have been made[112] in this way for frequencies greater than 500 cm^{-1}, the method becomes progressively less valuable as we go to lower and lower frequencies.

The solution to the corresponding problem in absorption spectroscopy was the application of the Michelson interferometer and we might ask whether Michelson interferometers can be adapted for the determination of refractive index spectra. The answer to this question is not only that they can, but that it is a natural consequence of their operation. The interference between the two beams in a Michelson interferometer arises because one beam has suffered a time delay, or a phase shift, which amounts to the same thing. The fact that the phase shift is a function of frequency is the basis of the process by which the interferometer can become a spectrometer. A beam of electromagnetic radiation traversing a slab of dielectric or refractive index n undergoes a phase shift $2\pi(n-1)d\bar{\nu}$ compared with the same wave travelling in a vacuum where, as before, d is the thickness. If such a slab of dielectric is inserted between the beam divider and the fixed mirror, and if n is constant, i.e. no dispersion, the effect will be to shift the position of the moving mirror, where the grand maximum of the symmetrical interferogram occurs, by an amount $2(n-1)d$. A measurement of this shift gives n immediately. We must now discover what will happen if we insert a dispersive plate into one arm of the interferometer. One immediate conclusion can be drawn: the optical path difference will no longer be independent of frequency and therefore the zero path difference position will occur at different settings of the moving mirror for different frequencies. The interferogram will therefore not only be shifted but will no longer be symmetrical about a grand maximum. It has to be admitted that the full theory of this phenomenon is very complex for, after all, we are faced with treating the propagation of a wavefront in a dispersive medium. A full outline has been given by Chamberlain, Gibbs and Gebbie[113] and all we will attempt here is to state their principal results and discuss the experimental realization of Fourier refractometry. The important practical consideration is to restrict the thickness of the sample so that the distortion of the interferogram is not too severe. One fringe will then be much brighter than the others. Suppose this occurs at a micrometer reading x_{max} and the undisplaced zero-path fringe (i.e. with no specimen in the beam) at $x = 0$. We now *define* a mean refractive index by the use of the relation

$$x_{max} = (\bar{n} - 1) d. \qquad (4.24)$$

The optical path difference, referred to the physical zero-path position as origin, is given by

$$\Delta = 2x - 2(n - 1) d \qquad (4.25)$$

and if we change to x_{max} as origin, the path difference becomes

$$\Delta = 2[x' - (n - \bar{n}) d] \qquad (4.26)$$

where

$$x' = x - x_{max} = x - (\bar{n} - 1) d.$$

The interferogram function is now given by

$$W'(x') = W(x') - \overline{W(x')} \propto \int_0^\infty S(\bar{\nu}) \cos 4\pi\bar{\nu}[x' - (n - \bar{n}) d] \, d\bar{\nu} \qquad (4.27)$$

that is

$$W'(x') \propto \int_0^\infty S(\bar{\nu}) \cos 4\pi\bar{\nu}(n - \bar{n}) d \cos 4\pi\bar{\nu}x' \, d\bar{\nu}$$

$$+ \int_0^\infty S(\bar{\nu}) \sin 4\pi\bar{\nu}(n - \bar{n}) d \sin 4\pi\bar{\nu}x' \, d\bar{\nu}.$$

Applying Fourier's integral theorem it follows that

$$S(\bar{\nu}) \cos 4\pi\bar{\nu}(n - \bar{n}) d \propto \int_{-\infty}^{+\infty} W'(x') \cos 4\pi\bar{\nu}x' \, dx' = P(\bar{\nu})$$

and

$$S(\bar{v}) \sin 4\pi\bar{v}(n-\bar{n})\, d \propto \int\limits_{-\infty}^{+\infty} W'(x') \sin 4\pi\bar{v}x'\, dx' = Q(\bar{v}).$$

Therefore

$$n-\bar{n} = (4\pi\bar{v}d)^{-1}\,[\arctan Q(\bar{v})/P(\bar{v})+m\pi], \quad m = 0\pm 1,\ \pm 2,\ \text{etc.}$$
$$(4.28)$$

Hence relative refraction spectra can be obtained by taking the full complex Fourier transform of the dispersive interferogram obtained with the specimen in the fixed mirror arm of the interferometer. It is to be noted that, for the determination of integrated band intensities, only relative refractive indices are required and therefore this method is very powerful. If absolute refractive indices are required two approaches are possible. Firstly one can attempt to determine $\bar{n}$ experimentally, that is, measure the shift of the grand maximum on introducing the specimen. Secondly, the refractive index can be measured absolutely at some frequency within the range over which we have relative values. The HCN laser operating at $29 \cdot 712$ cm^{-1} is a very convenient experimental tool for this purpose and some details of its use in this connection will be given later. In practical dispersive interferometry it is most desirable to work on only the principal branch of the arctan function, i.e. to have $m =$ zero. The range of the arctan function in its principal branch extends from $-\tfrac{1}{2}\pi$ to $+\tfrac{1}{2}\pi$ and hence it follows that

$$| (n(\bar{v})-\bar{n})\, d\,| < (8\bar{v})^{-1} \qquad (4.29)$$

or, in other words, the optical thickness of the sample at any frequency in the observed range must not depart by more than $(8\bar{v})^{-1}$ from a mean optical thickness $\bar{n}d$. If the specimen is displaying strong dispersion over the observed range of frequency then it will be necessary to study a range of specimen thickness to obtain the overall refraction spectrum. There are a few other considerations involved in the determination of refractive index spectra in this fashion. Firstly the interferogram function without any specimen in the beam may not be perfectly symmetrical due to instrumental imperfections, and so there will be a residual $Q(\bar{v})$ or phase from this cause which must be subtracted. Secondly, the largest ordinate of the digitized interferogram may not exactly coincide with the grand maximum in the distorted interferogram function. For normal transmission determinations this has no effect whatever, the double-sided complex transformation coping with this difficulty completely, but for refraction spectra it does matter since this time we are dealing with the ratio of $Q(\bar{v})$ to $P(\bar{v})$ rather than $[P^2(\bar{v})+Q^2(\bar{v})]^{\frac{1}{2}}$. The displacement is always small, of course, never being more than one sampling interval. If

H is the fraction of a sampling interval x_0 by which the largest digitized ordinate is displaced from the true grand maximum, the quantity $\frac{1}{2}Hx_0d^{-1}$ has to be added to the calculated values of $n(\bar{\nu})$. The third difficulty arises from absorption in the sample and it therefore follows that the two beams (one from each mirror) arriving at the detector will no longer have equal mean intensities. The fringe contrast will therefore be degraded. This is an unavoidable trouble for the determination of refraction spectra but, because of this phenomenon, it is generally better to determine absorption spectra in the conventional manner with the sample mounted before the detector.

The form of dispersive interferograms is particularly interesting. New features introduced into the interferogram by the presence of the specimen in one arm are always found only on the positive path difference side of the grand maximum. The reasons for this are very profound, having their origin in the principle of causality. A particularly spectacular illustration is provided by those gaseous samples which have a series of regularly spaced pure rotational absorption lines. It will be recalled (see Fig. 3.15) that in the conventional operation such a specimen will yield an interferogram having "signatures" regularly spaced each side of the zero path difference position. When the specimen is placed in the fixed mirror arm of the interferometer, the signatures occur on only the positive path difference side. This is illustrated[113] in Fig. 4.20 which shows the dispersive interferogram obtained with a gaseous sample of hydrogen chloride.

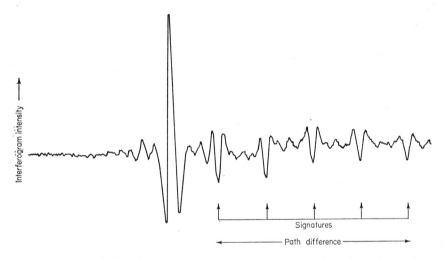

FIG. 4.20. Dispersive interferogram obtained with a sample of HCl gas in the fixed mirror arm. The spectral range was approximately 10–60 cm^{-1} and the one-sided signatures (indicated by arrows) arise due to absorption by the pure rotation lines at 20·88 and 41·76 cm^{-1} (after Chamberlain et al.[113, 114]).

Most forms of far infrared Michelson interferometers can be adapted for refraction work, but the modular construction of the modern types makes them particularly appropriate. Two configurations[113] for studying gases and liquids respectively are shown in Figs. 4.21 and 4.22. The arrangement for gases is quite straightforward with the gas specimen contained in a glass or metal cell sealed with a thin polyethylene window. A suitable filter F is mounted before the Golay window to isolate the region of interest. The arrangement for liquids is somewhat more complicated. The liquid is contained under gravity in a small cell R, the polished metal bottom of which serves as the fixed mirror of the interferometer. To keep the liquid sample plane parallel it is necessary for R to be mounted perpendicularly and, since this cell is rigidly connected to the interferometer, screw adjustments V must be provided. The greater part of the interferometer is evacuated so a window W is also necessary and this introduces some complications. The window must be as near the surface of the liquid as possible to minimize the unevacuated path length and then we run into the additional difficulty that the window looks to the interferometer like another fixed mirror. The effect of this is

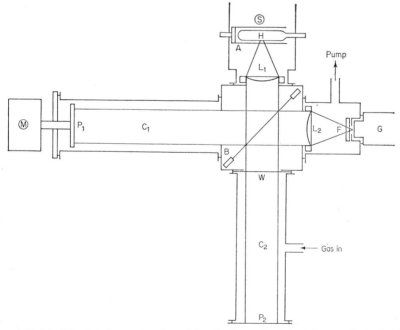

FIG. 4.21. Modular interferometer adapted for the determination of the complex refractive index spectra of gases. Key: C_1, evacuated compensation cell; C_2, specimen cell; W, melinex window; F, suitable filter; L, collimating lens introduced to increase energy throughput which would otherwise be low due to the long mirror arms. The Golay cell G can easily be replaced by an indium antimonide detector for very low wavenumber work.

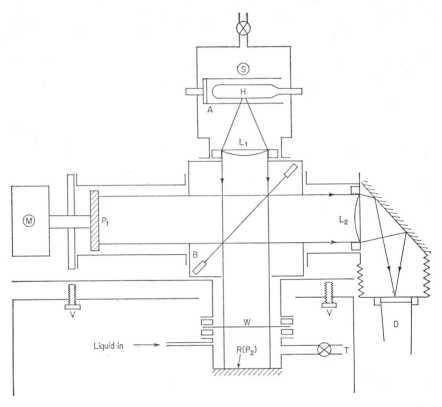

Fig. 4.22. Modular interferometer adapted for the study of the complex refraction spectra of liquids. Key as in Figs 4.2 and 4.21, but additionally: V, levelling screws; T, inlet valve for admitting dry air; R, a stainless steel vessel to contain the liquid under gravity; D, the entrance light pipe of Putley detector. The detector can easily be a Golay cell with the arrangement of Fig. 4.21.

that on each side of the true grand maximum there will be subsidiary features due to reflection from the window surface and also from its image in P_2. Very similar remarks apply to reflection from the upper surface of the liquid itself. In practice it is found that the effects of these phenomena can be eliminated from the final spectra by simply editing the subsidiary features out of the data tape before it is fed into the computer. Naturally it is necessary to have W sufficiently far from P_2 and the liquid sample must be thick enough to ensure that the unwanted features are far enough away from the true grand maximum. If this is not ensured, then there is the danger that meaningful oscillations of the interferogram function will also be edited out. In Fig. 4.22 is shown the variant arrangement used with a Putley-type indium antimonide detector.

Absolute refractive indices can be determined using either of the two methods mentioned earlier. The principal difficulty affecting direct measurements of the shift of the grand maximum (and hence $\bar{n}$) is backlash in the mirror drive system. This can be overcome by starting the drive a reasonable distance before the grand maximum with no specimen in, and recording the digitized interferogram. As soon as the grand maximum is past, the specimen is quickly inserted into the fixed mirror arm and the gain and zero back-off rapidly adjusted. The displaced grand maximum will then be observed and we will have both grand maxima on one tape and the precise value of x_{max} can be read off. The most accurate method at present consists in putting the relative values on an absolute scale by means of a single measurement of the refractive index at 29·712 cm^{-1}. Solid samples can be studied by mounting a plane parallel specimen in one arm of an interferometer irradiated by the parallel radiation from an HCN laser.[111] The sample is slowly rotated about an axis perpendicular to the optic plane of the interferometer and the fringes due to the varying effective thickness of the sample are observed. From a plot of fringes versus angle of rotation the refractive index can be deduced. Liquids are studied[115] in a variable path length cell. The cell has plane parallel quartz windows, the back one being aluminized on its front surface. It is mounted in the interferometer with the aluminized surface as one of the mirrors. The thickness of the liquid sample is varied and the detector output plotted as a function of thickness. From the rate of attenuation the absorption coefficient can be determined, and from measurements of the fringe positions the refractive index can be calculated. A list of measured optical constants at 29·712 cm^{-1} is given in Appendix 4.

4.6. Amplitude and Phase Modulation of Luminous Flux

In the early days of near infrared spectroscopy the spectrum was obtained by hand plotting the d.c. output of a thermopile or the change in resistance of a bolometer as the spectrometer was scanned over its working range. This procedure has a lot of disadvantages and the modern regimen is to "chop" the radiation periodically in time, so that a.c. amplifiers can be used after the detector. It is desirable to use as high a chopping frequency as possible to avoid the excessive noise which occurs in electronic devices at low frequencies —and whose power, as remarked earlier, varies inversely with the frequency— but the operating frequency is limited by the response time of the detector. For the Golay cell, for example, it is not desirable to use chopping frequencies in excess of 20 Hz, and 11 Hz seems to be the optimum value. The modular interferometers developed at NPL feature a cylindrical chopper mounted concentrically with the source lamp and running at $16\frac{2}{3}$ Hz. Chopping of this type is usually called amplitude modulation. If the interferometer is irradiated by monochromatic radiation, the power arriving at the detector as a function of mirror movement is given (in the absence of chopping) by

$$P(x) = \tfrac{1}{2}KP_i[1 + \cos 4\pi\bar{\nu}x] \tag{4.30}$$

where K is a constant giving a measure of the luminous throughput of the system and P_i is the incident power from the source. When we now introduce the chopper, P_i will become a function of time and the detector output will vary in a similar fashion. The varying electrical signal from the detector can be resolved into its Fourier components and the combination of limited detector frequency response, coupled with the narrow-band selectivity of the first stage amplification, will select just one of these. It is clearly most desirable that the form of the chopper should be such as to concentrate most of the power into that Fourier component which is passed by the detector amplifier combination. The ideal form of modulation would be if P_i were a pure cosine function of time for there would then be only one Fourier component. For this case

$$P_i(t) = \tfrac{1}{2}P_i(0)\,[1 + \cos 2\pi\bar{\nu}t] \tag{4.31}$$

and the power in the fundamental is one half the total incident power. The other half is absorbed on the chopper blades. It is always the case with amplitude modulation that some signal has to be lost to gain the advantage of a.c. amplification. In practice, the modulation wave form will be far from ideal and factors as high as three or four for the loss in signal have to be endured. Another disadvantage of amplitude modulation is that both terms in equation (4.30) are modulated. This means that if the lamp output or detector sensitivity vary, the mean level of the interferogram will drift, which can be a considerable nuisance.

It is worth while, in passing, pointing out that chopping is much more important in the far infrared than in other spectral regions. The detector is receiving radiation from all points in the field of view of the optical system and, whereas in the visible region, for example, only the source emits any significant power, in the far infrared this is far from being the case. The power radiated by a source in the far infrared region is as shown earlier, proportional to the first power of the temperature. It follows that one square centimetre of the source ($T \approx 1000$ K) is emitting only three times as much power as one square centimetre of the instrument wall. If the walls of the instrument are at the same temperature as the detector, there will be no net radiation flow from one to the other, but in practice thermal fluctuations will occur. We therefore want the detector to "see" only the source and to achieve this the chopper must be placed as near to the source as possible, so that the radiation from everywhere else will be unmodulated. In the visible or near infrared regions, on the other hand, it is a matter of convenience where the chopper is placed. One rather ingenious illustration of this phenomenon came in the work of Burroughs and Gebbie[116] who observed far infrared atmospheric absorption spectra at high altitude. To do this they placed a warm (300 K) Golay detector in the image plane of a combination telescope and Michelson interferometer. The telescope was pointed out into space and the chopper was mounted immediately in front of the Golay window. An interferogram was obtained corresponding to emission *from* the Golay; or looked at from another point of view, to radiation from a source at -300 C. The effect was that the interferogram was completely inverted compared to a normal interferogram but, nevertheless, it was successfully transformed to give spectra containing a great deal of information about the constituents of the atmosphere.

So far the discussion of chopping has been quite general and would apply to any spectrometer. Amplitude modulation is used in commercial grating and prism spectrometers and also in interferometers. The designers of commercial spectrometers invoke a rather clever trick and use a reflecting chopper, sometimes made of metal and sometimes of an alkali halide. The idea behind this is to use the energy not going through the specimen channel (i.e. cut off by the chopper blades) to pass through a reference or blank channel. The two beams are detected by a single detector but, since the beam transmitted by the chopper is $\frac{1}{2}\pi$ out of phase with that reflected by the chopper, a phase-sensitive detector will give two outputs—an in-phase signal and a quadrature signal. The ratio of these is the transmission of the specimen. Instruments with this feature are called double-beam spectrometers and are experimentally convenient since the transmission is obtained directly rather than by having to do two separate runs and taking their ratio. The factor of 3 to 4 in signal loss has, however, still to be endured. When we come to consider interferometers, a different form of modulation is available. This type, pioneered at NPL principally by Chamberlain, (see *Infrared Physics*, April 1971) is called phase modulation. In phase modulation, there is no chopper in the sense discussed above; instead, the fixed mirror of the interferometer is oscillated with a small amplitude a at a frequency ω. To see how this leads to a modulation of the signal arriving at the detector, imagine that the interferometer is irradiated by monochromatic radiation of frequency $\bar{\nu}$ and that the moving mirror is stationary. The time-dependent signal from the detector (assumed for the moment to have zero response time) will be given by

$$V(x, t) = K'[P_i/2 + P_i/2 \cos 4\pi\bar{\nu}(x + a \cos \omega t)]. \qquad (4.32)$$

To see what will be the effect in the real case when the detector has a finite response time and is followed by a narrow-band amplifier, we must resolve $V(x, t)$ into its Fourier components. We can rewrite equation (4.32) as

$$2V(x, t) = K'P_i + K'P_i \cos 4\pi\bar{\nu}x \cos (4\pi\bar{\nu}a \cos \omega t).$$
$$- K'P_i \sin 4\pi\bar{\nu}x \sin (4\pi\bar{\nu}a \cos \omega t). \qquad (4.33).$$

The time-dependent parts of this function are not elementary and the coefficients of their Fourier components turn out to be Bessel functions. The actual expansions are

$$\cos (4\pi\bar{\nu}a \cos \omega t) = J_0(4\pi\bar{\nu}a) - 2J_2(4\pi\bar{\nu}a) \cos 2\omega t$$
$$+ 2J_4(4\pi\bar{\nu}a) \cos 4\omega t - \text{etc.}$$

$$\sin (4\pi\bar{\nu}a \cos \omega t) = 2J_1(4\pi\bar{\nu}a) \cos \omega t$$
$$- 2J_3(4\pi\bar{\nu}a) \cos 3\omega t + \text{etc.} \qquad (4.34)$$

If the pass band of the detector plus amplifier is such as to admit only the fundamental, then the output of the amplifier will be given by

$$V(x, t) = K'P_i J_1(4\pi\bar{\nu}a) \cos \omega t \sin 4\pi\bar{\nu}x. \qquad (4.35)$$

The interferogram obtained by rectifying this will be

$$\mathscr{I}(x) \propto S(\bar{\nu}) J_1(4\pi\bar{\nu}a) \sin 4\pi\bar{\nu}x \, d\bar{\nu}. \qquad (4.36)$$

With broad-band radiation the interferogram function will be

$$\mathscr{I}(x) \propto \int_0^\infty [S(\bar{\nu}) J_1(4\pi\bar{\nu}a) \sin 4\pi\bar{\nu}x] \, d\bar{\nu}. \qquad (4.37)$$

Interferograms obtained in this way look completely different from those obtained using amplitude modulation. Whereas the latter are symmetrical about the zero path difference and reach an asymptotic value ideally equal to one half the zero-path ordinate, phase modulated interferograms are antisymmetrical about the zero-path position and the mean value (equal to the asymptotic value) is zero. This is illustrated in Fig. 4.23. The principal advantages of phase modulation are threefold. Firstly, at the maximum of $J_1(4\pi\bar{\nu}a)$—which occurs when $\bar{\nu}a = 0.146$—the modulation is close to 100 per cent which gives a large improvement on amplitude modulation. Secondly, the constant term of equation (4.33) is unmodulated, so drift problems are eliminated and noise due to source fluctuations is much reduced. Thirdly, the Bessel function $J_1(4\pi\bar{\nu}a)$ is frequency dependent, falling to zero when $\bar{\nu}a = 0.286$ and this gives us another non-absorptive method of limiting the frequency range of the interferometer. As pointed out earlier, it is always desirable to limit the band pass to the frequency range of interest if optimum quality spectra are to be obtained.

Experimentally, a light-weight front aluminized mirror is attached to the diaphragm of a small loudspeaker. The amplitude of oscillation is determined

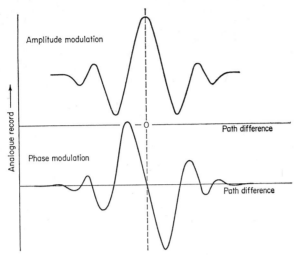

FIG. 4.23. Amplitude and phase-modulated interferograms near zero path difference.

by the audio-frequency power supplied to the speech coil from an oscillator. The loudspeaker assembly is then mounted in the interferometer in place of the usual fixed mirror. It is found, often, that the fabric diaphragms of loudspeakers tend to fatigue and are also subject to the effects of absorbed moisture. To obviate these difficulties the diaphragm may be replaced by a phosphor bronze "spider". Phase modulation has already proved very successful, especially for the region below 200 cm^{-1}, and is a standard fitment on the metrological version[117] of the submillimetre interferometer—the Teramet. Interferogram functions of the form of equation (4.37), i.e. involving sine terms instead of cosine terms, are just as readily transformed using the full complex programme as are the more usual forms and because of the advantages listed above, rather better spectra result. In practice, the ability to "tune" the maximum spectral frequency response merely by changing the power input to the loudspeaker is particularly felicitous. In the future we may expect to see increasing use of phase modulation when the prejudice against its novelty has been overcome.

4.7. Submillimetre Materials

There is not at present as wide a range of suitable materials for the far infrared as there is for the higher frequency regions.[118] As an example we do not have any substance suitable for use below 200 cm^{-1} which can rival the featureless transparency and good thermal stability of the alkali halides. Nevertheless, by careful choice of what is available, most experiments can be successfully carried through.

The only property of matter indisputably more easy to realize in the submillimetre region than at optical wavelengths is very high metallic reflectivity. In fact, first-class mirrors can be made directly from aluminium alloy blanks by cutting and machine polishing. Alternatively, by the evaporation of aluminium onto good quality glass blanks, mirrors can be made which perform excellently in the rigorous environ of a submillimetre laser. For the same reasons (see Chapter 5 for the theoretical background) good quality gratings can be made by evaporating aluminium onto plastic replicas.

Selective reflection from alkali halide discs was historically very important for by this means Rubens[4] succeeded in isolating narrow regions of the far infrared. It is still important in many practical applications where highly efficient filtering is required over a narrow frequency range. The very high reflection coefficients are a consequence of the great intensity of the "reststrahlen" absorption process which, in modern parlance, would be called the absorption due to the transverse optic mode. If the reststrahlen vibration were undamped, the complex dielectric constant would become real and negative between $\bar{\nu}_{TO}$ (i.e. the transverse optic frequency) and $\bar{\nu}_{LO}$, the frequency of the longitudinal optic mode. This implies that between these bounds the refractive index n is purely imaginary, and by equation (5.76) it follows that reflection is total, since the modulus of $(n-1)$ is the same as that for $(n+1)$. The motion is far from undamped in practice and, because of this, the absorption band has a finite width and the refractive index remains real. It does, however, drop to very low values on the high-frequency side of $\bar{\nu}_{TO}$ and consequently there is high reflectivity in the region where $n \ll 1$. The situation is similar to that shown in Fig. 4.19. It follows that the frequency of maximum reflection will be higher than that for maximum absorption and this is confirmed in practice. At room temperature a crystal of sodium chloride has $\bar{\nu}_{TO}$ equal to 164 cm^{-1}, yet the frequency of maximum reflectivity ($r^2_{max} = 90$ per cent) is 188 cm^{-1}. The fraction of the incident power reflected from seven plates of sodium chloride is shown in Fig. 4.24. The transverse optic mode frequency depends on the forces between the atoms and on their masses in the usual fashion (see equation 5.44) and it follows therefore that, by going to larger and heavier atoms, the reststrahlen region can be moved to lower frequencies. The heaviest material readily available at the moment is caesium iodide for which $\bar{\nu}_{TO} = 60$ cm^{-1} and $\bar{\nu}_{r=maximum} = 69$ cm^{-1}, both at room temperature. This material is essentially transparent down to 200 cm^{-1} and is usable in thin section as far as 180 cm^{-1}. The alkali halides are in common use as high-pass filters; thus potassium bromide is valuable for excluding the region below 300 cm^{-1} and sodium chloride for excluding the region below 500 cm^{-1}. The lightest of all, namely lithium fluoride, has $\bar{\nu}_{TO} = 313$ cm^{-1} at room temperature and because of this is opaque from this frequency to beyond 1000 cm^{-1}, but precisely because of

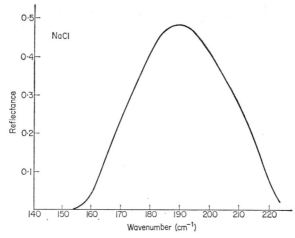

FIG. 4.24. Residual ray (reststrahlen) isolation by reflection from seven plates of crystalline sodium chloride.

the high value for $\bar{\nu}_{TO}$, opacity, on the low-frequency side, does not set in until the submillimetre region. Lithium fluoride is thus most welcome as a low-pass filter for the region below 60 cm^{-1}; lithium sulphate behaves likewise but cuts off above 40 cm^{-1}. Calcium fluoride, because of the heavier cation, cuts off at a still lower frequency, namely 30 cm^{-1}. Unlike, for example, sodium chloride, these materials are not hygroscopic which is a decided experimental convenience, but as filters it must be borne in mind that they are only relative in their action, absorbing submillimetre waves rather less heavily than higher-frequency waves. The absorption coefficients of lithium fluoride, lithium sulphate and calcium fluoride as functions of frequency are shown in Fig. 4.25. At low temperatures, the lattice vibration frequencies increase because the lattice shrinkage makes the atoms come closer to one another and this makes the interatomic forces larger. The reststrahlen bands also tend to sharpen since two phonon processes (the analogue of hot and difference bands for molecules) are reduced in intensity by the Boltzmann factor. As examples of the frequency shift, $\bar{\nu}_{TO}$ for NaCl changes to 174 cm^{-1}, $\bar{\nu}_{TO}$ for KBr goes from 114 cm^{-1} to 121 cm^{-1} and $\bar{\nu}_{TO}$ for CsI changes to 64·5 cm^{-1} as the temperature drops from 300 K to 90 K. Similar effects are shown by other ionic and molecular crystals and the net result in several cases is that the shifting and sharpening are sufficient to make the material useful for windows at low temperatures. For example, the spectra of ruby (essentially aluminium trioxide) at room and low temperature are shown in Fig. 4.26. Single crystals and sintered samples of beryllium oxide and magnesium oxide are now becoming available and should be useful in the

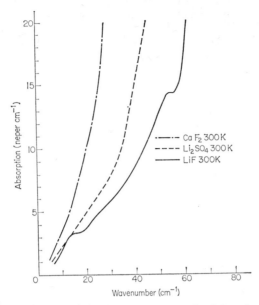

FIG. 4.25. Absorption characteristics for some extreme far infrared transmission filters.

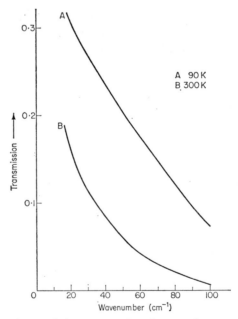

FIG. 5.26. Far infrared transmission spectra of a ruby crystal at room and liquid nitrogen temperatures.

extreme infrared ($< 100 \text{ cm}^{-1}$), especially at low temperature. There is a growing tendency to use cooled filters in submillimetre apparatus. This is especially convenient when the apparatus features one of the detectors which operate at liquid helium temperature, for the filter can be mounted in a cold part of the light pipe connecting the detector to the spectrometer. The idea is that there will be less unmodulated thermal radiation (from the filter) incident upon the detector if the filter is cooled. This is quite good practice but the changes in filter characteristic with temperature should be borne in mind when choosing a suitable filter.

Semiconductors such as silicon, germanium and indium antimonide are in wide use as windows and filters in submillimetre apparatus. Silicon is mostly used as a window, since it is essentially transparent throughout the infrared as far as $10\,000 \text{ cm}^{-1}$. It is important to have the material as pure as possible to avoid the types of absorption mentioned in Chapter 5 but, as purification processes such as zone refining seem to operate on cylinders no larger than 2 cm diameter, it is rather difficult to find large-size windows suitable, say, for gas cells. The purest samples presently available still show a band at 620 cm^{-1}, presumably due to impurity. Another difficulty with silicon is the high reflection loss (25 per cent per surface) arising from its large dielectric constant (≈ 10). Most semiconductors have high dielectric constants in the far infrared because of the existence of the enormously intense (in fact virtually metallic) valence band to conduction band transition for photons of energy greater than the band gap. As mentioned earlier, there is a "step" in refractive index or dielectric constant across an absorption feature proportional to its integrated strength. The infrared transmission of a 2 mm thick plate of germanium is shown in Fig. 4.27. The low level of transmission is in part due to reflection loss, but the complex absorption between 100 and 400 cm^{-1} probably arises from impurities. Doped samples of germanium containing phosphorus or arsenic are quite opaque below 400 cm^{-1}. The transmission spectrum of indium antimonide is shown in Fig. 4.28. The absorption rapidly increases below 100 cm^{-1} due to free carrier absorption, so this material has its principal application as a filter (combined with an appropriate alkali halide) to isolate a moderately narrow region between 500 and 1400 cm^{-1}.

Probably the first material to be used in transmission in the far infrared was paraffin wax. The discovery of its transparency was empirical but now we can understand it in terms of the non-polar character of the long-chain paraffin molecules. Polar materials exhibit relaxation phenomena which manifest themselves in strong and broad absorption bands throughout the radio, microwave and submillimetre regions. Non-polar materials show similar bands but they are very much weaker and, as a rough guide, we can say that in the submillimetre region a sample 1 cm thick will transmit 50 per

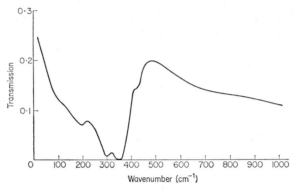

FIG. 4.27. Transmission of a 2 mm thick plate of germanium.

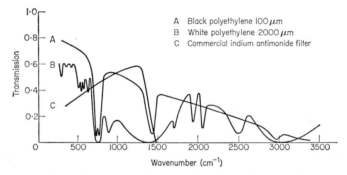

FIG. 4.28. Transmission characteristics of some low-pass filters.

cent of the radiant energy incident on it. Paraffin wax is no longer in common use because it is soft and low melting: it has been replaced by the most ubiquitous of all submillimetre materials—polyethylene. Polyethylene occurs in a number of forms varying in molecular weight and degree of crystallinity. They all have more or less the same absorption spectrum in the ordinary infrared (curve B of Fig. 4.28) but the more crystalline varieties show more distinctly the lattice band at 73 cm^{-1} (see Fig. 5.19). Polyethylene has been used for cell windows (the more crystalline versions such as "Rigidex" are the best), lenses and beam dividers in submillimetre apparatus, especially for observations below 700 cm^{-1}. It was stressed earlier how important it is to exclude unwanted radiation from the detector, but fortunately if one has more than a few millimetres of polyethylene in the beam one can rest assured that this has been achieved because of the heavy absorption by this material in the mid-infrared. Of course there will still remain some very high-frequency radiation, since polyethylene is translucent in the near infrared and visible regions, but fortunately a few sheets of thin "black" polyethylene (i.e. poly-ethylene loaded with carbon black) will completely exclude such radiation (see curve A of Fig. 4.28). It will be realized that the filtering in the modular interferometers which feature a polyethylene doublet lens and black poly-ethylene over the Golay window is quite efficient. Polypropylene is sometimes used instead of polyethylene, especially for low-temperature studies in the 70–80 cm^{-1} region, where the polyethylene lattice mode would interfere, and for studies at elevated temperatures (≈ 400 K) where polyethylene would soften. The absorption spectrum is shown in Fig. 4.29 where it will be seen that there is a series of bands beginning at 110 cm^{-1} and extending to higher frequencies. The presence of this set impairs the usefulness of polypropylene at frequencies greater than 100 cm^{-1}. The lower curve in Fig. 4.29 applies to a carefully purified nearly 100 per cent isotactic polypropylene. The less pure varieties as normally available commercially absorb far more heavily and in a broad-band sort of fashion—probably due to reststrahlen-type phenomena in polar additives such as calcium stearate—as shown in the upper curve. The presence of this rapidly rising absorption in impure poly-propylene has been turned to advantage as a filter. The observations of the sun (Burroughs et al.[116, 119]) made in the submillimetre region from high-flying aircraft require a window (or windows) for the aircraft if the operators are to work in reasonable comfort. Windows made from impure polypropylene up to 2 cm thick are quite suitable and exclude all radiation (apart from visible and near infrared) of frequency greater than 100 cm^{-1}. This is a fortu-

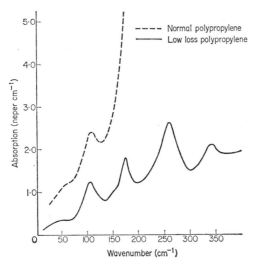

FIG. 4.29. Absorption spectra of carefully purified polypropylene as compared with normal commercial grade polypropylene.

nate (if fortuitous!) occurrence, but submillimetre filters can be deliberately made by loading a polymer such as polyethylene with ionic crystals and they have been described by several authors.[120] Atactic polypropylene is of little use as a material since it is soft and rubbery. It has an absorption characteristic similar to that of impure polypropylene but without the discrete bands. The absorption coefficient increases very rapidly above 160 cm^{-1}.

A new polymeric material which has come into prominence in the last few years is TPX, a substance based on poly-4-methylpentene-1 and manufactured by Imperial Chemical Industries Ltd in England. This polymer has the low absorption which is characteristic of aliphatic non-polar polymers in the region below 100 cm^{-1} and, although there are a few bands at higher frequencies, these are sufficiently broad and weak not to affect seriously its use as a window or lens.[121] TPX is harder and has a higher melting point than polyethylene, but its principal virtue is that it is transparent in the visible region and has there approximately the same refractive index as it has in the far infrared. The method of tracing the path of far infrared radiation through complex equipment by observing visible images can be carried out just as well when using TPX lenses as it can with mirrors and, in practice, refracting optics are very much easier to work with than are reflecting ones. Of course there are other transparent, readily mouldable plastics such as polymethyl methacrylate (Perspex) and polystyrene, but these absorb quite heavily and will be completely replaced by TPX in the future. The spectra of the three polymers are shown in Fig. 4.30. Polar polymers absorb very heavily, and thus polyethylene terephthalate has an average absorption coefficient of 70 neper cm^{-1} over the range 50–300 cm^{-1} and the polyimides have absorption coefficients of approximately 20 neper cm^{-1} up to 100 cm^{-1}. Both polymers have very intense low-frequency vibrational absorption bands,

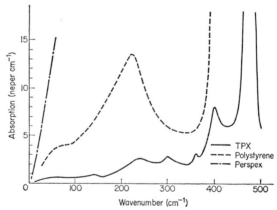

FIG. 4.30. Far infrared absorption characteristics of some visibly transparent polymers.

that for polyethylene terephthalate occurring at 360 cm⁻¹ and that for polyimide at 150 cm⁻¹. Because of these twin handicaps neither polymer can be used in transmission if thicknesses greater than a fraction of a millimetre are required. Fortunately they are both tough and quite thin films will be adequate as windows. They find their principal applications as beam dividers (polyethylene terephthalate) and as heat shields to safeguard more sensitive components (polyimide). Both applications require only thin films.

So far, not many molecular crystals or glasses have found important uses in submillimetre technology. The most significant is quartz which can be used as a window up to 220 cm⁻¹. At frequencies less than this it is fairly transparent, apart from a weak band at 125 cm⁻¹ whose intensity depends markedly on the orientation of the sample with respect to the plane of polarization of the incident radiation. Quartz is a very important material in applications such as refractive index determinations where rigid windows are required; it is also very valuable in high-temperature studies. The quartz envelope of the mercury arc lamp is the effective radiator at frequencies above 100 cm⁻¹ and the commonest form of Golay cell has a quartz window. Fused quartz is much less useful than the crystalline variety since it is far more heavily absorbing. The cost of diamonds precludes their extensive use in submillimetre apparatus. The spectral qualities of pure diamond are, however, so remarkable—essentially perfect transparency throughout the infrared with a low refractive index—that it is used as a window for Golay cells despite the steep rise in cost.

4.8. Submillimetre Polarizers and Interference Filters

The earliest device used to plane polarize the submillimetre radiation from a black-body source was the "pile of plates" polarizer. This features a number of plates of a transparent dielectric set at the Brewster angle (see equation 3.75). The radiation transmitted through the first plate will be partly polarized, as discussed in Chapter 3, with a degree of polarization

$$\rho = (I_{\parallel} - I_{\perp})/I_{\parallel} = 1 - (1 - R) \qquad (4.38)$$

where R is the reflectivity of the plate. If we have m plates the degree of polarization becomes

$$\rho = 1 - (1 - R)^m. \qquad (4.39)$$

The larger is R, the smaller can m become, so that ρ is still close to 100 per cent, but unfortunately large R (i.e. high n) is associated with high absorption, at least for the polymeric materials at present available, so the advantage is illusory. Polyethylene is the favoured material ($n = 1\cdot46$) though polyethylene terephthalate ($n = 1\cdot69$) has been used on occasion. With these rather low refractive indices, m has to be of the order of 16 if effective polarization is to be ensured and, as a consequence, the polarizer is bulky and awkward to use. Losses, even with polyethylene, are not negligible and the plates cannot be made too thin for fear of the difficulties with "channel" effects. A better prospect, using the same effect, is the silicon reflection polarizer. In principle, if we had perfectly parallel submillimetre radiation incident at the Brewster angle ($n = 3.4$, $\therefore$ $\theta_B = 73° 36'$) on a plate of transparent silicon, at the first surface we should have 65 per cent of the incident power transmitted with $\rho = 0.70$ and 35 per cent reflected with $\rho = 1.0$. It is not possible to get perfectly parallel beams (unless one is using a laser and then the polarization problem does not arise) and because of beam divergence the polarization is not perfect. The degree of polarization can, however, be brought very close to unity by reflecting the beam once more from a second plate also set at the Brewster angle. It will be noted that the angle of incidence is rather high and because of this the silicon plates need to be fairly large and there are all the optical problems of working in reflection rather than transmission, but nevertheless the polarizer is simple and has the great virtue of working over a very wide spectral range.

Polarizers and interference filters based on wire grids and wire meshes are becoming increasingly popular now that the technical problems of producing them have been overcome. The theoretical treatment of the interaction of an electromagnetic wave of wavelength λ with a metallic wire grid of spacing d and wire diameter a is in general very complicated.[122] The preferred method of approach is in terms of transmission line theory where the grid is regarded as a reactive shunt across perfect transmission lines. This approach can also handle the practical situation where the grid is either embedded in or deposited on the surface of a dielectric medium. Expressions for the impedance of the shunt have been given by several authors, but from their work it can readily be shown that for the two extremes, $\lambda \ll d$ and $\lambda \gg d$, the relations considerably simplify. The first extreme leads to the theory of the diffraction grating, whilst the second approaches approximately the situation of a large number of "tall" waveguides laid side by side. In a waveguide of long dimension l and short dimension w no wave of wavelength greater than $2l$ can propagate and waves having wavelengths between $2l$ and $2w$ can only propagate in the so-called dominant or TE$_{10}$ mode. Waves having wavelengths less than $2w$ can propagate in an increasing variety of modes approaching for $\lambda \ll 2w$ the situation where the resultant becomes the plane wavefront of geometrical optics. The dominant mode has the electric field lines perpendicular to the long dimension, so a grid with $d \ll \lambda$ will transmit only radiation polarized perpendicularly to the grid lines. The parallel component will be strongly reflected. From the point of view of diffraction theory it is interesting to note that for the case $\lambda \gg d$ only the zero order of diffraction is possible, so there is no spectral separation. The wire diameter is an important parameter at short wavelengths but in the far infrared has little effect. Commercial polarizers made either by evaporation or photolithography[123] on a suitable substrate (polyethylene or polyethylene terephthalate) are available from Buckbee Meers Inc. in the USA or from the AIM company in Cambridge, England. The grid spacing can be as fine as 0·002 cm leading to good performance as high as 200 cm^{-1}. The polarizers are easy to use in practice since they have the form of a stretched film 5 cm in diameter mounted in a small plastic frame.

Ulrich, Renk and Genzel[51] have discussed the behaviour of wire meshes in which the holes have square section. Because of this symmetry there are no polarization effects and the dominant mode can propagate for only a single wavelength. They describe a grid with wires parallel to the electric vector as an inductance and one with wires perpendicular as a capacitance. Clearly when both are present simultaneously (as in the square grid) we have a capacitance and an inductance in parallel or, in other words, a resonant circuit. As is well known, resonant circuits have sharply peaked reactances leading to a high transmission (for the grid) at a single wavelength, just as was deduced above from waveguide principles. These principles apply only poorly here, where $\lambda \approx d$, but the observed transmission of a square mesh does peak sharply at $(\lambda/d) = 1\cdot2$ and these meshes are very valuable as filters and as reflectors (when $\lambda > d$) in Fabry–Perot type spectrometers (see Chapter 2 and Fig. 6.8).

An extremely simple low-pass transmission filter has been described by Möller and McKnight.[124] They cut a 90° echellette grating into a brass former using a milling machine. Then, by heating the brass former and pressing polyethylene plates onto it, a polyethylene replica is obtained. If d is the spacing of the grooves the replica grating has no effect for $\lambda \gg d$ and simply transmits all the incident power, but for $\lambda < d$ interference effects are manifest and the incident power is distributed into the various possible transmission and reflection orders of the grating. For $(\lambda/d) < 0\cdot25$ virtually no energy is transmitted straight on in the zero order. These filters are now available commercially with d values giving cut-offs lying between 20 and 100 cm^{-1}.

4.9. Hybrid Submillimetre Spectrometers

Hybrid spectrometers, that is, instruments which have both dispersive and interferometric features, are rapidly coming into favour in the near and mid-infrared where they represent a good compromise between resolving power and luminous throughput. Examples are the SISAM[125] and Girard[126] spectrometers. So far, however, they have not found any applications in the

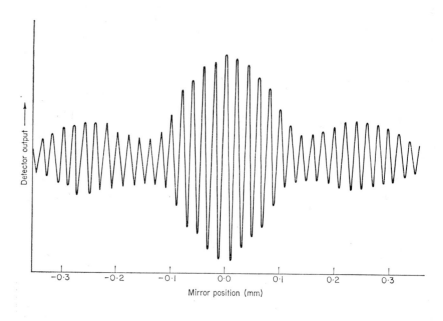

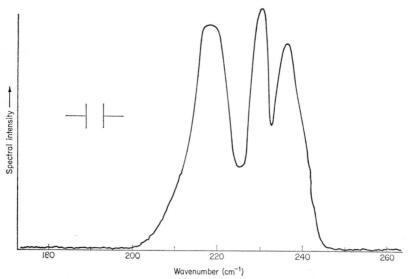

FIG. 4.31. Interferogram and resulting spectrum from hybrid spectrometer.

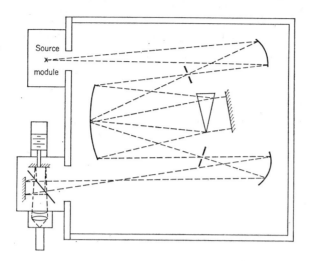

FIG. 4.32. Hybrid spectrometer for the range 200–1000 cm⁻¹.

far infrared. The simplest type of hybrid spectrometer is a prism or grating monochromator followed by a Michelson interferometer. This type of hybrid might be valuable for ultra-high resolution work in the submillimetre region when, as discussed earlier, it will become necessary to severely restrict the radiant bandwidth. The band pass of the system can be altered merely by changing the slit-widths, and the centre frequency of the band pass can be altered simply by rotating the prism or grating. The combination does have some of the luminous throughput restrictions common to most dispersive spectrometers, but it will be realized on reflection that in effect it enables high resolutions to be achieved (via the band-pass restricted interferometer) equivalent to narrow slit-widths whilst retaining the reasonable luminous throughput corresponding to the actual rather wide slits. So far this pro-gramme has not been carried out fully and in practice it will need the most sensitive detectors, but the preliminary results shown in Fig. 4.31 obtained with the prototype instrument shown in Fig. 4.32 are promising. This set-up featured a Littrow mounted caesium iodide prism and a Golay detector. The whole apparatus was deliberately held at atmospheric pressure so as to introduce some sharp features, namely, the two water-vapour absorption bands shown in the Figure. The interferogram shown in Fig. 4.31 is a smoothed version of the original which had a signal-to-noise ratio of 5 to 1 and, because of this rather noisy record and the pressure of other work, the spectrum was only computed to 4 cm⁻¹ resolution. Nevertheless, with detectors operating at liquid helium temperature it should be possible to achieve resolutions of up to 0·01 cm⁻¹ using equipment of this type. The application will most likely be in resolving vibration–rotation bands in the range 200–1000 cm^{-1} for, as discussed elsewhere, high resolution studies in the pure rotation band are often disappointing, merely serving to confirm what had been predicted from microwave observations.

4.10. Polarized Interferometric Spectroscopy

The conventional interferometer, with amplitude modulation and thin-film beam division, suffers from two principal difficulties. Firstly there is the array of beam divider minima which lead to poor performance in certain spectral regions, and secondly there is the strong mean level of the inter-ferogram, variations of which, due to instrumental instabilities, will produce spurious features in the resulting spectrum. Methods of avoiding these difficulties have been discussed earlier, but recently a very novel type of interferometer which bypasses both, whilst retaining the facility for refracto-metry, has been proposed and its action experimentally tested by Martin and Puplett (*Infrared Phys.* **10**, 105, 1970). The instrument is basically a Michelson interferometer but with a beam divider constructed from a flat wire-grid polarizer. The radiation from the lamp is first polarized by an external polarizer so that the electric vector is equally inclined (45°) to both the interferometer axis and the vertical direction. The polarized radiation then encounters the wire-grid beam divider and half is transmitted with horizontal polarization and half is reflected with vertical polarization. After reflection from the interferometer mirrors, the beams once more encounter the beam divider and then pass through an analysing polarizer. The outputs with the analyser parallel and perpendicular to the sense of the initial polarizer are

$$W_{\parallel} = \tfrac{1}{2}W_0[1+\cos 4\pi\bar{\nu}x],$$
$$W_{\perp} = \tfrac{1}{2}W_0[1-\cos 4\pi\bar{\nu}x]. \qquad (4.40)$$

The two outputs are both modulated as the interferometer mirror scans and the resulting interferograms may be used to obtain spectra. The per-formance should be good over the entire range of the polarizing action of the beam divider, and Martin and Puplett give this as 10 to greater than 500 cm^{-1}. With the use of appropriate rocking motions for the analyser it is possible to obtain the difference signal

$$V = V_0 \cos 4\pi\bar{\nu}x$$

which oscillates about a true zero, just as do phase-modulated interfero-grams. If two detectors are used it is possible to arrange the instrument to give essentially double-beam action with one detector determining the background interferogram and the other the sample interferogram. This instrument has clearly considerable potential and properly engineered it may be a strong contender in the commercial field.

CHAPTER 5

Submillimetre Physics

The various types of submillimetre spectrometer and ancilliary equipment described in the earlier chapters are now so well developed and so readily available—often commercially—that spectroscopy in the region from 1 to 500 cm^{-1} is no longer difficult and is certainly no longer the perquisite of a few favoured laboratories. This is a very satisfactory state of affairs, since the submillimetre region of a spectrum is a particularly rich source of information on a diverse array of physical phenomena. Part of this bounty comes from the overlap which occurs here of the normal infrared with the microwave region, and we might expect to observe types of spectra in the far infrared usually found only in the one or the other of its neighbours. Thus both pure rotation and rotation–vibration spectra of molecules are commonly observed in the submillimetre region. But this is far from being the whole story and very many more types of spectra belong naturally in the far infrared—a consequence of the numerical magnitudes of certain fundamental physical quantities. As one example of this, consider phonons in a crystal; the shortest phonon wavelength which can be present is equal to twice the lattice spacing, and this latter usually varies from about 1 to 3 Å. The phase velocity of sound waves in the crystal will be of the order 10^4 cm s^{-1} and so the frequency at the zone boundary will be of the order 10^{12} Hz, that is ∼33 cm^{-1}. Another way of looking at what is really the same situation is to note that the forces between molecules in a crystal are an order of magnitude weaker than those between covalently bonded atoms in a molecule. The masses to be moved in an intermolecular vibration are again roughly an order of magnitude larger than those for an intramolecular vibration and, bearing in mind the square root dependence of frequency on the product of force constant and reciprocal mass, we predict a ten-fold drop in vibration frequency. This is just about what is observed; the symmetrical ring-stretching mode of benzene occurs near 1000 cm^{-1}, whereas the strongest infrared-active lattice mode of crystalline benzene occurs near 100 cm^{-1}. For these reasons, lattice modes tend to be found in the range 10 to 100 cm^{-1}, i.e. in the submillimetre region. In thermodynamics, a constant thread running through the argument is the energy of a degree of freedom, i.e. $\frac{1}{2}kT$. For room temperature the frequency for which $h\nu = kT$

141

corresponds to a wavenumber of ~ 200 cm^{-1}. Many phenomena are characterized by excitation energies $h\nu$ which have equivalent temperatures in the range 10 K to 100 K; an example would be the behaviour of the specific heat of solids at low temperatures as discussed by Debye. Other examples of these elementary excitations are phonons and magnons which are discussed later in this chapter; these serve to introduce the topic and in the remainder of the chapter an attempt will be made to present a more systematic survey of the fields of physics where submillimetre observations are important.

5.1. Pure Rotational Absorption of Submillimetre Waves

For a discussion of the absorption or emission of electromagnetic waves by isolated molecules undergoing pure rotational transitions, four factors have to be considered:

a. the nature of the energy levels involved;
b. the appropriate selection rules;
c. the molecular population distribution amongst the available energy levels;
d. the nature of the molecular electric or magnetic multipole responsible for the electromagnetic interaction.

5.1.1. *Energy Levels*[127]

As in the classical case, the energy of the quantum mechanical rotor is determined by the three principal values of the momental ellipsoid, I_A, I_B and I_C. When these three values are different, the molecule is said to be an asymmetric rotor and no closed form expression can be derived for the energy levels. The total angular momentum J (as always) and its projection M on an axis fixed in space are constants of the motion. For each value of J there are $(2J+1)$ sub-levels, each of which has $(2J+1)$ degenerate components, due to the quantum number M. No "good" quantum number can be defined to label the sub-levels of a given J, and a pattern results which is extremely complicated. If the molecule possesses a three-fold or higher axis of symmetry, two of the moments of inertia become necessarily equal and the molecule is said to be a symmetric top; it is oblate if $I_A < I_B = I_C$ and prolate if $I_A > I_B = I_C$. For symmetric tops the $(2J+1)$ sub-levels can be labelled in terms of the quantum number K,

$$K = -J \ldots 0 \ldots +J,$$

which is the projection of J onto the symmetry axis, and the energy levels can now be written down in the simple form

$$E(J, K) = BJ(J+1) + (A-B)K^2 - D_J J^2(J+1)^2$$
$$- D_{JK}J(J+1)K^2 - D_K K^4, \quad (5.1)$$

where $A = h/(8\pi^2 cI_A)$, $B = h/(8\pi^2 cI_B)$ and D_J, D_{JK} and D_K are very small quantities introduced to take account of centrifugal distortion of the non-rigid molecule. From this equation two special cases can be picked out: first, linear rotors for which I_A is zero (or very small if electronic motion is considered), and secondly spherical rotors for which $I_A = I_B = I_C$ and therefore $A = B$. Linear rotors have A very large so that $E(J, K)$ is of the order of many thousands of cm^{-1} unless K is zero. Consequently, at ordinary temperatures only the levels with $K = 0$ are populated, and for purposes of pure rotational transitions in the microwave through submillimetre regions the energy levels take on the very simple form

$$E(J) = BJ(J+1) - D_J J^2 (J+1)^2. \qquad (5.2)$$

This equation also describes the energy levels of a spherical top for which $(A - B)$ = zero. Nevertheless, it should be borne in mind that, whereas every level of a linear rotor is $(2J+1)$ degenerate, every level of a spherical rotor is $(2J+1)^2$ degenerate.

5.1.2. Selection Rules

The absorption or emission of electromagnetic radiation by a molecule takes place by interaction between the electromagnetic field and the electric or magnetic moments, either fixed or varying, possessed by the molecule. Pure rotational transitions require the molecule to possess a permanent moment. By far the commonest type of transition is that due to an electric dipole moment, since such transitions are very much more intense than those due to higher-order electric moments or to magnetic dipole moments. For electric dipole absorption the principal selection rule is

$$\Delta J = 0, \ \pm 1. \qquad (5.3)$$

Additionally, for the transition to have measurable intensity the dipole moment must not be zero. However, all molecules, except those that have two or more non-coincident axes of symmetry or a centre of inversion, or else a rotation–reflexion axis, possess a non-zero permanent moment, and consequently the large majority of molecules have electric dipole pure rotation spectra. When the molecule has no symmetry whatever the selection rule given above is the only one applicable, and all transitions between adjacent values of J and between the various sub-levels of a given J are possible; and the spectrum will be extremely complex. Many asymmetric rotors possess some symmetry elements and these necessarily prescribe the direction of the permanent moment; when this is the case, additional selection rules become operative. Perhaps the most interesting example is the water molecule, especially since the three rotational constants are such (A_0 27·877,

B_0 14·512 and C_0 9·285 cm^{-1}) that most of the absorption spectrum lies in the submillimetre region.[128] The energy levels of an asymmetric rotor are usually written

$$E(\text{cm}^{-1}) = \tfrac{1}{2}(A+C)\,J(J+1)+\tfrac{1}{2}(A-C)\,E(J_{K_aK_c})$$

where $E(J_{K_aK_c})$ is a dimensionless function of the asymmetry parameter $\kappa = (2B-A-C)/A-C$. $E(J_{J_aJ_c})$ has been listed in the standard works, but as examples we have $E(0_{00}) = 0$, $E(1_{01}) = \kappa-1$, $E(1_{11}) = 0$, $E(1_{10}) = \kappa+1$, $E(2_{12}) = \kappa-3$, $E(2_{20}) = 2[\kappa+(\kappa^2+3)^{1/2}]$. The energy levels for the first three J values of H_2O ($\kappa = -0\cdot437\,72$) are shown in Fig. 5.1. The dipole moment of the water molecule lies along the two-fold

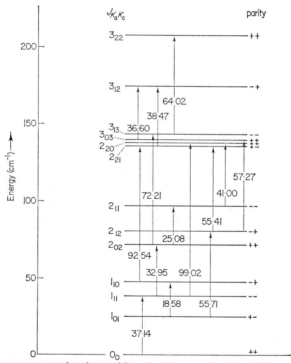

FIG. 5.1. Some pure rotational transitions in the ground state of the water molecule. The figures parenthesized in the vertical arrows are the observed wavenumbers of the lines.

axis of symmetry which is also the intermediate (in value) axis of inertia, so that the molecule can be classified as a case b asymmetric rotor. Only J is defined (i.e. is a "good" quantum number) for an asymmetric rotor, but, by invoking the principle that energy levels must change smoothly with molecular configuration, one can label any level additionally by the two K values, K_a and K_c, which it would have if smoothly deformed into either the limiting prolate or oblate symmetric top. The values of K_a and K_c are restricted by the relations $0 \leqslant K \leqslant J$ and $K_a + K_c = J$, or $(J+1)$, which between them give the proper number, i.e. $(2J+1)$, of sub-levels for a given J. In the older literature a number, $\tau = K_a - K_c$, was used as a subscript to label the various sub-levels. The parity of a level is defined in terms of the symmetry of the underlying wave functions with respect to reflection in two perpendicular planes, and this can be immediately deduced from inspection of K_a and K_c. If both are even the level is $(+ +)$, but if both are odd it is $(- -)$; there are also the two intermediate cases, i.e. $(+ -)$ and $(- +)$. The additional selection rules which apply to the water molecule are $(+ +) \leftrightarrow (- -)$ and $(- +) \leftrightarrow (+ -)$. All possible transitions obeying these rules for the low J levels are shown in the Figure and it will be seen that many absorption features in the submillimetre region will be expected. The dipole moment of H_2O is quite large $(1 \cdot 85 \; D)$, so the lines will be intense. Water vapour is present in the atmosphere and absorption by atmospheric water vapour leads to severe attenuation of submillimetre waves travelling therein. This attenuation is most serious in the vicinity of the actual transitions, but in between the lines the absorption coefficient need not necessarily be large and some so-called "windows" may occur; a well-known one lies between the strong absorption lines at $25 \cdot 085$ and $32 \cdot 95$ cm^{-1}. Because of the occurrence of this window, atmospheric attenuation in the 29 to 30 cm^{-1} region is not too severe. This is very fortunate since one of the most powerful submillimetre lasers (the 337 μm HCN laser) radiates in this region at $29 \cdot 712$ cm^{-1}. We can therefore carry out experiments with this device in the open air rather than having to work in a vacuum tank. The attenuation of the $29 \cdot 712$ cm^{-1} radiation is found[129] to be approximately 10 dB km^{-1} when the humidity corresponds to 1 g of water per cubic metre.

Symmetric rotors always have the dipole moment along the unique momental axis and it is worth remarking in passing that, whereas several asymmetric rotors, cf. $P^{35}Cl_2{}^{37}Cl$, can be discussed as slightly perturbed symmetric rotors (the perturbation taking the form of a removal of the $\pm K$ degeneracy), the water molecule cannot; for, although if the bond angle were near 90° the molecule would have $I_B = I_C$, the dipole moment would *not* be parallel to I_A. The selection rules for symmetric rotor transitions are

$$\Delta J = 0, \pm 1, \qquad \Delta K = 0, \tag{5.4}$$

so that the transition frequencies are given by the expression

$$\bar{\nu} = 2B(J+1) - 4D_J(J+1)^3 - 2D_{JK}(J+1)K^2 \tag{5.5}$$

and, since D_J and D_{JK} are small compared to B, the result is a regular series of lines spaced, to a good approximation, by $2B$. A well-known example

G

is found in the pure rotation spectrum of ammonia which has lines near 19, 38, 57 cm^{-1} etc. If symmetric top spectra are studied at high resolution some complications arise. Firstly, a splitting of the line into its $(J+1)$ components, due to the term involving D_{JK}, may be discernible and, secondly, a doubling of the lines due to "inversion tunnelling" may occur. The splitting of a line into the $(J+1)$, K components can often be resolved in the microwave spectrum, but generally not in the submillimetre spectrum unless this has been observed by the harmonic multiplication methods discussed in Chapter 2. Even in the lower resolution grating or interfero-metric spectra the effect may be noticed by a shift of the absorption maximum away from the position of the $K = 0$ component. This shift can lead to an incorrect determination of B and D_J values unless corrections are applied: thus for NF$_3$ the usual plot of "line" frequency (from the spectra of Fig. 5.2) divided by $(J+1)$ against $(J+1)^2$ gives[130] $B_0 = 0 \cdot 3558$ cm^{-1} and $D_J = 0 \cdot 3 \times 10^{-6}$ cm^{-1}, whereas the correct[63, 130] values are $B_0 = 0 \cdot 3563$ cm^{-1} and $D_J = 0 \cdot 94 \times 10^{-6}$ cm^{-1}.

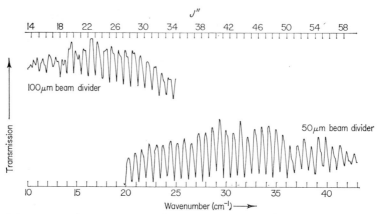

FIG. 5.2. Pure rotation spectrum of nitrogen trifluoride (NF$_3$). The transmission is that of an interferometer with the indicated beam divider and with a path length of 1m of the gas (pressure 700 torr) included in the beam. The two observations are separated vertically for greater clarity.

Inversion doubling of pure rotation lines is a consequence of the ability of atoms in quantum mechanics to "tunnel" through potential barriers which would be impassable according to classical mechanics. The best-known example occurs with the pyramidal NH$_3$ molecule, which can go over to an equivalent (but inverted) position if the nitrogen atom passes through the plane of the three hydrogen atoms. The barrier to inversion is determined by the energy required to deform the molecule into a planar con-figuration, and this is experimentally found to be approximately 2077 cm^{-1}.

Because of the "tunnelling", molecules are able to rapidly invert even in the vibrational ground state, and this effect modifies the vibrational wave functions and energy levels. For each vibrational state the two equivalent levels, which would constitute a doubly degenerate level in the absence of tunnelling, interact in its presence and the result is the familiar quantum mechanical mixing, leading to a removal of the degeneracy. The split levels in the vibrational ground state of ammonia are separated by approximately $0·7934$ cm^{-1}, the actual amount being slightly dependent on J and K, and transitions between the two components lead to a rich (because of the variation with J) spectrum in the microwave region near $23·786$ GHz. The observation of this absorption was an early puzzle since, by an extrapolation of Badger's results[10] to lower frequencies, one could deduce that the first pure rotation line should not occur until 19 cm^{-1}. This $J = 0 \rightarrow J = 1$ line has since been observed frequently by interferometric methods and has recently been detected[131] by microwave techniques at $572·49669$ GHz $(19·096$ cm$^{-1})$. Under moderate resolution all the lines in the pure rotation spectrum of ammonia appear as doublets (splitting $\approx 1·6$ cm^{-1}), with the exception of the first at $19·1$ cm^{-1}. The reason for this anomaly is that, because of the effect of the nuclear spins, the overall wave function for one component of the doublet would be totally symmetric if K were zero and this would violate the Exclusion Principle. All levels with $K = 0$ are therefore single and the first pure rotation line which has only the one component,

$$J = 0, \quad K = 0 \rightarrow J = 1, \quad K = 0,$$

is likewise a singlet,† apart from the hyperfine splitting due to interaction with the ^{14}N quadrupole. So far this splitting (~ 1 MHz) has not been observed experimentally.[131] For ND$_3$, because of the different nuclear spin, the $J = 0 \rightarrow J = 1$ line is also a doublet (intensity ratio 10 : 1), and two components are observed[131] at centre frequencies $309·909\,49$ and $306·736\,71$ GHz. Each of these has been resolved into a hyperfine triplet. Under moderately high resolution each of the doublet components of the lines with $J'' > 0$ breaks up into two or more lines because of the D_{JK} splitting mentioned above.

The pure rotation spectrum of a linear molecule can be thought of as equivalent to that of a symmetric top with $K = 0$; we thus obtain, from equation (5.5),

$$\bar{\nu} = 2B(J+1) - 4D(J+1)^3, \tag{5.6}$$

---

† Although this transition appears as a single line, both its upper and its lower states are displaced by the inversion tunnelling. The 572 GHz line can thus be thought of as the low-frequency component of a doublet whose high-frequency component does not exist. With[131] $B_0 = 298·114\,68$ GHz and $D_J = 24·33$ MHz the unperturbed line centre would occur at $596·132$ GHz.

and once again we have a series of more or less equispaced lines. There are only a few molecules whose B values are sufficiently high to make their entire pure rotation spectrum lie at submillimetre or shorter wavelengths. An example is HCl with $B_0 = 20 \cdot 68$ cm^{-1}. For the remainder, as remarked in Chapter 2, the submillimetre observations, made with delay-type instruments, can add little to the information gleaned from microwave studies. The only exception to this general rule is when there is some other form of angular momentum present in the molecule, in addition to that arising from the molecular rotation. When this is the case, J is the resultant of the various contributions and some much more complicated spectra result. The molecules NO and NO$_2$, which contain unpaired electrons, are examples and their submillimetre spectra have proved good tests for the resolving powers of interferometers.[132]

Centrosymmetric linear molecules such as N_2, CO_2 and C_2H_2 have necessarily a zero electric dipole moment. In group theoretical language, an electric dipole moment transforms as a translation and, if the molecule possesses a centre of symmetry, no translation can belong to the totally symmetric representation and, since this representation includes the ground state of the molecule, what has been said above follows. A magnetic dipole moment, on the other hand, transforms as a rotation and it is possible for the ground state representation to include one of these. The oxygen molecule has electronic symmetry $^3\Sigma_g^-$ and this representation of the point group $D_{\infty h}$ also contains the primitive rotation R_Z. Oxygen has therefore a permanent magnetic moment which can be thought of as arising from the presence of the two unpaired electrons. The transitions involving magnetic dipole moments are typically 10^5 times weaker than those involving electric dipole moments, so that under normal circumstances they might not be observed. However, because of the large amount of oxygen in the atmosphere, and because the observing path lengths can be so long, submillimetre spectra of the sun obtained at high altitudes show strong absorption features due to magnetic dipole pure rotation transitions in oxygen. These features have now been duplicated[101] under laboratory conditions, an example having been presented in Fig. 4.14. Each line of the spectrum is a widely-spaced triplet, the origin of which will be explained in Chapter 6. Electric quadrupole transitions are in principle possible but so far no example is known. Moments created by isotopic substitution are likewise expected to be very small, but here an exciting astrophysical application arises since, if it proves possible to observe HD in absorption in galactic spectra, it should be possible to estimate the at present unknown concentration of molecular hydrogen in various regions of the universe. On a humbler plane it has been pointed out[15] that spherical rotors, such as CF_4 and SF_6, should possess a small moment when excited to a degenerate vibrational level.

If CF_4 were excited to the ν_4 level which lies at 628 cm^{-1}, it would then have symmetry F_2 (which includes the three translations) and a very weak pure rotation spectrum might be observed. So far this possibility remains unproven.

5.2. Intensities and Line-shapes in Pure Rotation Spectra

With the development of intense monochromatic laser sources in the submillimetre region, and with the increasingly successful efforts to extend radio techniques into this part of the spectrum, the study of the line profile of pure rotation absorptions is becoming increasingly important. One can always hope to have the source frequency well away from the centre frequency of the various atmospheric lines, but necessarily there will always be the attenuation at the source frequency due to the "wings" of remote features. We therefore need to know the variation of absorption coefficient with frequency, i.e. the line-shape function, for all atmospheric lines if we are to be in a position to judge the utility or otherwise of submillimetre systems operating in the atmosphere. The line-shape function is also important in meteorological connections, since the absorption of solar and terrestrial radiation in the somewhat optimistically labelled "window regions" influences the heat balance of the earth. An excellent account of line-shape theory with an emphasis on the microwave region has been given by Townes and Schawlow;[15] so here we will simply quote their results, sketch in the physical background and then go on to discuss in more detail the changes to be expected at the higher submillimetre frequencies.

A pure rotation line has a shape other than the delta function because the radiation wavetrains involved are not pure cosine waves of limitless extent. This can come about in three ways. Firstly, since a finite quantum of energy is involved in the transition of a molecule from one rotational state to another, the emitted or absorbed wavetrain can only have a finite length. Line broadening by this phenomenon is called "uncertainty broadening" since another way of looking at it is to say that, because of the finite transition probabilities, all states of a molecule except the ground state will be broadened because molecules may only spend an average finite time Δt in a given state. If this is so, then, by Heisenberg's uncertainty principle,

$$\Delta E \Delta t \approx h, \tag{5.7}$$

it follows that the energy levels have a finite width, ΔE. Since $E = h\nu$, this equation can also be written

$$\Delta \nu \Delta t \approx 1. \tag{5.8}$$

Lifetimes of the states involved in pure rotational transitions vary inversely as the cube of the frequency, but even at 30 cm^{-1} the lifetimes are as long as 1 second and the uncertainty broadening is therefore only of the order 10^{-10} cm^{-1}. Whilst this is of theoretical importance, it has little practical relevance in submillimetre spectroscopy where line-widths of the order of 10^{-2} cm^{-1} are encountered.

The second cause of line broadening lies in the chaotic and random velocities of the molecules in the gaseous sample. Due to the Doppler effect, the observed frequency will rise when a molecule is travelling towards the detector and fall when it is travelling away from the detector. The equation giving the Doppler shift in the non-relativistic case is

$$\Delta \bar{\nu}/\bar{\nu} = u/c, \tag{5.9}$$

where u is the component of velocity along the line of observation. A rough idea of the line broadening to be expected from this effect can be deduced from the equipartition principle which gives the average kinetic energy of the molecules in the gas as

$$\tfrac{1}{2}\overline{mu^2} = kT,$$

and thus

$$\bar{u} = \sqrt{(2kT/m)}.$$

Substituting this in the Doppler equation gives

$$\Delta \bar{\nu}/\bar{\nu} = \sqrt{[2kT/(mc^2)]}. \tag{5.10}$$

For the case of HF, putting in the values of the physical constants, with $T = 300\,K$, a value of $\Delta\bar{\nu} \approx 3 \times 10^{-4}$ cm^{-1} for $\bar{\nu} = 40$ cm^{-1} is obtained. This is much larger than the uncertainty broadening but is still rather small. Townes and Schawlow[15] give a more accurate version of equation (5.10) from a consideration of the resolved components of the velocities and deduce that the line-shape will be Gaussian with a half-width

$$\Delta \bar{\nu}/\bar{\nu} = \sqrt{[2kT \ln 2/(mc^2)]}. \tag{5.11}$$

The third cause of line broadening, and by far the most important in most practical situations, is molecular collision. The basic physical principle underlying the various treatments of this phenomenon is the assumption of "strong collisions"; by this we postulate the collisions to be so violent that the phase of the molecular rotation, or vibration after the collision, is not correlated at all with that before collision. With this assumption the line-shape to be expected can be derived using correlation function theory.[133] The correlation function $f(t)$ is a measure of the chance that a dipole originally aligned along a given direction in either a stationary or rotating frame of reference, at zero time, has still that alignment after the passage of a time t. In terms of it, the complex dielectric constant (see Appendix 3) may be written

$$(\hat{\epsilon} - \epsilon_\infty)/(\epsilon_0 - \epsilon_\infty) = - \int_0^\infty \dot{f}(t) \exp(-2\pi i \nu t) \, dt, \tag{5.12}$$

where ϵ_0 and ϵ_∞ are the dielectric constants at zero and very high (i.e. optical) frequencies and the dot signifies differentiation with respect to time. If we have an oscillator of natural (time) frequency ν_0 undergoing random collisions, the correlation function may be written†

$$f(t) = \exp(-t/\tau) \exp(2\pi i \nu_0 t), \tag{5.13}$$

where τ is an average collision time. Substituting this in (5.12) and carrying through the integration, we arrive at

$$(\hat{\epsilon} - \epsilon_\infty)/(\epsilon_0 - \epsilon_\infty) = (1 - 2\pi i \nu_0 \tau)/[1 + 2\pi i (\nu - \nu_0)\tau]. \tag{5.14}$$

From equations (10) and (14) of Appendix 3 we can write down an explicit relation between α, the absorption coefficient, and the real (ϵ') and imaginary (ϵ'') components of $\hat{\epsilon}$, i.e.

$$\alpha = 4\pi\bar{\nu}\left(\frac{\epsilon'}{2}\right)^{1/2}\left\{\left[1 + \left(\frac{\epsilon''}{\epsilon'}\right)^2\right]^{1/2} - 1\right\}^{1/2}. \tag{5.15}$$

This expression is rather formidable but fortunately, in the far infrared and microwave regions, ϵ' is usually very much greater than ϵ'', so we may simplify it using familiar approximations to give

$$\alpha = 2\pi\bar{\nu}\epsilon''(\epsilon')^{-1/2}, \tag{5.16}$$

and for gases we may still further simplify the expression by setting $(\epsilon')^{1/2} = 1$. When the imaginary component of $\hat{\epsilon}$ is extracted from equation (5.14) and substituted in the simplified form of (5.16), the result is

$$\alpha = 4\pi^2\nu^2\tau(\epsilon_0 - \epsilon_\infty)/c[1 + 4\pi^2(\nu - \nu_0)^2 \tau^2]. \tag{5.17}$$

From dispersion theory it may be shown that, if the difference in population between the upper and lower levels of the transition is ΔN per unit volume,

$$\epsilon_0 - \epsilon_\infty = 4\pi\Delta N \, |\mu_{tj}|^2/(3h\nu_0), \tag{5.18}$$

---

† The use of a simple exponential decay correlation function is not physically justifiable, except in the long time limit, and it leads to erroneous predictions of finite absorption at all frequencies greater than ν_0. Nevertheless, this type of function and the line-shape equations derived therefrom are in such common use that we have chosen to follow this approach here. More accurate treatments will be discussed later.

where μ_{ij} is the dipole moment matrix element for the transition.[134] If $h\nu_0$ is much less than kT, this reduces to

$$\epsilon_0 - \epsilon_\infty = 4\pi N_i \mid \mu_{ij} \mid^2/(3kT), \qquad (5.19)$$

where N_i is the number of molecules per unit volume in the lower state. Substituting (5.19) into (5.17) we have

$$\alpha = \{16\pi^3 N_i \mid \mu_{ij} \mid^2/(3ckT)\}\{\nu^2\tau/[1+4\pi^2(\nu-\nu_0)^2 \tau^2]\}. \qquad (5.20)$$

N_i can be evaluated in terms of N (the total number of molecules per unit volume) by calculating the Boltzmann distribution over all the available rotational and vibrational levels. Vibrational effects are not usually of much significance unless the molecule has a very low vibrational frequency, but the summation over the rotational levels is most important. The matrix element of the dipole moment for a pure rotational transition is a standard result of quantum mechanics, i.e.

$$\mid \mu_{ij} \mid^2 = \mu^2(J+1)/(2J+1) \text{ for } \Delta J = +1. \qquad (5.21)$$

The summation over the rotational levels of the ground vibrational state is complicated by the $(2J+1)$ dependence of the statistical weights. The fraction of molecules in a state with angular momentum J, ignoring centrifugal distortion, is given by

$$f_i = \frac{N_i}{N} = \frac{(2J+1) \exp [-hcBJ(J+1)/kT]}{\sum\limits_{J=0}^{J=\infty} (2J+1) \exp [-hcBJ(J+1)/kT]}. \qquad (5.22)$$

It is rather difficult to evaluate the sum over all J with a view to finding the rotational partition function, but fortunately $hcB/(kT)$ is usually sufficiently small for the sum to be approximated as an integral, and when this is done it is found that

$$N_i = N [hcB/(kT)](2J+1) \exp [-hcBJ(J+1)/(kT)]. \qquad (5.23)$$

Therefore

$$N_i \mid \mu_{ij} \mid^2 = N\mu^2[h\bar{\nu}_0c/(2kT)] \exp [-hcBJ(J+1)/(kT)], \qquad (5.24)$$

and, of course,

$$2B(J+1) = \bar{\nu}_0,$$

where $\bar{\nu}_0$ is the line frequency in cm^{-1}. Substituting (5.24) in equation (5.20), and changing throughout to cm^{-1} as the unit of frequency, the final expression for the line-shape is found to be

$$\alpha = \frac{8\pi^3 hN\bar{\nu}_0c^2\mu^2}{3(kT)^2} \frac{\bar{\nu}^2\tau}{1+4\pi^2c^2(\bar{\nu}-\bar{\nu}_0)^2 \tau^2} \exp [-hcBJ(J+1)/kT]. \qquad (5.25)$$

This equation can also be written in terms of the line-width parameter, $\Delta\bar{\nu} = [2\pi c\tau]^{-1}$, the expression being

$$\alpha = \frac{4\pi^2 hN\bar{\nu}_0 c\mu^2}{3(kT)^2} \frac{\bar{\nu}^2\Delta\bar{\nu}}{(\Delta\bar{\nu})^2+(\bar{\nu}-\bar{\nu}_0)^2} \exp\left[-hcBJ(J+1)/kT\right]. \quad (5.26)$$

Line-shape functions of the above type have some interesting properties. Firstly, if $\Delta\bar{\nu}$ is much less than $\bar{\nu}_0$, the peak absorption occurs at a wavenumber very close to $\bar{\nu}_0$ and, if we put $\bar{\nu} = \bar{\nu}_0$, we may write to a good approximation

$$\alpha_{max} = \{4\pi^2 hNc\bar{\nu}_0^3\mu^2/[3(kT)^2\Delta\bar{\nu}]\} \exp\left[-hcBJ(J+1)/(kT)\right]. \quad (5.27)$$

The collision time τ will be inversely proportional to the pressure, from which it follows that the half-width of the line $\Delta\bar{\nu}$ will be directly proportional to the pressure. The number of molecules per unit volume N will also be proportional to the pressure and because of this the effects cancel and α_{max} is a pressure invariant. This has been confirmed in the microwave region where, with the availability of ultra-high resolving power (see Chapter 2), it is possible to scan over the line with a spectral window whose width is very much less than $\Delta\bar{\nu}$. The second point is that the peak height increases initially as the cube of the frequency until the effect of the exponential term takes over. This means that, whereas in the microwave region with $\mu = 1$ Debye (10^{-18} e.s.u.) and a pressure such that $\Delta\bar{\nu} = 5 \times 10^{-4}$ cm^{-1}, the peak absorption at 1 cm^{-1} will be 10^{-4} neper cm^{-1}; in the submillimetre region the corresponding absorption at 30 cm^{-1} will be of the order of 2 neper cm^{-1}. It follows, therefore, that in most experiments done to observe pure rotation spectra in the submillimetre region, using delay-type spectrometers, the central regions of the strongest lines are essentially "black" since path lengths of the order of 10 cm are commonly employed. The absorption which is apparently observed at the place in the spectrum corresponding to the centre frequency of a line represents roughly the fraction of the observing bandwidth which is "blacked out". Clearly very high resolving powers (i.e. very narrow observing bandwidths) will be necessary before any meaning whatever can be attached to measured transmissions at the centre frequencies. This point is illustrated graphically in Fig. 5.3, which shows the pure rotation spectrum of HCN observed with a resolution of $0\cdot25$ cm^{-1}. The "peak" absorptions of the H^{13}CN lines are roughly 25 per cent of the corresponding H^{12}CN lines, although H^{13}CN forms only 1 per cent of a natural sample. The third point is that, since the line-width $\Delta\bar{\nu}$ is proportional to pressure, the fraction of the observing bandwidth which is "blacked out" will increase with pressure. The effect in the observed spectrum is that the apparent transmission at the line-centre frequency falls as the pressure rises. This is such a familiar and reasonable observation that it is not

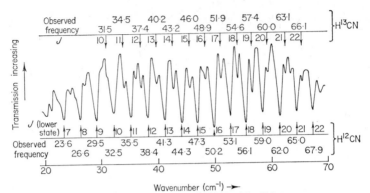

FIG. 5.3. Far infrared transmission spectrum of HCN with all isotopes present at natural abundance. Pressure 6 torr, path length 5 m, temperature 293 K, resolution $0 \cdot 25$ cm^{-1} (from unpublished results of G. W. Chantry and Helen M. Evans).

frequently realized that the effect is due entirely to increasing line-width, the true peak absorption being invariant. The fourth point, which is highly germane to discussions of the transmission of submillimetre laser radiation through polar gases, is that the absorption coefficient in the "wings" of the line, i.e. when $(\bar{v} - \bar{v}_0)^2 \gg (\Delta \bar{v})^2$, is proportional to the square of the pressure. This is because in such a region the term $(\Delta \bar{v})^2$ in the denominator may be ignored and therefore

$$\alpha \sim N \Delta \bar{v} \sim p^2. \tag{5.28}$$

The fifth point is that for very large $\bar{v}$ the absorption coefficient does not fall to zero but reaches a constant asymptotic value given by

$$\alpha_\infty = [4\pi^2 h N \bar{v}_0 c \mu^2 \Delta \bar{v}/3(kT)^2] \exp [-hcBJ(J+1)/(kT)]. \tag{5.29}$$

Behaviour of this type has indeed been found in the microwave region, but in general the asymptotic value is lower than would be expected. This topic is one engaging active interest at the moment, and it is becoming clear that the simple exponential decay type of correlation function will need modification for small time values. The correlation function approach is relatively modern and the early work of Debye, Lorentz and Van Vleck and Weisskopf derived the line-shape functions by the solution of appropriate equations of motion (see Appendix 3). These equations did not contain terms involving the molecular moment of inertia, and therefore the line-shape functions would not be expected to agree with the observed shape in the high-frequency wing of the line at frequency displacements of the order of pure rotational transitions. Several attempts[135] were made to introduce the molecular moments of inertia explicitly into the equations of motion and thus to obtain, in the theoretical treatment, the observed recovery of transparency at a sufficiently high frequency. Equivalent work, using the correlation function approach by Brot and Lassier[136] and by Birnbaum and Cohen,†[137] has led to significant advances. In particular they have shown that to be physically acceptable $f(t)$ must be a real even function of time. Quite clearly the simple exponential decay function $\exp(-t/\tau)$ does not satisfy this criterion but, by analytically modifying it near $t = 0$, line-shape functions result which are far more satisfactory and agree well with observation. That the two different types of approach are really equivalent can be seen by noting that modification of $f(t)$ for $t \approx 0$ is really the same thing as altering the line-shape at very high frequency displacement.

The treatment given above is approximate also from a mathematical point of view in that the correlation integral should involve $\exp(2\pi i \nu t)$ as well as $\exp(-2\pi i \nu t)$; in other words, $\cos 2\pi \nu t$. If this is done the full line-shape (Van Vleck and Weisskopf) equation is found to be

$$\alpha = \frac{4\pi^2 h N \bar{\nu}_0 c \mu^2}{3(kT)^2} \exp\left[-hcBJ(J+1)/kT\right]$$

$$\times \left[\frac{\bar{\nu}^2 \Delta \bar{\nu}}{(\Delta \bar{\nu})^2 + (\bar{\nu} - \bar{\nu}_0)^2} + \frac{\bar{\nu}^2 \Delta \bar{\nu}}{(\Delta \bar{\nu})^2 + (\bar{\nu} + \bar{\nu}_0)^2}\right]. \qquad (5.30)$$

The second of the two terms in parentheses is very small compared with the first in the vicinity of $\bar{\nu}_0$, which justifies the approximation, but in the region $\bar{\nu} \gg \bar{\nu}_0$ the two terms become approximately equal. This function is compared and contrasted with the Lorentz line-shape function in Appendix 3.

So far we have discussed line broadening by collision of identical molecules—the so-called "self broadening". A very important practical problem is to determine the absorption to be expected when the polar gas is dispersed at low partial pressure in a transparent foreign gas such as nitrogen. The first thing to note is that we will have contributions to the line-width from both molecule–molecule collisions and from molecule–foreign gas molecule collisions; it is usual to assume a linear form and to write

$$\Delta \bar{\nu} = p_1 \sigma_1 + p_0 \sigma_0, \qquad (5.31)$$

where p_1, p_0 are the pressures of the polar and the foreign gas respectively and σ_1 and σ_0 are the appropriate broadening parameters. The foreign-gas broadening is less effective than the self broadening and, typically, we might

† The correlation integral used by these workers is

$$(\hat{\epsilon} - \epsilon_\infty)/(\epsilon_0 - \epsilon_\infty) = 1 - i\omega \int_0^\infty \phi(t) \exp(-i\omega t)\, dt,$$

which can be shown to be equivalent to our equation (5.12) by application of the rule for integration by parts and, of course, identifying their $\phi(t)$ with our $f(t)$.

have $\sigma_0 = 2\,\text{MHz torr}^{-1}$ whereas $\sigma_1 = 10\,\text{MHz torr}^{-1}$. However, p_0 is usually much larger than p_1, either deliberately or naturally, and, despite the disparity of σ_0 and σ_1, the term in $p_0\sigma_0$ dominates. Substituting (5.31) into (5.26) we have

$$\alpha \propto [p_1\bar{\nu}^2(p_1\sigma_1 + p_0\sigma_0)]/[(p_1\sigma_1 + p_0\sigma_0)^2 + (\bar{\nu} - \bar{\nu}_0)^2], \qquad (5.32)$$

and for $p_0 \gg p$

$$\alpha_{\max} \propto (p_1/p_0)(\bar{\nu}_0^2/\sigma_0). \qquad (5.33)$$

The absorption coefficient at the resonant frequency is no longer invariant and is simply proportional to the ratio of pressure of absorbing gas to pressure of broadening gas. In general, this ratio can be made small enough so that the peak absorption becomes a measurable quantity, even when one is restricted to the lower resolving powers available in the submillimetre and infrared regions. Essentially the line intensity becomes spread out over a much larger spectral region, and the absorption coefficient becomes a much less rapidly varying function of frequency. This phenomenon is the basis of the method suggested by Wilson and Wells[138] for determining the intensities of spectral lines in the gas phase. Foreign-gas broadening is particularly important in connection with the transmission of submillimetre waves through the atmosphere. The effect of the nitrogen and oxygen is to pressure broaden the pure rotational lines of water vapour, and thus to reduce the transmission in the "window" regions. In fact, the transmission falls to such low values that submillimetre radiation from the sun is not normally observable at ground stations and observations have to be made from high-altitude laboratories, or else from balloons or aeroplanes. Very careful studies of atmospheric absorption of the radiation from the various submillimetre lasers (see Chapter 6) by Burroughs, Jones and Gebbie[139] has indicated that simple pressure-broadening theory cannot account for all the atmospheric absorption in the regions remote from the line centres. They postulate the existence of a continuum absorption, arising from pure rotational transitions in an unstable dimer $(H_2O)_2$, and additionally suggest that there is excess absorption in the extreme wings of the lines, due to collision-induced absorption, arising from interaction between the dipole moment of the polar molecules with the quadrupole moment of the foreign-gas molecules. Both these effects are relatively small and near the line centres they may be neglected and the simple theory outlined above applied with confidence.

It was remarked earlier that the peak height of a rotational line increases initially as the cube of the centre frequency. This has an interesting effect on the intensity distribution in the pure rotational band as compared with that in a vibration–rotation band. For the latter, the absolute frequency does not change much over the entire band, so that the most intense rotational line corresponds to a transition from the most populated level. This level can be found by determining the J value at which equation (5.22) has a maximum. The answer, found by standard methods of differential calculus, is

$$J_{max} = [kT/(2Bhc)]^{\frac{1}{2}} - \frac{1}{2}; \qquad (5.34)$$

for HF as an example, $J_{max} = 2$. In the pure rotation band, on the other hand, the transition which is most intense is found to correspond to a J value which is a root of the equation

$$(2J+1)(J+1) = 3kT/(hcB), \qquad (5.35)$$

and for HF again this is found to be $J = 3$. The relative displacement increases as B becomes smaller and T larger. The overall result of this effect is that the pure rotation spectrum can often be observed to higher J values than is the case with vibration–rotation bands, and even moderately heavy molecules, whose first few rotational lines lie in the microwave region, will still have an observable spectrum in the submillimetre region.

In conclusion, we have a satisfactory phenomenological theory of line-shapes which is quite satisfactory—apart from some discrepancies in the "wings"—for understanding the propagation of submillimetre waves through polar gases. Unfortunately, as Townes and Schawlow[15] have emphasized, the theory contains a parameter $\Delta\bar{\nu}$ which ought really to be reducible to other physical quantities. These would include, for example, mean free paths, collision cross-sections and multipole moments, but little progress seems to have been made in effecting this synthesis.

5.3. Microwave and Submillimetre Absorption in Non-polar Gases at High Pressure

As was remarked earlier, it is necessary for a molecule to possess a permanent electrical or magnetic moment for absorption of radiation by pure rotational transitions, and for most purposes only an electric dipole moment is of significance. Nevertheless, at pressures greater than a few atmospheres many non-polar gases exhibit absorption which is much higher than can be accounted for by direct interaction of their higher moments with the radiation field. It can readily be shown that absorption by isolated molecules is not the cause of the phenomenon by noting that the absorption varies, not as the first power of the pressure, but rather as the square. This absorption is also in general very diffuse with no discernible sharp peaks. These two facts taken together are strong evidence that the absorption is due to interaction between molecules in close contact. Pressure-induced absorption in the

infrared was first† reported by Welsh and his colleagues.[140] They observed
the forbidden vibrational fundamental of H_2 at 4200 cm^{-1}, and showed that
its intensity depended on the square of the density. Unambiguous proof
that pairs of molecules were involved came with the observation of simultaneous transitions by Welsh, Crawford, McDonald and Chisholm,[141] in
which one photon is absorbed but its frequency is either the sum or the
difference of two transitions, one in one molecule and the other in another.
Microwave absorption in compressed CO_2 was reported in 1954 by Birnbaum, Maryott and Wacker.[142] Again the absorption was proportional to
the square of the pressure and at X band (3·3 cm wavelength) frequencies
the absorption coefficient was $2·3 \times 10^{-5}$ neper cm^{-1} for a gas pressure of
45 atm and a temperature of 298 K. This absorption is thought to arise
both from translational and rotational types of motion of one molecule in
the field of the other. Mid-infrared pressure-dependent absorption was
reported by Colpa and Ketelaar[143] in 1957 when they studied hydrogen in
a 100 cm gas cell at pressures between 20 and 150 atmospheres and over
the frequency range 420–1300 cm^{-1}. Their spectra show a broad absorption
covering this region with distinct features at 587, 814 and 1035 cm^{-1}. The
B value for hydrogen is known to be 59·3 cm^{-1}, so these observed features
occur at frequencies corresponding to the transitions $J = 1 \rightarrow J = 3$,
$J = 2 \rightarrow J = 4$ and $J = 3 \rightarrow J = 5$; in other words, the selection rule is
$\Delta J = \pm 2$ and the line positions, disregarding centrifugal distortion, are
given by

$$\bar{\nu} = 2B(2J+3). \tag{5.36}$$

The first line of the series expected at 354 cm^{-1} was outside the range covered
in the experiments. Hydrogen gas consists of a mixture of molecules in
either *para* or *ortho* states, which correspond respectively to the two proton
spins, being either antiparallel or parallel, and interconversion of one form
into the other is very slow. *Para*-hydrogen can only exist with J even and
ortho-hydrogen with J odd; so another way of looking at the selection rule
is that it forbids *ortho–para* conversion by pure rotational transitions.‡
The peak in the pressure-induced rotation spectrum of H_2 ought not, in
principle, to be found by direct application of equation (5.35), since the
spin statistics which make the *ortho* levels three times more populated than
the *para* levels have to be taken into account. By direct solution of equation

† Absorption in the $0 \rightarrow 2$ and $0 \rightarrow 3$ vibration–rotation bands of H_2 had been reported
earlier in the same year by Herzberg[144] who used atmospheric pressure and very long
path lengths. However, it seems likely that Herzberg's suggestion that his observations
could arise from quadrupole absorption by isolated molecules is in fact correct.

‡ The $J = 0 \rightarrow J = 1$ *para* to *ortho* transition in H_2 has, however, been observed in the
inelastic neutron scattering spectrum.[146] This is because the only selection rules which
apply here are conservation of energy and momentum.

(5.35), we find that $J_{max} = 1 \cdot 5$, so that the 587 and the 814 cm^{-1} lines should be equally intense on this count, but the 587 cm^{-1} line is an *ortho* transition and therefore, in agreement with experiment,[143] is expected to be the more intense. A comprehensive account of pure rotational absorption in H_2 has been given in a series of papers by the group at Toronto led by Welsh.[145]

The commonest form of pressure-induced pure rotational absorption arises from a dipole moment induced in one molecule by the quadrupole field of another. For a homonuclear diatomic molecule, both the quadrupole moment and the molecular polarizability are sent into themselves (i.e. they do not change sign) by the application of either the operation of inversion at the centre of symmetry, or by the operation of rotation through π about an axis perpendicular to the internuclear axis. It follows that the induced moment will rotate at twice the speed of the molecular rotation and, by the correspondence principle, we recover the self-same selection rule, $\Delta J = \pm 2$. The intensity of absorption will depend very strongly on the intermolecular separation and will only be significant for the time of closest approach. The line-width will therefore be very broad since, by the uncertainty principle, the line-width is inversely proportional to the lifetime of the absorbing state. This is confirmed[143] for hydrogen where the discrete features become sharper at lower temperatures, due to reduced molecular velocities, and there is a consequent increase in the time during which the two molecules are in close contact. A similar interpretation[143] is offered to account for the sharper lines observed at the same positions when compressed mixtures of hydrogen and nitrogen are studied, for a nitrogen molecule approaching a hydrogen molecule will be travelling much slower than would another hydrogen molecule. Very similar behaviour has now been observed in the far infrared region for nitrogen[147] and carbon dioxide.[148] No discrete features are observed (see Fig. 5.4), presumably because the line spacing (now very much less because of the reduced B values) is smaller than the widths of the component lines. The absorption band of nitrogen peaks at 100 cm^{-1}, but as the band is very broad absorption due to its low frequency "tail" has been observed[149] in the microwave region and a value for the quadrupole moment has been derived from the experimental results. The quoted result is $Q = 1 \cdot 0 \times 10^{-26}$ e.s.u.

The broad absorption band in compressed CO_2, whose low-frequency tail was detected in the microwave experiments of Birnbaum and Maryott,[142, 150] has been extensively investigated. At microwave frequencies the translational or non-resonant branch ($\Delta J = 0$) dominates the absorption, but at frequencies greater than 10 cm^{-1} the rotational or resonant branch is by far the more intense. The theoretical expressions giving the integrated absorption of the band in terms of the molecular quadrupole moment are rather complex

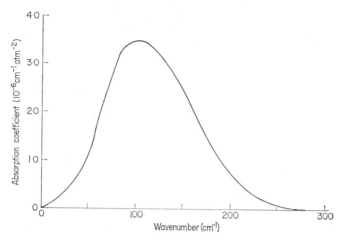

Fig. 5.4. Pressure-induced far infrared absorption in gaseous nitrogen. The spectrum is a smoothed plot of the data of Gebbie, Stone and Williams[147] together with that of Heastie and Martin.[157]

and involve some non-elementary functions, so they will not be explicitly listed here, but from them Birnbaum and Maryott[150] estimated for CO_2, $Q = 5 \cdot 9 \times 10^{-26}$ e.s.u. The quadrupole moment enters the expressions as Q^2, so the absolute sign of Q may not be inferred. The far infrared portion of the band was first described by Gebbie and Stone,[148] whose results are shown in Fig. 5.5. Combining this data with microwave results, Ho Kauffman and Thaddeus[151] calculated Q to be $6 \cdot 7 \times 10^{-26}$ e.s.u. Temperature variation studies by Harries[152] showed that the simple treatment in terms of point moments was inadequate and, by using corrections which took explicit account both of the quadrupole–quadrupole interaction energy and of the anisotropy of polarizability, this author subsequently obtained consistent values of Q which were, as they should be, independent of temperature. His mean value was $(4 \cdot 45 \pm 0 \cdot 3) \times 10^{-26}$ e.s.u., which agreed quite well with the absolute measurement of Buckingham, Disch and Dummur,[153] namely, $Q = 4 \cdot 3 \times 10^{-26}$ e.s.u.

Molecules belonging to the cubic point groups (T_d and O_h), such as CH_4, CF_4 and SF_6, are not only non-polar but are also forbidden to have a quadrupole moment. Nevertheless, absorption in the submillimetre region is observed with compressed samples and this is ascribed to dipole moments induced in the polarizable molecule by the octapole (T_d) or hexadecapole (O_h) fields of another molecule in close contact.[154] An octapole field has trigonal symmetry and a hexadecapole field four-fold symmetry so that again, by the correspondence principle, the selection rules for an octapole

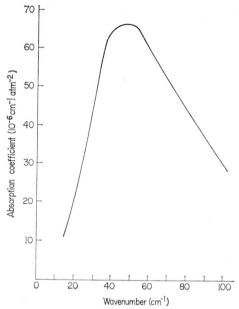

FIG. 5.5. Pressure-induced far infrared absorption in gaseous carbon dioxide (after Gebbie and Stone[148]).

absorption are $\Delta J = \pm 1, \pm 2$ and ± 3. The selection rules for a hexadecapole absorption do not appear to have been explicitly derived but, arguing from analogy, one may assume them to be $\Delta J = \pm 1, \pm 2, \pm 3$ and ± 4. Because of these selection rules, the observed band extends to much higher frequencies than might be expected from conventional reasoning in terms of the known B values. Values for the octapole moments have been derived from the data: for CH_4 this is[155] $\Omega = 2 \cdot 5 \times 10^{-34}$ e.s.u. with a very similar value for CD_4; for CF_4 the value found[156] is $4 \cdot 5 \times 10^{-34}$ e.s.u. Some complications are encountered when polyatomic molecules are being investigated, for difference bands of the type $\nu_i - \nu_j$ may occur in the same region. Fortunately the intensity of such a band will be a linear function of pressure, whereas the intensity of the induced band will depend on the square of the pressure, so that if spectra are recorded over a range of pressures the two effects can be separated.

It will be seen, therefore, that investigations of absorption in non-polar gases at high pressures can give a great deal of information about molecular properties. Pressure-induced absorption is important in astrophysical connections, especially when such problems as heat exchange in the atmospheres of the larger planets are being discussed. Even in the case of the earth's atmosphere, induced absorption in nitrogen may be significant. Perhaps also a consideration of the induced absorption in nitrogen and oxygen, due to the polar water-vapour molecules, may be necessary in gaining a complete understanding of the transmission of submillimetre radiation through the atmosphere.

5.4 Translational Absorption by Molecules Trapped in Clathrates

One of the first problems to be solved in the early days of quantum mechanics was that of the "particle in a box". This phrase was visual imagery for the problem of deriving the wave equation and energy levels for a particle of mass m which moves in the region from $x = -d/2$ to $x = +d/2$ without experiencing any forces, but which encounters infinitely high potential walls at these two values of x. The boundary conditions clearly demand that the wave function should vanish at $x = -d/2$ and $x = +d/2$, and the solutions are a set of standing waves with nodes at these two extremities. It follows that there must be an integral number of half wavelengths inside the "box", i.e. $n = 2d/\lambda$ and, since the energy is purely kinetic,

$$E = n^2h^2/(8md^2); \qquad n = 0, 1, 2, \text{etc.} \tag{5.37}$$

It is not reasonable, of course, to expect potential discontinuities of this type in real molecular systems and, for this reason, the treatment outlined above has only illustrative value, but we might notice that, for an argon atom with $d = 2$ Å the first excited state would occur at 1 cm^{-1}. One of the more interesting attempts to make the treatment more realistic was that of Pöschl and Teller[158] who used the potential function

$$V(x) = [h^2/(8md^2)]\{a(a-1)/[\sin^2 \pi(x/d-\tfrac{1}{2})]\}, \tag{5.38}$$

where a is a parameter. If $a = 1$, this function reproduces the classic case, whilst for large values of a the function more nearly resembles that for the harmonic oscillator, since $V(x)$ has a quadratic dependence on x for small x. This is therefore a very flexible function capable of describing both extremes and, furthermore, the wave equation in terms of it can be analytically solved, leading to energy levels given by

$$E = [h^2/(8md^2)](a+n)^2; \qquad n = 0, 1, 2, \text{etc.} \tag{5.39}$$

The $0 \rightarrow 1$ transition of such a system will occur at a frequency

$$\bar{\nu} = [h/(8mcd^2)](2a+1). \tag{5.40}$$

The "stiffness" parameter a will be expected to be much larger than unity (that is, there will be a distinct minimum at $x = 0$) and, taking a value of 20, the translatory absorption band for argon, with $d = 2$ Å, will lie at 40 cm^{-1}.

Some years ago, Powell and his colleagues[159] at Oxford showed that hydroquinone, when crystallized in its β-quinol modification, forms a lattice with a very open structure containing regularly spaced holes. The effective size of these holes is between 3 and 4 Å and, if the crystals are grown under a moderate pressure of a gas made up of small molecules, these molecules can be trapped in the holes leading to the formation of what has been called a clathrate. The encaged molecules in the β-quinol lattice realize in practice the theoretical situation described above, and it is expected that argon trapped in such a clathrate could absorb electromagnetic radiation at submillimetre wavelengths by undergoing transitions between quantized translation states. The first indication that this was indeed the case came from the work of Van Vleck[160] who, from an analysis of the magnetic susceptibility of an NO clathrate, concluded that the trapped molecules had a first excited vibrational state near 31 cm^{-1}. Direct observations of far infrared absorptions by clathrates were reported in 1965 by Burgiel, Meyer and Richards[161] who studied a wide range of monatomic and diatomic species. They found, in addition to the absorption near 70 cm^{-1} which is ascribed to the host lattice, several further bands which were assigned to translation and hindered rotational modes of the "guest" molecules. For NO, bands were observed at 32 and 47 cm^{-1} and for argon a single band at 35 cm^{-1} was noted. This band shifts to higher frequencies as the temperature is lowered, presumably mostly due to the shrinkage of the host lattice, with a consequent reduction of d.

More extensive spectral data have recently been given by Davies,[162] who included in his study some further "guests" such as HCl, HBr, SO$_2$ and HCN. His results agree, where there is a comparison, with those of Burgiel *et al.*, and for a temperature of 90 K he found: N$_2$ 52 cm^{-1} ($a = 12$, $d = 1 \cdot 7$ Å); CO$_2$ 74 cm^{-1} ($a = 18$, $d = 1 \cdot 4$ Å); CO 51 cm^{-1} ($a = 16$, $d = 2$ Å); and HCl 55 cm^{-1} ($a = 15$, $d = 1 \cdot 6$ Å). No evidence was found— again in agreement with Burgeil *et al.*—for a hindered rotational mode of N$_2$, which is in accord with theoretical expectations based on the centrosymmetric character of the hole. However, it should be borne in mind that the n.m.r. evidence suggests that this mode should have a frequency of 54 cm^{-1} and lie uncomfortably near the translational mode, so the present evidence is not totally conclusive. With non-centrosymmetric molecules, on the other hand, such as CO, the hindered rotational modes are observed, that for CO lying at 80 cm^{-1}. Obviously the barrier to free rotation is high and no quantized free rotation spectrum is expected in the lower frequency region. For HCl, however, features are observed at 20 and 40 cm^{-1} which are very likely due to the $0 \rightarrow 1$ and $1 \rightarrow 2$ pure rotational transitions.

This last observation brings out the importance of clathrate studies, for a clathrate may be legitimately regarded as a kind of intermediate between a gas and a crystal. As we have already seen, both translational and rotational types of motion have been invoked to explain the pressure-induced spectrum of a non-polar gas and, as we shall see later, the lattice modes of a regular crystal may be discussed on a basis of translatory and rotatory modes. The far infrared studies of clathrates have shown unambiguously that quantized molecular rotation can take place in condensed phases, as well as in the gas phase.

5.5. Submillimetre Absorption in Crystals

In the crystalline state, the constituent entities, either molecules, atoms or ions, are held very strongly in their equilibrium positions by a balance of attractive and repulsive forces. There is a long range order which ideally extends throughout the macroscopic specimen and this order may be specified by the space-group symmetry of the crystal lattice. If the crystal contains N atoms or ions, there will be $3N-6$ (or roughly $3N$ since N is large) vibrational degrees of freedom and our problem in determining the infrared absorption spectrum of a crystal is to decide the frequencies of these modes and their spectral activity. In general, this problem cannot be solved exactly, even for the simplest lattices, but one can make a great deal of progress using a semi-phenomenological theory. Many workers have contributed to this topic, but the simple exposition given here is inspired mostly by the work of Born and Huang,[163] as summarized by Mitra and Gielisse.[164]

It is usual to begin by discussing the idealized case of a simple linear diatomic lattice. We consider such a chain made up of two particles of masses M and m and connected by springs whose force constant is f. The model is shown schematically in Fig. 5.6, where the interatomic distance is a. To each lattice point is assigned a number—even $2l$ for the M sites, and odd $2l+1$ for the m sites.

FIG. 5.6. Simple linear diatomic chain.

If the displacements from the equilibrium positions are denoted by the coordinate u, the equations of motion are

$$M(d^2u_{2l}/dt^2) = f(u_{2l+1} + u_{2l-1} - 2u_{2l}),$$

and

$$m(d^2u_{2l+1}/dt)^2 = f(u_{2l+2} + u_{2l} - 2u_{2l+1}). \tag{5.41}$$

Assuming simple harmonic solutions of the form

$$u_{2l} = A_1 \cos (2\pi vt + 2l\bar{k}a)$$
$$u_{2l+1} = A_2 \cos (2\pi vt + (2l+1)\bar{k}a), \qquad (5.42)$$

and substituting in the equations of motion gives two simultaneous linear equations for A_1 and A_2, and these equations have a solution other than $A_1 = A_2 = 0$ only if

$$\begin{vmatrix} 2f - 4\pi^2 v^2 M & -2f \cos \bar{k}a \\ -2f \cos \bar{k}a & 2f - 4\pi^2 v^2 m \end{vmatrix} = 0, \qquad (5.43)$$

which gives

$$v^2 = (1/4\pi^2)\{f/\mu \pm [f^2/\mu^2 - 4f^2 \sin^2 \bar{k}a/(Mm)]^{1/2}\}, \qquad (5.44)$$

where

$$\mu^{-1} = M^{-1} + m^{-1}.$$

The quantity $\bar{k}$ which appears in these equations is known as the wave vector since its direction indicates the polarization of the wave. Its magnitude is a measure of the momentum carried by the wave because in quantum mechanics momentum and wavelength are inversely proportional and the magnitude of $\bar{k}$ is given by

$$|\bar{k}| = 2\pi\lambda^{-1}, \qquad (5.45)$$

where λ is the wavelength of the wave. Clearly, the minimum value of λ will occur when alternate lattice sites of a given kind are moving in phase, i.e. $\lambda_{min} = 4a$; $|\bar{k}|$ is therefore restricted to the range

$$-\pi/2a \leqslant |\bar{k}| \leqslant \pi/2a. \qquad (5.46)$$

The region between these limits of $\bar{k}$ is termed the first Brillouin zone.

The relation between the vibration frequencies and the wave vector are shown in Fig. 5.7 and this takes the form of two branches corresponding to the two signs of the radical in equation (5.44). Diagrams such as Fig. 5.7

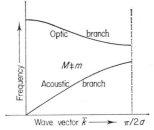

FIG. 5.7. Dispersion diagram for the vibrations of a simple linear diatomic chain.

have extensive use in physics and are known as dispersion diagrams. The name comes from the fact that for any wave propagating in any medium

$$\nu\lambda = v_\phi, \tag{5.47}$$

where v_ϕ is the phase velocity. Therefore, the phase velocity for any value of $\bar{k}$ can be immediately read off from the dispersion diagram by dividing the frequency of intercept on the branch by the value of $\bar{k}/2\pi$. The branches are not linear so that the phase velocity is a function of $\bar{k}$ and varying phase velocity is synonymous with dispersion. The lower of the two branches in Fig. 5.7 is called the acoustic branch since it corresponds to the propagation of sound waves. For low values of $\bar{k}$, this branch is sensibly linear with a slope equal to the velocity of sound along the chain

$$v_s = (2a^2 f)^{1/2} (M+m)^{-1/2}.$$

At higher wavenumbers the slope becomes less and the branch intercepts the zone edge at a frequency $\nu = (f/2\pi^2 M)^{1/2}$ for $M > m$. That this frequency commonly occurs in the submillimetre band was mentioned in the introduction to this chapter. The upper branch is called the optical branch since for low $\bar{k}$ the phase velocities are very high, corresponding roughly to light velocities; for $\bar{k}$ zero the phase velocity is infinite, which is just another way of saying that the vibrations are in phase everywhere. Infinite phase velocities do not conflict with special relativity, since it is the group velocity given by $v_g = \partial\nu/\partial\bar{k}$ which determines the speed of flow of energy or information. As the ν versus $\bar{k}$ curve has a horizontal tangent at $\bar{k} = 0$, the group velocity is actually zero here. Both acoustic and optical types of waves propagating along the chain are quantized in energy and for this reason are called "phonons".

We now have to consider the absorption of radiation by this system. In quantum mechanical language this involves the absorption of a photon with the corresponding generation of one or more phonons and, as always in physics, it is necessary that both energy and momentum be conserved. The momentum of an infrared photon, $p = h\lambda^{-1} = \hbar\bar{k}$, is very small compared with that of an average phonon, so absorption of radiation will be confined in the dispersion diagram to the region of very low $\bar{k}$. In fact solution of the relevant equations shows that there exists only one frequency for which both energy and momentum are both conserved, and this corresponds to the point of intersection of the optical branch with the dispersion curve for photons (i.e. a straight line through the origin of slope $c/2\pi n$, where n is the refractive index). It follows, therefore, that the infrared spectrum of such an idealized system would consist of a single infinitely sharp line at a frequency given to a very good approximation by

$$\nu = (2\pi)^{-1} \sqrt{(2f/\mu)}, \tag{5.48}$$

which is the frequency of intersection of the optical branch with the frequency axis. This system is discussed in more detail and from a different point of view in Appendix 2.

When we come to consider real three-dimensional crystals, the situation, not unexpectedly, is much more complicated, but certain key concepts still remain; thus, again we find optical and acoustic branches and the selection rule is still $\Delta \bar{k} = 0$. In three dimensions it is possible to have transverse as well as longitudinal vibrations and so in general we expect to encounter Transverse Optical (TO), Longitudinal Optical (LO), Transverse Acoustic (TA) and Longitudinal Acoustic (LA) modes. The dispersion diagrams can get very complicated and they will vary with direction in the crystal. The more symmetrical the crystal lattice is, the less complex becomes the problem of its dynamics and therefore, not surprisingly, the bulk of the investigations undertaken by physicists have been confined to the cubic systems. Chemists, less fortunately, have to accept whatever crystal structure their chosen molecule happens to adopt, and for this reason less reliance can be placed on their interpretations as compared with, say, the highly detailed assignments possible with such well studied systems as the alkali halides. The $\Delta \bar{k} = 0$ selection rule for infrared absorption implies that the infrared absorption spectrum can only tell us the frequencies of intersection of some of the optical branches with the $\bar{k} = 0$ axis. This is clearly a rather restricted amount of information and because of this the art of neutron spectroscopy has been developed. A neutron may have any amount of momentum and, by studying the inelastic scattering of neutrons from crystals, the entire dispersion diagram may be explored. This phenomenon has much in common with Raman spectroscopy which is essentially the inelastic scattering of photons, but even an optical photon has negligible momentum as compared with a phonon, so the normal first-order or one-phonon Raman spectrum of a crystal is much like the one-phonon infrared, apart from any variation in the selection rules (see p. 199). However, the Raman effect is an emission phenomenon, so it is possible to satisfy the energy and momentum conservation conditions with the creation of several phonons. This gives rise to the second-order Raman effect of crystals where the observed frequency shift is the sum (or difference) of two or more phonons. Any given frequency shift can be arrived at in a large number of ways, since there will be very many pairs of phonons which can be so combined. From this it follows that the second-order Raman effect will be a continuum whose maxima (if any) reflect the peaks in the combined density of states function $g(\nu_i + \nu_j)$ rather than any fundamental vibration frequency of the lattice. The density of states function $g(\nu)$ is the number of phonons whose frequencies lie between ν and $\nu + d\nu$; it shows maxima whenever $\partial \nu / \partial \bar{k}$ is zero, i.e. at the origin and at the zone boundary. Knowing

$g(\nu)$, the thermodynamic functions of the crystal may be computed and indeed one of the principal objects of the determination of dispersion diagrams is to arrive at this function so that its predictions may be compared with the experimental data, such as specific heats etc. Although the infrared spectrum is limited in its usefulness because of the restrictive selection rule, this very fact permits an enormous simplification in the treatment of the problem. If $\bar{k} = 0$, the vibrations of corresponding lattice sites are in phase everywhere, which means that all the unit cells are vibrating together with the same frequency and phase. Since this is so, the spectrum can be regarded as made up of the superposition of a very large number of identical spectra one from each unit cell. We need therefore only consider the vibrations of a unit cell as the basic entity. If the unit cell contains N atoms, there will be $3N$ phonon branches of which 3 will be acoustic and have zero frequency when $\bar{k} = 0$. As an example, consider the NaCl crystal which has a face-centred-cubic structure with one Na^+ ion and one Cl^- ion per unit cell. N therefore equals 2 and there are three optical branches and three acoustic branches. The symmetry, frequencies and spectral activities of the normal modes of the unit cell can be calculated by the same group theoretical and matrix mechanical methods which are used for molecules, but in the case of lattices a larger range of types of interatomic force are encountered. Thus, a crystal may be held together by chemical bonds (e.g. diamond), by Coulombic forces (e.g. sodium chloride), by Van der Waals forces (e.g. argon) and by free electron exchange bonding such as occurs in all metals. The nature and physical extent of the interatomic forces decides the symmetry of the potential function and it is this, rather than the symmetry of the unit cell, which decides the symmetry of the vibrational problem. To illustrate this it must be remembered that, for a system such as diamond where there are only short-range forces, and these only between nearest neighbours, the vibrations of a unit cell in isolation can be considered. Not surprisingly, the three optical branches are degenerate when $\bar{k} = 0$, since they can be assigned to identical vibrations in the x, y and z directions respectively. The unit cell is centrosymmetric and the vibrations are symmetrical with regard to the centre of symmetry. Transitions involving the optical modes are therefore forbidden in infrared absorption but do occur in the first-order Raman effect. It is the absence of any allowed far infrared transition which makes diamond such a valuable window material. The case of the alkali halides is quite different, for here the Coulombic forces fall off very slowly with distance and the force between second nearest or third nearest neighbours is not that much different from that between nearest neighbours. There is an interaction between quite remote unit cells, even for $\bar{k} = 0$, and as a result the triple degeneracy of the optical modes is removed, giving a doubly degenerate mode corresponding to transverse optical phonons and a non-degenerate mode corresponding to a longitudinal optical phonon. The latter occurs at a higher frequency than the TO mode but is inactive spectrally† because the electromagnetic field is itself transverse and may only excite transverse phonons. The absorption spectrum of an alkali halide is therefore in principle very simple, consisting of a single sharp line at the TO frequency which will be very intense because the oscillating dipole moment is very large. This sort of spectrum is in fact observed, NaCl, for example, having an absorption maximum at 164 cm^{-1} for 300 K, but the bands are much broader than expected. The broadening is mostly due to multiphonon processes, some of which are the exact analogues of "hot" bands in molecular spectroscopy; they likewise owe their displacement from the fundamental to anharmonicity of the potential energy function. The momentum conservation condition can always be satisfied with three phonons. Just as the intensity of hot bands falls as the temperature falls, so the width of the TO absorption decreases at low temperatures and at $4 \cdot 2$ K the band is quite sharp. At room temperature, however, the situation is that we have a band whose peak absorption coefficient is enormous (> 1000 neper cm^{-1}) and whose half-width may be 50 cm^{-1}; it follows that the absorption coefficient may be large over some hundreds of cm^{-1} and that the alkali halides will be opaque over large regions of the far infrared. The use of this quality in the manufacture of absorption filters was discussed in Chapter 4.

The existence of an extremely intense absorption band at the TO frequency necessarily involves a strong dispersion (see Appendix 3). This can be discussed at several levels of approximation, but fortunately always with the same qualitative result. Mitra and Gielisse[164] have shown that the equations of motion of the lattice under the influence of the electromagnetic field may be written

$$\partial^2 \bar{w} / \partial t^2 = -4\pi^2 v_{\text{TO}}^2 \bar{w} + (\epsilon_0 - \epsilon_\infty)^{1/2} \, v_{\text{TO}} \bar{E},$$

$$\bar{P} = (\epsilon_0 - \epsilon_\infty)^{1/2} \, v_{\text{TO}} \bar{w} + \frac{\epsilon_\infty - 1}{4\pi} \, \bar{E}, \qquad (5.49)$$

where $\bar{w}$ is a reduced displacement vector equal to $\bar{u}(\mu/V)^{1/2}$ with $\bar{u}$ the displacement of the positive ions relative to the negative, μ the reduced mass of the unit cell and V the cell volume. $\bar{P}$ is the dielectric polarization and from the solution to these equations we have

$$\bar{P} = \{(\epsilon_\infty - 1)/4\pi + (\epsilon_0 - \epsilon_\infty) v_{\text{TO}}^2 / [4\pi^2 (v_{\text{TO}}^2 - v^2)]\} E, \qquad (5.50)$$

† This is for normal or near normal incidence. At oblique angles of incidence LO modes may sometimes be detected (see D. W. Berreman, *Phys. Rev.* **130**, 2193, 1963).

which, since (Equations 24 and 28 of Appendix 3)

$$\bar{P} = [(\epsilon - 1)/4\pi]E \qquad (5.51)$$

gives

$$\epsilon = \epsilon_\infty + (\epsilon_0 - \epsilon_\infty)\nu_{TO}^2/(\nu_{TO}^2 - \nu^2). \qquad (5.52)$$

The second term in equation (5.49) is responsible for the splitting of the TO and LO modes and the frequencies of these two modes are necessarily related, therefore, to the dielectric parameters by the Lyddane, Sachs and Teller[165] equation,† i.e.

$$\nu_{LO}/\nu_{TO} = (\epsilon_0/\epsilon_\infty)^{1/2}, \text{ when } |\bar{k}| = 0. \qquad (5.53)$$

Reverting to equation (5.52), it will be seen that ϵ rises from its static value ϵ_0 as ν increases, that it becomes infinite at $\nu = \nu_{TO}$ and then negative for ν infinitesimally greater than ν_{TO}; it remains negative until

$$\nu = (\epsilon_0/\epsilon_\infty)^{1/2} \nu_{TO},$$

i.e. $= \nu_{LO}$. The dielectric constant is therefore negative between $\nu_{TO} < \nu < \nu_{LO}$, and this implies that the refractive index is purely imaginary. The crystal is therefore perfectly reflecting (equation 3.47) between these two limits. The treatment is, of course, unrealistic in that no damping term is present in equation (5.49) and we know from experience that the TO resonance is very broad. The effect of damping is to make n real everywhere, but it is nevertheless very small between ν_{TO} and ν_{LO}. Alkali halide crystals are therefore very highly reflecting in this region—a property which makes them rather valuable as reflection filters in the far infrared. Taking NaCl again as our example, $\nu_{TO} = 164 \text{ cm}^{-1}$ and $\nu_{LO} = 259 \text{ cm}^{-1}$ and, as was shown earlier (Fig. 4.24), there is strong reflectivity between these bounds. The effect of the strong damping is, however, to make the reflectivity less than unity and to make it peak at a frequency near ν_{TO} on the high side. The peak in the reflectance spectrum was exploited by Rubens who succeeded in isolating far infrared radiation by allowing the radiation from a hot body to undergo successive reflection from alkali halide plates. The resulting "residual rays" or "reststrahlen" were much studied in the early days of far infrared spectroscopy and the name "reststrahlen" is still in common use to describe the absorptive and reflective properties of ionic crystals in the far infrared.

Many compounds of the general formula ABX_3 where A and B are metals and X is oxygen, or a halogen, crystallize in the cubic system. The typical

---

† It should be noted that ϵ_0 must exceed ϵ_∞ by Kramers–Kronig arguments, since their difference is a measure of the integrated strength of the TO band. If this latter is zero, as it is for diamond, $\epsilon_0 = \epsilon_\infty$ and $\nu_{LO} = \nu_{TO}$, as remarked earlier.

example is calcium titanate, or perovskite ($CaTiO_3$), and such materials are commonly referred to as "perovskites" and are said to adopt the perovskite structure. They are particularly interesting physically because, below a certain transition temperature, many of them become spontaneously polarized and are therefore ferroelectric.[166] This transition temperature is commonly around 50 K and, additionally, at a higher temperature there occurs another transition where the elastic constants of the crystal show anomalous behaviour. Strontium titanate ($SrTiO_3$) undergoes this latter transition[167] at 110 K. The elastic constants of a crystal are intimately connected with the velocity of sound therein, and anomalous behaviour of the elastic constants implies some extraordinary behaviour of the acoustic branches of the dispersion diagram. Cochran[168] has suggested, and subsequent calculations and experiments have confirmed, that the ferroelectric transition arises in some cases because the lattice becomes unstable with respect to the lowest frequency transverse optical mode. This mode has come to be known as a "soft" mode and intense interest has been shown in the lattice dynamics of perovskites because of this singular behaviour.

The perovskite structure has one formula unit per unit cell and the symmetry of the unit cell is octahedral with point group O_h. There are fifteen branches to the dispersion diagram, but at the zone origin these form the representation

$$\Gamma_Q(\bar{k} = 0) = 4F_{1u} + F_{2u} \tag{5.54}$$

to first order. However, just as for the alkali halides, the effect of the macroscopic electric field is to split the triple degeneracy of the F_{1u} modes into a doubly degenerate transverse mode and a non-degenerate longitudinal mode. One of the F_{1u} modes corresponds to zero frequency when $\bar{k} = 0$, i.e. is equivalent to an overall translation of the crystal and therefore represents the acoustic branches. The net result is that we have three TO modes active in infrared absorption, three LO modes inactive and one triple degenerate F_{2u} mode which is also inactive. The infrared spectrum should show three lattice modes and there should be no first-order Raman effect. This is observed, for at room temperature the far infrared spectrum of strontium titanate shows three bands at 100, 178 and 510 cm^{-1}, and the Raman spectrum is entirely second order.[169] Under normal circumstances the frequency of a lattice mode will rise as the temperature falls, since the interatomic forces will increase as the lattice shrinks and the atoms come closer together. Just the opposite sort of behaviour is noticed for the lowest frequency TO mode, which for $SrTiO_3$ has dropped to 40 cm^{-1} when the temperature has been reduced to 90 K. Cochran[168] has shown that if ϵ_0 follows a Curie law, i.e.

$$\epsilon_0 = C(T - T_c)^{-1}, \tag{5.55}$$

then the frequency of the lowest TO mode should be given by

$$\nu^2_{TO} = K(T-T_C). \tag{5.56}$$

Both quantities follow these equations quite well with a Curie temperature $T_C = 35$ K. Cowley[167] has pointed out that, at the ferroelectric transition in barium titanate, the displacement of the ions away from their cubic positions are all in the same sense as the oscillations of the atoms in the lowest frequency TO mode of strontium titanate. It is most plausible to argue, therefore, that as the TO mode frequency falls, its amplitude to maintain quantization must rise and eventually will be big enough to take the whole lattice over into the ferroelectric phase. The transition near 110 K has been explained as due to a near degeneracy of the lowest TO mode and the highest (i.e. longitudinal) acoustic mode over a wide range of wave vector for this temperature.

The few examples given above are intended to illustrate what is currently one of the most active fields of physics. The successful development by Cochran[170] of the "shell model", which takes account of the polarizability of ions, has opened the way to accurate calculation of the dispersion relations, ν versus $\bar{k}$, for both ionic and covalent crystals. The rapid advances in inelastic neutron spectroscopy have permitted the accurate testing of these over a wide range of $\bar{k}$. Far infrared spectroscopy, especially reflection spectroscopy, has enabled the $\bar{k} = 0$ intersections to be determined and their temperature and pressure variations explored. The current availability of high-power gas lasers for the visible region has increased the experimental reach of Raman spectroscopy enormously, and nothing illustrates this more than the new technique of electric field induced Raman spectra. This phenomenon occurs when a perovskite crystal is exposed to a high electric field. There is no first-order Raman effect at zero field, essentially because each ion is on a centre of symmetry of the lattice; when the field is present, the ions are slightly displaced† and a first-order Raman effect occurs.[171] If the electric field is modulated at an audio frequency, the first-order Raman effect can be picked out from the unmodulated second-order effect by the use of suitable narrow-band amplifiers and phase detectors following the photomultiplier detector. The importance of this technique is that the induced Raman spectrum may show zone-centre phonons which are not present in the far infrared spectrum. Another field of interest at the moment is in the far infrared spectra of small crystals. All the theory given above applies strictly to an infinite crystal, or at least to one very much larger than the wavelength. When this condition is not satisfied, the modes of vibration

---

† The converse, i.e. electric field induced infrared absorption, has been observed with diamond.[172] A weak band appears at 1336 cm^{-1} which agrees with the frequency of the $\bar{k} = 0$ optical mode found from first-order Raman scattering.

have to satisfy the boundary conditions set by the particular size and shape of the specimen. The separation of the TO and LO modes of an alkali halide is particularly sensitive to crystallite geometry. Balthes and his colleagues have obtained[173] interesting emission spectra from small alkali halide crystallites evaporated onto a gold substrate. The spectra show structure which is interpreted as arising from surface phonons.

The lattice spectra of molecular crystals are much less intense than those of ionic crystals and are therefore much easier to study experimentally, since they can be observed in transmission. There is no macroscopic electric field and, because of this, the unit cell symmetry or factor-group method applies rigorously. The simplest way of interpreting the spectrum of a molecular crystal is to assign the high-frequency bands, which occur more or less where those of the free molecule do, to purely intramolecular modes and to assign the low-frequency bands to the vibrations of the unit cell regarded as made up of a number of rigid molecules. Even at moderate resolution this approximation fails, since the true normal modes of the unit cell are mixtures of the two types and the failure is evident from the splitting of the "intramolecular" modes into several components and from the fact that some of the "intermolecular" modes have observable intensity, whereas the zero-order calculation would indicate vanishingly small matrix elements. The situation is quite akin to the corresponding problem in molecular dynamics where any given normal mode of a given symmetry is made up of a linear combination of the simple internal coordinate modes of the same symmetry. The degree of mixing depends on the frequency separation, and we therefore expect that the lowest frequency "intramolecular" modes will show the largest factor group or correlation splitting. The lattice modes themselves can be thought of as made up of a combination of translational and librational motion of the constituent molecules. If the molecules are situated on centres of symmetry, the two types are rigorously separate and any given mode belongs strictly to one type or the other but even when this condition does not apply the division is useful in practice, since usually a mode is mostly either translational or else librational in character. With the assumption that the intermolecular and intramolecular modes are separable, there will be $3N-3$ translatory and $3N$ rotatory lattice modes for a unit cell containing N non-linear polyatomic molecules. Extensive investigations on a range of molecular crystals have been published by Anderson and his co-workers.[174] A particularly interesting point which emerges from their work comes from a comparison of the lattice spectra of a hydrogen-containing compound with that of the corresponding deuterium compound. Crystalline hydrogen chloride for example gives[175] six absorption bands at 86, 109, 217, 296, 496 and 650 cm^{-1}, whereas crystalline deuterium chloride absorbs at 89, 113, 169, 209, 258 and 328. The effective temperatures of the samples were close to 90 K. The two lowest frequency modes show little shift on deuteration and are therefore principally translational in character, whereas the four higher frequencies arise from modes which are mostly librational. Analogous studies of the halo-benzenes and their deuterated derivatives have been published by Fleming and his colleagues.[176] The symmetry of the unit cells are known for these compounds, unlike the crystalline hydrogen halides, and, armed with this information, Fleming has calculated the activity of the various modes and has assigned the observed spectra. A typical spectrum is shown in Fig. 5.8.

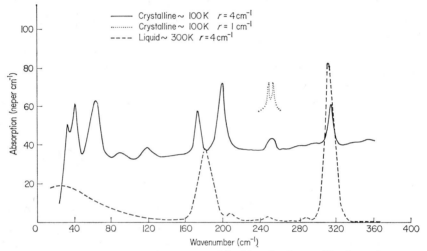

FIG. 5.8. Far infrared absorption spectra of liquid and polycrystalline bromobenzene.

Fifteen lattice modes made up of six translatory and nine rotatory types are expected for the D_{2h} unit cell containing 8 molecules; five are observed for C_6H_5Cl, C_6H_5Br, C_6H_5I and their deutero derivatives, and five are also observed for C_6H_5F, which has a different crystal structure with four molecules per unit cell. The five lattice bands of C_6H_5Br shown in Fig. 5.8 occur at $33(T)$ cm^{-1}, $44(L_y)$ cm^{-1}, $66(L_x)$ cm^{-1}, $88(T)$ cm^{-1} and $120(L_z)$ cm^{-1}, where the letters in brackets indicate translational assignment T or librational assignment L_x, L_y, L_z. Three intramolecular modes are also evident in Fig. 5.8. The lowest of these of B_2 symmetry occurs at 182 cm^{-1} for the liquid phase and shows a large correlation splitting in the crystalline phase; the second lowest of B_1 symmetry occurs at 246 in the liquid and shows a very small crystal state splitting; the third lowest of A_1 symmetry has not so far been resolved into split components. The broad-band peaking at a wavenumber less than 40 cm^{-1} for liquid bromobenzene is typical of the liquid state and bands of this type will be discussed in the next section.

A very interesting application of crystal-phase far infrared spectroscopy is the detection of weak complex formation between molecules.[177] It is known, for example, that the crystals which separate from a mixture of chloroform and benzene on cooling are not pure crystals of either component, but contain both. The question arises of whether they are simply solid solutions or crystals of stoichiometric complexes. It is not readily answered by X-ray methods since single crystals would have to be isolated for study and it is possible that several types of complex are being formed simultaneously. However, if stoichiometric complexes are being formed with defined crystal structures showing long-range regularity, the far infrared spectra of polycrystalline samples may show new bands arising from the vibrations of unit cells which contain both chloroform and benzene. If this is observed, it provides conclusive evidence for the formation of stoichiometric complexes. Studies of the intensities of the new bands as functions of composition of the original mixture will indicate, via the well-known plots versus mole ratio, the exact stoichiometry of the various complexes present. Some results for chloroform and benzene are shown in Fig. 5.9. From these and similar spectra, the existence of the two complexes, $2CHCl_3 : C_6H_6$ and $CHCl_3 : C_6H_6$, is firmly established, since the spectra

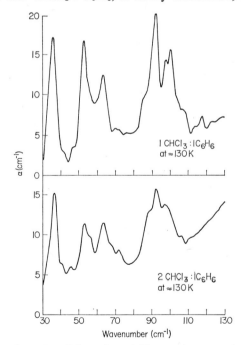

FIG. 5.9. Far infrared spectra of the polycrystalline specimens produced by freezing two different liquid mixtures of chloroform and benzene.

show several sharp lines and these vary in a regular manner with composition of the original mixture. By contrast the crystalline spectra of $CHCl_3$ and of C_6H_6 are simple (Figs. 5.11 and 5.13).

Observations of crystal-phase spectra have some relevance to purely molecular spectroscopy, either perforce because the spectroscopist is studying a compound which does not dissolve in any convenient solvent or else by design in that, by choosing the crystalline phase, the experimentalist might hope to observe fundamentals which would be forbidden for the free molecule. In the first case great care must be taken to ensure that the various components of a split fundamental are not misidentified as separate fundamentals; and the spectroscopist has also the considerable problem of identifying which observed bands are molecular fundamentals and which are lattice bands. If the crystal can be studied at various temperatures, or at various hydrostatic pressures, this identification can be made more easily, since in general the lattice modes show much bigger shifts than do the intramolecular modes. The observation of forbidden fundamentals in the crystal phase arises because the selection rules in this phase are dictated by the symmetry of a molecule's environment (i.e. the site symmetry) rather than by the molecular symmetry itself, and frequently a molecule will occupy a site whose symmetry is lower than that of the molecule itself. This has been demonstrated[178] for sulphur, S_8, where some of the Raman-active (only) fundamentals appear in the infrared crystal spectrum (Fig. 4.13) and for naphthalene $C_{10}H_8$, where the lowest frequency A_u mode, which is forbidden for the free molecule, does appear[179] at medium intensity in the far infrared spectrum of the crystal at 210 cm^{-1}.

It was remarked earlier that the infrared spectrum can give only a limited amount of information so far as the density of states function $g(\bar{\nu})$ is concerned. Specific heats are, however, often discussed in terms of approximate forms of $g(\bar{\nu})$ and the classic example is that chosen by Debye[180] who postulated that the density of states function for the acoustic branches was a quadratic function of $\bar{\nu}$ up to a limiting wavenumber $\bar{\nu}_m$ and was zero for all higher $\bar{\nu}$. At low temperature, when by the Boltzmann factor only the acoustic phonons are significant, the specific heat is then given by

$$C_v = (12\pi^4 R/5c^3)(kT/h\bar{\nu}_m)^3. \qquad (5.57)$$

The Debye temperature θ_D is that temperature for which $k\theta_D = hc\bar{\nu}_m$. This equation satisfactorily accounts for the behaviour of many solids at cryogenic temperatures, which is surprising in view of the crude model used in its derivation, but if $\bar{\nu}_m$ is reinterpreted as the wavenumber of the centroid of the density of vibrational states, as suggested by Plendl,† the

† See the article by this author in "Optical Properties of Solids" (Ed. S. S. Mitra), Plenum Press, New York.

treatment becomes physically much more acceptable. It is therefore most interesting to note that for crystalline HCl $\bar{\nu}_m$ is $89 \cdot 6$ cm^{-1}, and that this is close to the mean of the two translational mode frequencies. For NaCl, as another example, $\bar{\nu}_m$ is 196 cm^{-1}, which is quite close to the "reststrahlen" frequency (164 cm^{-1} at 300 K, 174 cm^{-1} at 90 K).

5.6. Submillimetre Absorption in Liquids

The submillimetre spectra of low-pressure gases are simple because the molecules spend a great deal of time without undergoing interaction with other molecules and, even when interactions do occur, only binary collisions need be considered. The submillimetre spectra of crystalline solids are simple because, although strong interactions are always present, the translational symmetry of the lattice prevents most of the phonons from being optically active. When we come to consider the liquid state both these simplifying features are absent, for the principal characteristics of a liquid are that strong attractive forces are present and there is no long-range order.

The first attempt to provide a theory of the radio-frequency absorption in polar liquids came from Debye[181] in 1929. He considered a highly detailed physical model of dipoles attempting to rotate in response to the electromagnetic field, but impeded by the frictional drag of the surrounding viscous medium. His derivation of the frequency dependence of the complex dielectric constant is now only of historical interest, and attention is currently focussed on the approximations which Debye found necessary to make the problem tractable. Principal amongst these was that the flow of dipole moment component into the angular region $\theta+d\theta$, where θ is the angle subtended by the electric field, is independent of frequency; that is, there is no inertial effect. This approximation will clearly fail at a sufficiently high frequency which later we shall show to lie in the submillimetre region. Another important approximation—and this time of much more general applicability—is that $\mu E/kT \ll 1$. If this is assumed, the mean dipole moment in the direction of the field, which arises from the Boltzmann weighting of the lower energy states and which is given by the Langevin function

$$\bar{\mu} = \mu L(y) = \mu(\coth y - 1/y), \tag{5.58}$$

where $y = \mu E/kT$, may be approximated to read

$$\bar{\mu} = \mu[\mu E/(3kT)]. \tag{5.59}$$

With this approximation, the dielectric constant of the medium may be written

$$\epsilon_0 = 1 + (4\pi N_A \rho/M)[\chi_e + \mu^2/(3kT)], \tag{5.60}$$

H

where χ_e is the electronic molecular polarizability, N_A is Avogadro's number, ρ is the density and M the molecular weight. The frequency dependence of the dielectric constant can now be obtained by writing down and solving a differential equation for the response of the medium to the time-varying electric field. We may neglect the term in χ_e since this arises from electronic effects which may surely be regarded as instantaneous so far as infrared frequencies are concerned. With this assumption, the polarization $\hat{P}$, i.e. the dipole moment per unit volume, may be found from the equation

$$d\hat{P}/dt = -\tau^{-1}\{\hat{P} - [N_A\rho\mu^2/(3MkT)]E_0 \exp(2\pi i\nu t)\}, \quad (5.61)$$

where τ is a relaxation time. The solution of this equation is

$$\hat{P} = [N_A\rho\mu^2/(3MkT)](1 + 2\pi i\nu\tau)^{-1} E_0 \exp(2\pi i\nu t). \quad (5.62)$$

From which, by the application of the relation (equation 5.51)

$$\hat{\epsilon} = 1 + 4\pi P/E,$$

we find that

$$\hat{\epsilon} = 1 + [4\pi N_A\rho\mu^2/(3MkT)](1 + 2\pi i\nu\tau)^{-1}. \quad (5.63)$$

If we retain the electronic contribution, the effect is to replace the first term on the right-hand side of this equation by a quantity which we shall call ϵ_∞, i.e. the dielectric constant at very high (i.e. optical) frequencies, and we may write

$$\hat{\epsilon} = \epsilon_\infty + (\epsilon_0 - \epsilon_\infty)(1 + 2\pi i\nu\tau)^{-1},$$

or

$$(\hat{\epsilon} - \epsilon_\infty)/(\epsilon_0 - \epsilon_\infty) = (1 + 2\pi i\nu\tau)^{-1}. \quad (5.64)$$

This is the form in which the Debye equation is most often quoted. Cole[182] has shown that the result is general and follows from any relaxational model. That this is so can be seen by noting that equation (5.64) is a special case of equation (5.14) with ν_0 equal to zero. In Appendix 3 it is also shown that the Debye equation results in the limit of the rigorous Van Vleck–Weisskopf equation as the resonant frequency tends to zero. Debye's original derivation was, however, much less phenomenological and the parameter τ was explicitly given as a function of the macroscopic viscosity η and the effective molecular radius; in fact

$$\tau = [4\pi\eta a^3/(kT)]. \quad (5.65)$$

For chloroform, as an example, $\eta = 5.5 \times 10^{-3}$, and, assuming a to be ≈ 2 Å, τ is found to be of the order of 10^{-11} second. The form of ϵ' and ϵ'', and also of n and α for liquid chloroform, assuming the Debye equation to hold, is shown in Fig. 5.10. A maximum in ϵ'' and a most rapidly changing region of ϵ' are found where $2\pi\nu\tau = 1$, with similar phenomena for n and

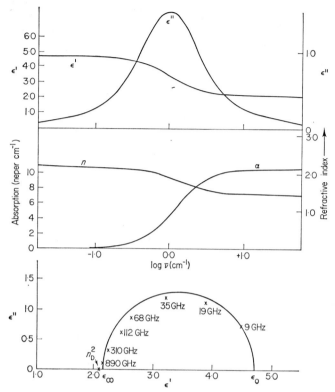

FIG. 5.10. Dielectric dispersion in liquid CHCl₃ at 300 K assuming a perfect Debye relaxation. The Cole–Cole plot includes some experimental[183] data for comparison.

α. Taking $\tau = 10^{-11}$, the frequency where the dispersion is most intense will be of the order of 10^{10} Hz in the high microwave region.

A priori calculations of τ do not unfortunately agree very well with the values found from dielectric experiments, not only because of uncertainty about the value of a but also because of the simplicity of the model, and the answers must be taken as having only indicative value. Thus for chloroform, τ at room temperature is[183] 5×10^{-12} s with a resulting maximum dispersion near 30 GHz or 1 cm⁻¹. But, although τ does not depend on η and T in quite the simple manner indicated in equation (5.65), there is nevertheless a strong dependence on these two quantities and, since η is itself sensitively dependent on temperature, it follows that τ will rapidly vary as the temperature is altered. One might therefore hope to bring the maximum of ϵ'' into any chosen frequency region by a suitable choice of temperature and this is the basis of the commonest form of dielectric investigation in which the loss (i.e. ϵ'' or tan δ) is studied, at a fixed frequency, as a function of temperature. Clearly, however, the best form of data presentation would be a three-dimensional plot of ϵ'' versus both ν and T and, whilst this would be difficult, the next best thing, i.e. contour maps, are becoming popular. However, at the present time the most popular form of data presentation is undoubtedly the so-called Cole–Cole plot.[184] This is a plot of ϵ'' as ordinate against ϵ' as abscissa. Simple algebraical manipulation of equation (5.64) leads to the result

$$[\epsilon' - \tfrac{1}{2}(\epsilon_0 + \epsilon_\infty)]^2 + (\epsilon'')^2 = \tfrac{1}{4}(\epsilon_0 - \epsilon_\infty)^2, \tag{5.66}$$

from which it follows that, if the Debye equation holds rigorously, the Cole–Cole plot will be a semicircle in the right upper quarter of the complex plane with intercepts ϵ_0 and ϵ_∞ on the real axis. The theoretical plot for chloroform is also shown in Fig. 5.10, together with the observed plot. It will be seen that there is fair agreement for the lower frequencies but that increasing discrepancies occur as the frequency rises.

The first suggestion that submillimetre dispersion processes existed in polar liquids as well as the lower frequency Debye process came from Poley[185] who noted the small departures from the semicircle for the higher frequency points. These departures are slight for the frequencies available to Poley and for some years there was controversy as to whether his suggestion was correct. Hill[186] developed a theory in which vibrations of a polar molecule in the cage formed by its neighbours would lead to submillimetre absorption in the $30\ \mathrm{cm}^{-1}$ region. Her motive for developing this theory came from the observation that the parameter ϵ_∞, deduced from radiofrequency measurements, was seldom equal to the square of the visible refractive index (i.e. n_D^2). Now, ϵ_∞ is a rather loose concept and is often regarded just as a parameter, but initially it was thought of as the square of the refractive index somewhere in the nether region between the microwave (where the Debye process was located) and the infrared (where the vibrational resonances were located) regions. The effect of the infrared resonances will make n_D^2 differ from ϵ_∞, but the calculated amount does not agree with the observed discrepancy. All these arguments are, however, indirect in that the properties of a submillimetre absorption process are being deduced from observations outside this region. The unequivocal establishment of the validity of the Poley hypothesis had to await the development of submillimetre spectroscopy and the first clear evidence came in 1964 when the newly developed HCN laser was used to study the halobenzenes. But before discussing this experiment we need to develop a Debyelike theory valid for the submillimetre region.

In this region, as we anticipated earlier, the conventional Debye theory must be expected to fail, for now the frequency is much greater than $(2\pi\tau)^{-1}$. The failure is most graphically illustrated by calculating the absorption coefficient at high frequencies, assuming the equation to hold. The real and imaginary parts of $\hat{\epsilon}$, from the Debye equation are

$$\epsilon' = \epsilon_\infty + (\epsilon_0 - \epsilon_\infty)/(1 + 4\pi^2 \nu^2 \tau^2) \tag{5.67}$$

and

$$\epsilon'' = 2\pi\nu\tau(\epsilon_0 - \epsilon_\infty)/(1 + 4\pi^2 \nu^2 \tau^2).$$

When $2\pi\nu\tau$ is much greater than unity we may assume that $n^2 \approx \epsilon_\infty$ and then use equation (10) of Appendix 3 to calculate α; the result is

$$\alpha = 4\pi^2 \nu^2 \tau(\epsilon_0 - \epsilon_\infty)/[c(\epsilon_\infty)^{\frac{1}{2}}(1 + 4\pi^2 \nu^2 \tau^2)] \tag{5.68}$$

which, for very high ν, reduces to

$$\alpha_\infty = (\epsilon_0 - \epsilon_\infty)/(c(\epsilon_\infty)^{\frac{1}{2}}\tau). \tag{5.69}$$

The Debye equation therefore predicts a large constant absorption through-out the infrared and optical regions, which is in conflict with the observed recovery of near transparency at a sufficiently high frequency. The origin of the paradox lies in the approximations made by Debye. In modern language these would be said to be equivalent to the use of a correlation function whose behaviour was incorrect near $t = 0$. The topic has been compre-hensively discussed from a theoretical point of view by Lassier and Brot[136] and by Birnbaum and Cohen[137] and from an experimental point of view by Davies, Pardoe, Chamberlain and Gebbie.[187] A clear and readable review of the subject has been given by Leroy and his colleagues[188] at Lille. The early work of Rocard[189] and Powles,[190] which introduced inertial terms explicitly, has now been shown to be equivalent to the use of

$$f(t) = (\tau_1 - \tau_2)^{-1} [\tau_1 \exp(-t/\tau_1) - \tau_2 \exp(-t/\tau_2)] \tag{5.70}$$

as the correlation function. This leads to a dielectric constant given by

$$(\hat{\epsilon} - \epsilon_\infty)/(\epsilon_0 - \epsilon_\infty) = [(1 + i\omega\tau_1)(1 + i\omega\tau_2)]^{-1} \tag{5.71}$$

and to an absorption coefficient which at high frequencies has the form

$$\alpha = (nc)^{-1}\{(\epsilon_0 - \epsilon_\infty)\omega^2(\tau_1 + \tau_2)/[(1 + \omega^2\tau_1^2)(1 + \omega^2\tau_2^2)]\}. \tag{5.72}$$

At a sufficiently high frequency, set by the magnitude of τ_1 and τ_2, α will asymptotically fall to zero and we have the desired recovery of transparency. Other functions have been proposed which also give more acceptable be-haviour at high frequencies. Sack[191] proposed that

$$(\hat{\epsilon} - \epsilon_\infty)/(\epsilon_0 - \epsilon_\infty) = (1 + i\omega\tau_1 - \omega^2\tau_1\tau_2)^{-1} \tag{5.73}$$

which, as Kubo[192] and others have commented, is equivalent to the use of a complex and frequency-dependent relaxation time in the Debye equation, i.e.

$$\tau = \tau_1(1 + i\omega\tau_2). \tag{5.74}$$

Birnbaum and Cohen have shown that to be physically acceptable $f(t)$ must be an even symmetric function of time and must behave like $\exp(-t/\tau)$ for large t. Few of the numerous correlation functions which have been proposed meet this specification exactly, but it seems sufficient merely to make the linear term zero in the series expansion of $f(t)$ for the calculated absorption coefficient to tend to zero for a sufficiently high frequency. Thus we desire $f(t)$ to begin

$$f(t) = 1 - at^2 + \dots , \tag{5.75}$$

and it will be seen that the Rocard–Powles correlation function satisfies this requirement. Other correlation functions still more intricate such as

$$f(t) = \exp[1 - t/\tau - \exp(-t/\tau)] \tag{5.76}$$

have been proposed, but the principal difficulty in putting these to the experimental test is that, as we will soon see, it is impossible to observe the high-frequency wing of the Debye process. What one can say with certainty is that the absorption coefficient arising from the relaxation process will, in general, reach a maximum value for wavenumbers of the order 1 cm^{-1}, and will then asymptotically fall to zero at higher wavenumbers. At submillimetre frequencies, therefore, α will be less than the hypothetical α_∞.

The laser measurements at $29 \cdot 712 \text{ cm}^{-1}$ demonstrated[193] to the contrary that $\alpha_{29.7}$ was at least twice α_∞ for a wide range of polar liquids (see Fig. 5.14). This surprising observation was followed by interferometric spectroscopic studies which established the existence of very broad absorption bands located in the submillimetre region which were additional to the Debye process.[194] Poley and Hill were thus vindicated. It is now clear that all polar liquids show, in the submillimetre region, an excess absorption and the details for individual liquids have been reported widely in the scientific literature. It is the presence of this additional absorption which prevents the observation of the high-frequency wing of the Debye process. The observed spectrum for liquid chloroform is shown in Fig. 5.11, together with dispersion data and the spectrum of a polycrystalline sample for comparison. The liquid state results should be compared with those given earlier (Fig. 5.10) for the ideal Debye case. Absorption spectra for both liquid and crystalline chlorobenzene are shown in Fig. 5.12. This liquid was the first to be completely characterized in the far infrared though there was a strong hint of the additional absorption from microwave data and the high-frequency wing of the combined absorption had been detected by Gunthard and his colleagues.[195] Non-polar liquids also show broad absorption bands in the submillimetre region.[196, 197] These were first suggested by Whiffen[198] who noted a weak microwave absorption in liquid carbon

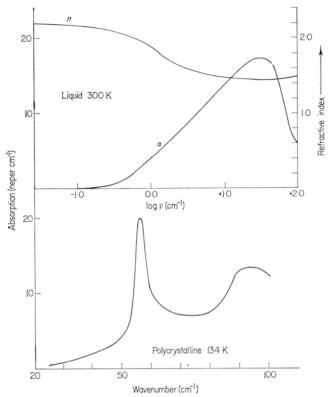

FIG. 5.11. Far infrared spectra of liquid and polycrystalline chloroform.

tetrachloride and benzene with intensity varying as the square of the frequency. It will be seen from equation (37) of Appendix 3 that a resonant absorption process will have exactly this dependence of α on $\bar{\nu}$ when $\bar{\nu}$ is very much less than $\bar{\nu}_0$. Whiffen conjectured that $\bar{\nu}_0$ for his liquids must be somewhat less than 70 cm⁻¹. The absorption spectrum of liquid benzene at 300 K is shown in Fig. 5.13: it will be seen that Whiffen's conjecture has turned out to be remarkably accurate.

We must now consider what explanations can be offered for this additional submillimetre absorption. The phenomenon is general, so we may not invoke absorption by fundamentals to explain it; thus, for chlorobenzene, the lowest frequency normal mode (see Fig. 5.14) occurs at 195 cm⁻¹ which is well clear of the region where the additional absorption is located. Difference bands such as $\nu_i - \nu_j$ could also be a possibility but no plausible combinations can be found to fit all the observed spectra; furthermore, the great width of the band would still have to be explained. Difference

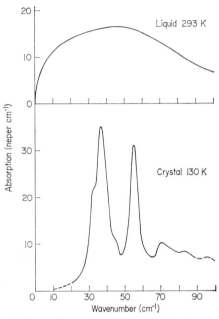

FIG. 5.12. Far infrared absorption spectra of liquid and polycrystalline chlorobenzene.

bands are also very temperature sensitive as regards their intensities, since the band strength depends on the population of the lower level which itself depends on temperature via the Boltzmann function (see equation 6.6). The spectrum of chlorobenzene has been studied in the supercooled state at $-55°$ C, but the integrated strength of the band hardly alters as compared with that for a room-temperature sample. All that happens on cooling is that the band slightly sharpens and shows a small displacement of its peak to higher frequencies. This is quite reminiscent of the behaviour of lattice bands. The only plausible explanation is that the bands arise from inter-molecular effects. Clearly there are two possibilities: either we are dealing with the same phenomenon that occurs in compressed gases or else we are observing a smeared-out lattice spectrum. Detailed discussions of both these approaches have been given by Chamberlain and Davies and their colleagues.[197] Their conclusions are that, as first suggested by Kroon and Van der Elsken,[199] rotational modes well account for most of the absorption, but that there is a residual component which arises from translational motion. Clearly this has to be the case if we are to explain the absorption in non-polar liquids where the rotational component would have zero intensity to first order. The rotation cannot in any sense be regarded as quasi-free for the maxima do not occur where the maximum of the gas-phase pure

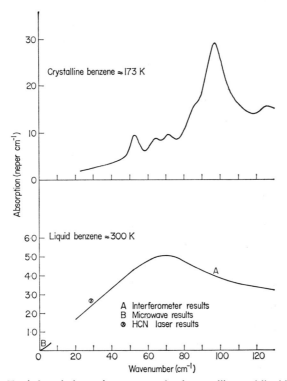

FIG. 5.13. Far infrared absorption spectra of polycrystalline and liquid benzene.

rotation envelope occurs and, even if we invoke $\Delta J = +2$ selection rules for benzene, the discrepancy still remains. There is also the difficulty that the peak of the pure rotation band shifts to lower frequencies (see equation 5.35) as the temperature falls. From this it follows that the rotatory and translational motion of a molecule in a liquid has the same physical essence as it does in a crystal, and so the broad bands have been called "liquid–lattice" bands. The use of this term does not imply the existence of any save the most local order in a liquid. One can think of the liquid spectrum as corresponding to a "smeared-out" version of the equivalent crystal spectrum; generally it is found that the two occur in the same region and have roughly similar integrated strengths. The breadth of the band arises from two causes: firstly, there is no long-range order and the $\Delta \bar{k} = 0$ selection rule breaks down; secondly the immediate vicinity of the absorbing molecule will fluctuate, because of diffusion at the Brownian frequency and therefore, by the Uncertainty Principle, each line must have at least this (i.e. $\approx 10 \text{ cm}^{-1}$) width. Consequently we assume that the model is a set of closely spaced and very broad resonances and Chamberlain[200] has shown, as one might

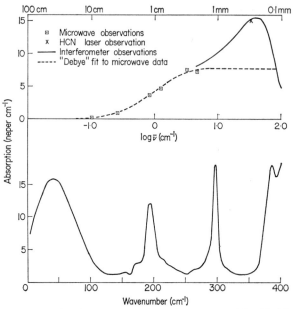

Fig. 5.14. Far infrared and microwave absorption spectra of liquid chlorobenzene.

expect, that this accounts for the observed absorption profile; but he has also shown that the refraction spectrum calculated from this model differs significantly from that expected in the case of a relaxation. In particular, the shallow minimum in n, which tends to occur near the peak of the α curve, is strong evidence that the broadened resonances type of theory is applicable. This can be seen by considering the difference between the monotonic fall of n for a relaxation (Fig. 5.10) and the oscillatory behaviour of n near a resonance; the refraction data does not therefore support the alternative suggestion that the Poley absorption is due to another Debye-type absorption at higher frequencies. Brot and Lassier[136] have gone a long way towards developing a satisfactory integrated theory producing relaxational behaviour at low frequencies and broadened resonant behaviour at higher frequencies. Basically they postulate molecules librating in shallow potential wells, but able to undergo essentially irreversible (on the short time-scale that is) flips into other configurations where again they undergo librational motion. The model thus incorporates both relaxational (i.e. the flipping) and resonant (i.e. the libration) features and, by suitably adjusting the parameters, absorption and refraction curves have been produced which look remarkably like those observed. The theory has been expressed in mathematical form with explicit correlation functions and the expected Cole–Cole plots indicated. Because of the resonant nature of the high frequency process ϵ' will be expected to be less than ϵ_∞ somewhere in this region and the Cole–Cole plot will therefore be re-entrant. This type of behaviour has not so far been observed, probably because the refractive index of a polar liquid in the 40 cm^{-1} region is significantly affected by the dispersion arising from the intramolecular modes in the region above 100 cm^{-1}. The rising contribution to n, due to these remote features, will probably be sufficient to ensure that ϵ' is always greater than n_D^2.

On the experimental front too, considerable advances are currently under way, aimed at bettering our knowledge of the submillimetre properties of liquids. Much higher accuracy is now possible in determining α which can usually be determined to at least 1 per cent; the refractive index can readily be measured to three decimal places, and Chamberlain and his colleagues are developing sophisticated refractometers which will give the fourth place. With this improved accuracy, much more certainty attaches to observed departures from the Cole–Cole semicircular arc. High-pressure apparatus has been developed[201] which permits the study of liquids up to the hydrostatic pressure where they crystallize. With these experimental advances it is now possible to detect small differences from additivity of the submillimetre absorption spectra of liquid mixtures[202] and to show that the intensity of the submillimetre band of non-polar liquids increases rapidly as the pressure rises.[203] This latter observation agrees with expectation, since dipole moments induced by multipole interactions will depend on the molecular separation to a high inverse power. Brot and his colleagues at Orsay[204] have studied the absorption spectrum of OCS, carbonyl sulphide, in the gas phase and through the critical point into the liquid phase. By this experiment, which virtually means a continuous study of the change in absorption characteristic in going from the gas phase to the liquid, they have been able to quantify the basic assumption that the bulk of the absorption arises from a rotational type of motion of the dipolar molecules. The experiment is the analogue of the study of clathrates which provide a sort of intermediate between the gas and solid phases and which help to clarify the notion of translational absorption. As we shall see in the next section, the study of plastic crystals completes the circle since these are a half-way house between liquids and true crystals. The subject is advancing rapidly and we can already view the panorama which is emerging of an integrated approach which envelops absorption in all three phases of matter.

5.7. Submillimetre Absorption in "Plastic" Crystals

In general, the distinction between the liquid and the crystalline state is profound. Crystals normally have long-range order and show the large changes of entropy on melting, characteristic of first-order thermodynamic

transitions. There does exist, however, a class of materials in which the
change in entropy on melting is relatively small and because these materials,
in the crystalline state and at temperatures just below the melting point,
lack the rigidity commonly observed with normal crystals they have come
to be called "plastic" crystals. These plastic crystals undergo a series of
solid-state transitions at progressively lower temperatures and the entropy
change at one of these lower transitions has usually a value more appropriate
to a melting phenomenon. As an example,[205] methyl chloroform, CCl_3CH_3
crystallizes at 240·5 K with $\Delta S = 1·85$ e.u., undergoes a phase transition
at 224·3 K with $\Delta S = 7·92$ e.u. and has a still lower transition at 205 K
with $\Delta S = 0·244$ e.u. Calorimetric observations and magnetic resonance
measurements have suggested that these phenomena are consequences of
the relatively free molecular motion in the crystalline higher temperature
phases. In terms of molecular dynamics, this freedom to rotate probably
arises from the near equality in effective "size" of a chlorine atom and a
methyl group, so that any molecule of the general formula $CCl_n(CH_3)_{4-n}$
is effectively spherical so far as interactions with neighbouring molecules
in the lattice is concerned. Electrically, of course, these molecules can be
far from spherical and can in fact have quite large dipole moments. We
thus have the interesting situation of molecules which are mechanically
isotropic, whilst being electrically anisotropic, located in a lattice which
has positional order but rotational disorder. The ensemble has features of
both the liquid and the crystalline state (hence the small entropy change on
melting) and it is illuminating, therefore, to compare the submillimetre
spectra with those of normal crystals and liquids.

All the compounds of the above general formula, ranging from carbon
tetrachloride to neopentane, $C(CH_3)_4$, are now known to exhibit the phenomenon of plastic crystal formation, but since the spectral intensity is correlated with the dipole moment only methyl chloroform[205] and tertiary
butyl chloride,[206] $CCl(CH_3)_3$, have been investigated in depth. The spectra
of the latter are shown in Fig. 5.15. The transition temperatures are 244 K
(melting), 219 K and 183 K. The most important point which arises from
these results is that the spectra of the two higher temperature solid phases
are essentially "liquid-like". The spectrum of the lowest phase does show
discrete maxima but the absorption bands are quite broad. The chlorine
pure quadrupole magnetic resonance spectrum has shown[207] that the
molecules are undergoing some type of overall rotation in Phase I (> 219 K),
that they have restricted rotational freedom about a fixed C–Cl bond in
Phase II, and that only rotation of the methyl groups occurs in Phase III.
The spectra thus show conclusively that sharp lattice bands are only observed
when rigorous long-range order prevails in the crystalline lattice. Even a
lack of order in the hydrogen atom positions is sufficient to introduce

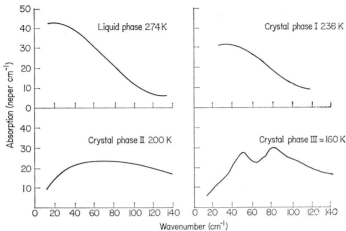

FIG. 5.15. Submillimetre wave spectra of liquid and polycrystalline *t*-butyl chloride.

considerable breadth to the lattice bands. In this connection it is interesting to point out the spectrum of crystalline toluene at liquid nitrogen temperatures is very broad, and to speculate that the spectrum might sharpen at liquid helium temperatures when methyl-group rotation is known to stop.

Another class of compound—not strictly plastic crystals but exhibiting some of the phenomena described above—is typified by the hexasubstituted chloromethylbenzenes. Because of the approximate equality of interaction radius of a chlorine atom and a methyl group (3·56 and 3·58 Å respectively) these molecules have effectively hexagonal symmetry. As a result, the molecule can librate for a time in a potential well before rotating through 60° to an essentially identical position. The librational frequencies have been estimated, from nuclear magnetic resonance determinations of the barrier to rotation, to be in the range 30–60 cm⁻¹. Submillimetre spectra observed[208] with three compounds of this type are shown in Fig. 5.16. The librational bands are certainly observed and show the expected shift to higher frequency as the temperature is lowered. The intensities of the bands show a satisfactory correlation with dipole moment, since the upper two spectra are of molecules with dipole moments of approximately 3D, whereas the bottom spectrum is for a molecule with $\mu = 1·55$ D. The bandwidths are much closer to those observed in normal molecular crystals and this is interpreted as a consequence of the much slower rate of molecular reorientation compared with that prevailing in plastic crystals.

These types of crystal are very valuable since they provide a sort of half-way house between true liquids and truly crystalline solids. They therefore give us an opportunity for studying the effects of various departures from

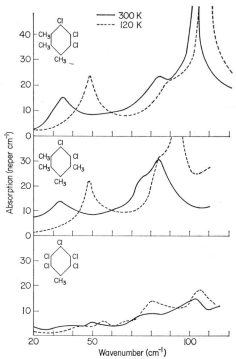

FIG. 5.16. Far infrared absorption spectra of some hexasubstituted chloromethylbenzenes. The specimens were pressed discs of polycrystalline material.

the strict long-range order of true crystals one by one. This has already provided a basis for a theory[209] of liquid spectra based on a model of molecules librating in potential wells but undergoing relatively rapid reorientation.

5.8. Submillimetre Absorption in Polymers

High polymers are another class of material in which the usually clear-cut distinction between amorphous and crystalline solids becomes rather blurred. A molecule such as that of polyethylene is so long and so flexible that it can easily become entangled with other molecules to produce a chaotic ensemble which has been likened to "micro-spaghetti". On the other hand, the molecule has such a simple repeat unit ($-CH_2-$) and one chain can fit together so nicely with another (or with itself for that matter after a fold) that stereochemical forces strongly favour crystallization. As the melt cools down through the freezing point small crystallites form, but the chain entanglement prevents these from growing much more than a few microns in size and eventually the crystallite growth (in the form of globular spherulites) ceases altogether. The result is that a sample of polyethylene will contain crystalline regions embedded in an amorphous matrix, and a given molecule can pass from the amorphous regions through a crystallite and then back out again into the matrix. As may be imagined, such a system will not show a clearly defined melting point; in fact, many polymers do not melt in the ordinary sense at all but pass instead into a "rubbery" state. This is very important technologically since polymers are available which are rubbers at ordinary temperatures.

Amorphous polymers also undergo another transition at a temperature usually considerably below the melting point. At this temperature, the material changes from being soft and flexible and becomes hard and rigid. The phenomenon is called the glass transition and is thought to be associated with rotation of polymer segments about single bonds. Glass transition temperatures vary widely because the ease of segment rotation can differ considerably. Gee has given a comprehensive review of this topic in which all the relevant factors are considered,[210] but roughly one can say that the presence of bulky sidegroups is a dominating factor in increasing the glass transition temperature T_g. Thus for polyethylene ($T_g = 250$ K) and poly-tetrafluorethylene ($T_g = 160$ K) there are no side groups, whilst for poly-methylmethacrylate ($T_g = 334$ K) and polystyrene ($T_g = 373$ K) there are. Whether the glass transition temperature is above or below room temperature is a most important question technologically and the widespread use of nylon and polystyrene in engineering applications depends on these materials having high values of T_g. Conversely, the use of polyethylene in the food industry and in domestic applications depends on the room-temperature flexibility of this material, and this is a consequence of its low T_g.

Because polymeric materials are so technically important, and because they exhibit such a range of interesting transition phenomena, they have been extensively investigated by dielectric relaxation methods. In these, the real and imaginary parts of the complex dielectric constant (see Appendix 3) are observed over as wide a frequency and temperature range as possible. A three-dimensional plot of ϵ'' versus frequency and temperature shows peaks which are associated with various relaxation mechanisms. A series of sections through such a three-dimensional plot is shown in Fig. 5.17, which gives some data for dry highly crystalline polyethylene terephthalate. As will be seen, there is a peak in each section which moves to lower frequency as the temperature falls. The relation between frequency of maximum loss ν_m and temperature is found to follow an Arrhenius equation, i.e.

$$\nu_m = A \exp(-E/RT), \tag{5.77}$$

from which an activation energy E for the process in question can be derived.

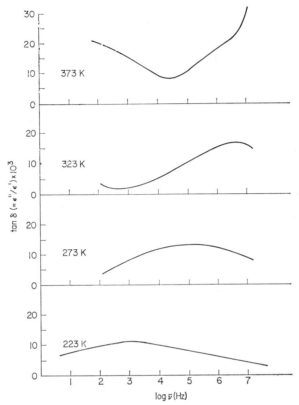

Fig. 5.17. Dielectric loss in highly crystalline polyethylene terephthalate.

The alternative section in which ϵ'' or tan δ is plotted as a function of temperature at constant frequency is also often used and brings out nicely the fact that the properties of polymers depend on how quickly they are measured. Thus, at a low frequency such as 178 Hz, the plot for polytetra-fluorethylene shows[211] a single peak at 188 K, whereas at 1 GHz this peak has shifted to 273 K. Now this peak can only correspond to the glass transition, so we can say that the glass transition temperature is 273 K if the measurement is to take only 10^{-9} seconds. For measurements taking relatively long times, as for example a dilatometric measurement of T_g, we arrive at the much lower value quoted earlier. There is an interesting philosophical point here, for clearly a static value of any physical property is unmeasurable since we do not have an infinite time available to us for measurement. The point is mostly academic since the difference in T_g measured over a few hours or a few days is infinitesimal, but there are cases where phenomena reminiscent of ferroelectricity have been observed in polymers. Thus for polyvinyl chloride Reddish[212] has shown that the dielectric constant shows progressively larger oscillations through the glass transition (347 K) as the frequency of measurement falls. For a sufficiently low frequency—and Reddish went down to 10^{-4} Hz—the dielectric constant starts to exhibit an approach to Curie-type behaviour, so that

$$\epsilon = 1 + 3T_g/(T-T_g). \tag{5.78}$$

In addition to loss peaks corresponding to the melting and glass transitions, the dielectric spectra of amorphous polymers frequently show other features which are associated with the motion of smaller units of the macromolecule. It is conventional[213] to name the loss peak which corresponds to the highest temperature α, the next β and so on, it being understood that low audio-frequencies are chosen for this convention. In the case of polyethylene we have an α peak, a β peak (glass transition) and also a γ peak which is thought to involve a "crankshaft" motion of four CH_2 units.[214] The activation energies of the β and γ processes are very different $(E_\beta \gg E_\gamma)$ and so, although the two processes are quite distinct at low temperatures, at higher values (≈ 300 K) they overlap. The overlap occurs in the 10^8–10^9 Hz region. The particular interest of these relaxation processes so far as submillimetre spectroscopy is concerned is firstly that at still higher temperatures the loss peaks may move into the 10^{11}–10^{12} Hz region, and secondly that if they can be represented by Debye-type formulae there will be high-frequency plateaux which will contribute to the submillimetre absorption coefficient even if the peak in ϵ'' is at a lower frequency. So far, not much work has been done in this field, but clearly an investigation of the temperature dependence of the millimetre wave spectrum of polytetrafluorethylene might be expected to reveal the glass transition peak shifted into this region. Measurements on polyethylene and polypropylene should be even more interesting, for Reddish and Buckingham[211] have published spectra which show tan δ for pure polypropylene to be only 50 μ radian and *decreasing* at 10^{10} Hz. By extrapolation, at 30 cm^{-1} one would expect absorption coefficients in the range $0\cdot01$ neper cm^{-1} (equation 5.15, with $\epsilon' = 2\cdot2$), a low value which would interest the submillimetre engineer very much. Spectra of low-loss polypropylene have been given earlier (Fig. 4.29) and a more detailed spectrum of the low-frequency region is given in Fig. 5.18. It will be seen that the observed absorption coefficients are ten times higher than expected, indicating the presence of new absorption processes in the submillimetre region.[215]

What kind of absorption processes might we expect from a polymer in the far infrared? The sequence of repeating units in the polymer molecule is very much akin to the one-dimensional crystal discussed in Section 5.5

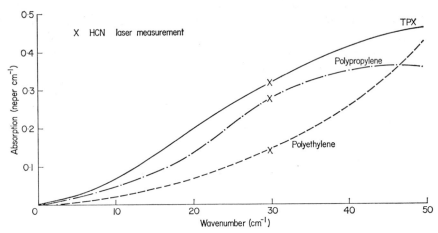

FIG. 5.18. Far infrared spectra of some low-loss polymers.

and in Appendix 2, and we may apply the same theory to predict its infrared spectrum. The ideal linear polyethylene molecule has the repeating unit

$$\ce{\backslash CH_2 / \quad / CH_2 \backslash \quad \backslash CH_2 / \quad /}$$

with symmetry D_{2h}. There will therefore be three acoustic branches and fifteen optical branches whose intersections with the $\bar{k} = 0$ axis will indicate potentially active modes. The fifteen $\bar{k} = 0$ modes form the representation

$$\Gamma_{\bar{k}=0} = 3A_g + A_u + 3B_{1g} + B_{1u} + 2B_{2g} + 2B_{2u} + B_{3g} + 2B_{3u} \qquad (5.79)$$

of the point group D_{2h} and, since the three translations T_x, T_y and T_z form the representation $B_{1u} + B_{2u} + B_{3u}$, it follows that there will be five infrared active modes. The frequencies are expected to be ≈ 2850 (B_{3u} CH stretch), ≈ 2920 (B_{2u} CH stretch), ≈ 1470 (B_{3u} CH$_2$ bend), ≈ 1180 (B_{1u} CH$_2$ wag) and ≈ 720 (CH$_2$ rock) cm^{-1} respectively, and this is what is more or less observed in the infrared spectrum of polyethylene (Fig. 4.28). Interbranch or multiphonon processes are possible but will be very weak and temperature sensitive. Absorption of this type has not yet been definitely established in polymers but has been seen in some simple hydrocarbon liquids. In the normal forms of crystalline polyethylene, the chains are folded after the fashion of a concertina, resulting in the formation of lamellar crystallites some 100 Å thick. The folds destroy the translational symmetry of the chain and will make $\bar{k} \neq 0$ transitions possible and give a continuum absorption. This too has not yet been properly investigated.

Under moderate resolution the 770 and 1470 cm^{-1} bands of polyethylene are found to be doublets. This splitting arises from intermolecular effects, since the actual unit cell of crystalline polyethylene contains two segments of two distinct chains. The intermolecular forces couple the vibrations of the two chains and one can have the vibrations of a given kind either in phase or out of phase and the two states will have slightly different energies. Quantum mechanically—and equivalently—one can say that the double degeneracy which would prevail in the absence of interchain interactions is destroyed by their presence and a splitting into two components occurs. All the fifteen branches are doubled by this interaction, but only in some cases is the splitting experimentally observable. The acoustic branches also couple, leading to three in-phase branches which have zero frequency at $\bar{k} = 0$ and to three anti-phase branches which now have a finite frequency at $\bar{k} = 0$. The $\bar{k} = 0$ modes of the two chain unit cell can also be discussed as irreducible representations of the point group D_{2h} and for the particular case of the three antiphase (and therefore lattice optical) modes one finds

$$\Gamma_{\text{lattice}} = A_u + B_{1u} + B_{2u}. \tag{5.80}$$

The A_u vibration is forbidden in absorption, but the other two are allowed. The B_{1u} vibration is well known, occurring as a medium-intensity band near 73 cm^{-1} for room temperature (Fig. 5.19), but the B_{2u} band is much weaker and can only be discerned[216] at all clearly at liquid helium temperature where its frequency is 105 cm^{-1}. That the 73 cm^{-1} is truly a lattice mode was established by Krimm and Bank[217] who noted the shift to higher frequency of this band as the temperature was lowered. This shift, together with the intensification of the band, makes polyethylene unsuitable as a window material for low temperature studies in the 70–80 cm^{-1} region.

In addition to the sharp absorption band at 73 cm^{-1}, there is also a continuum absorption, part of which is shown in Fig. 5.18. Some of this continuum must arise in the amorphous regions of the polymer, as may be seen from the reduction of absorption coefficient in the 100 cm^{-1} region in going from less to more crystalline material shown in Fig. 5.20. However, at frequencies below 50 cm^{-1} the distinction disappears and the absorption coefficient of reasonably pure polyethylene may be represented by the formula[218]

$$\alpha = (8 + 1 \cdot 4 \,\bar{\nu})\bar{\nu}\, 10^{-4}. \tag{5.81}$$

The refractive index of polyethylene hardly varies over the radio-frequency and submillimetre regions and we may therefore write

$$\tan \delta = (0 \cdot 85 + 0 \cdot 15 \,\bar{\nu}) \times 10^{-4} \tag{5.82}$$

for the loss tangent of polyethylene. It is most interesting to observe that this

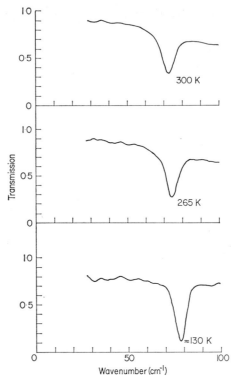

FIG. 5.19. Transmission of a 2 mm plate of high-density polyethylene (Rigidex).

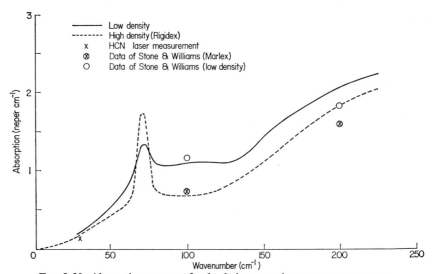

FIG. 5.20. Absorption spectra of polyethylene samples at room temperature.

equation predicts a constant loss tangent of 85 μ radians in the radio-frequency region where $\bar{\nu} \ll 1$, and that to within a factor of two this is observed. We thus have an equation which roughly gives us the losses in polyethylene over the enormous frequency range $10–10^{12}$ Hz. Whilst this is technologically satisfying it is not so physically, for we still lack a good understanding of the physical processes leading to the absorption. More work on samples of more widely varying composition and especially in the little-explored $10^9–10^{11}$ Hz region will be necessary if a physical understanding is to be achieved, but one can speculate that some part of the continuum absorption is analogous to that shown by non-polar liquids.

The macromolecules in isotactic polypropylene take the form of helices with four such helices passing through each unit cell. The vibrations of an isolated helix have been considered by Snyder and Schachtschneider[219] who have calculated the frequencies assuming reasonable force constants. The vibrations divide into A and E type because of the trigonal symmetry of the helix. The calculated values do not agree with observation very well at the low frequency end but one may use them to make a reasonable assignment. Thus from Fig. 4.29 it can be seen that there are bands at 50 cm^{-1} (E, chain torsion), 103 cm^{-1} ($A+E$), 170 cm^{-1} ($A+E$), 248 cm^{-1} (A), and 311 cm^{-1} (E). That the band at 103 cm^{-1} is indeed a doublet becomes obvious at liquid nitrogen temperatures where it is clearly resolved[215] into two components at 98 and 110 cm^{-1}. No lattice bands have ever been observed for polypropylene although they should exist since there are four segments per unit cell. There is very probably a continuum absorption just as for polyethylene but it is less obvious because of the series of resonances. Nevertheless, one cannot make a resolution of the lower curve of Fig. 4.29 into a series of Lorentzian bands without involving a continuum. Of course one has to bear in mind that "pure" polymers do not exist and polypropylene in particular is liable to contain catalyst residues (principally titanium) and these may be responsible for the continuum absorption. This is another point in polymer physics which is worthy of deeper investigation.

As will be seen from the above account, the broad outlines of the topic of submillimetre absorption in polymers are reasonably understood. Thus the low absorption coefficient of non-polar polymers matches the low absorption of non-polar liquids: the vibration frequencies of the chains and of the unit cells can be calculated with fair accuracy and the refractive indices can be correlated well with the polar character of the molecule. However, in detail there is much that is still puzzling. Some of these points have been mentioned above, but another is that polyethylene is more heavily absorbing at frequencies above 50 cm^{-1} than either polypropylene or TPX (poly-4-methylpentene-1) in their clear interband regions. Why a simple polymer should be more heavily absorbing than a complex one is not at all clear, nor is the fact that this pattern is reversed below 50 cm^{-1}. There are clearly some interesting discoveries still to be made.

5.9. Submillimetre Aspects of Molecular Physics

A knowledge of the complete vibration–rotation spectrum of a molecule is a great help in understanding its physics, for with this information one may hope to determine the equilibrium geometry of the molecule, to understand the forces operating between the atoms making up the molecule and to understand the complex phenomena of energy transfer between molecules in collision. For many molecules, the vibration–rotation bands occur at high frequencies in the mid- and near infrared, and the submillimetre spectrum is only required to complete the data. Submillimetre spectroscopy therefore, though valuable, is not of first-order importance in these cases and, for this reason and because the underlying theory has been amply developed in several well-known textbooks,[60, 220] we will confine ourselves here to a brief exposition illustrated by some examples where submillimetre observations are particularly important.

The equilibrium configuration of molecules can be determined from vibrational spectra because the selection rules depend on molecular symmetry. Consider as an example stannic bromide, $SnBr_4$. If we were investigating the structure of this molecule for the first time, we might imagine various possible structures for it: it might be tetrahedral, square planar, pyramidal or distorted pyramidal. The symmetry operations, which transform the molecule into an identical configuration, form a group and the various structures can be labelled in terms of the point groups which are isomorphous with these groups of molecular symmetry elements. The $3N-6$ normal vibrations of a molecule can be assigned to the various irreducible representations of the molecular point group and, as an example, in the present case the nine normal modes of vibration are distributed in the following fashion:

$$
\begin{aligned}
&\text{Tetrahedral } T_d && \Gamma_Q = A_1 + E + 2F_2 \\
&\text{Square planar } D_{4h} && \Gamma_Q = A_{1g} + A_{2u} + B_{1g} + B_{2g} + B_{2u} + 2E_u \\
&\text{Pyramidal } C_{4v} && \Gamma_Q = 2A_1 + 2B_1 + 1B_2 + 2E && (5.83) \\
&\text{Distorted pyramidal } C_{2v} && \Gamma_Q = 4A_1 + 1A_2 + 2B_1 + 2B_2.
\end{aligned}
$$

In these equations, Γ_Q is the reducible representation of the molecular point group formed by the normal coordinates. The selection rules are readily derived by group theoretical methods and are listed in the standard works. They may be summarized as follows: (1) only those vibrations which belong to an irreducible representation, which itself contains a primitive translation along the coordinate axes x, y or z, may be infrared active; (2) only those vibrations which belong to the most symmetric irreducible representation (A_1 or A_{1g} as the case may be) may give rise to polarized lines in the Raman spectrum; (3) only those vibrations which belong to irreducible representations containing the products xy, xz, yz or $x^2 - y^2$ may give rise to depolarized lines in the Raman spectrum. Applying these rules to the four cases listed above leads to the following predictions: the tetrahedral model should lead to four lines (one polarized) in the Raman spectrum with two coincident lines in the infrared spectrum; the square planar model should lead to three lines (one polarized) in the Raman spectrum with three non-coincident lines in the infrared; the pyramidal model should lead to seven lines (two polarized) in the Raman spectrum with four coincident lines in the infrared; and, finally, the distorted pyramidal model should lead to nine lines (four polarized) in the Raman spectrum with eight coincident lines in the infrared. The observed Raman spectrum[221] has four lines which occur at 279, 220 (polarized), 88 and 64 cm^{-1}, and the infrared spectrum[222] has two bands at 280 and 86 cm^{-1}. It follows, therefore, that the molecule is tetrahedral in its ground-state configuration.

This method has been applied to the elucidation of the structures of a large number of molecules and has become especially valuable in recent years with the renaissance of interest in inorganic chemistry.[223] Some care is, however, required in the observation and interpretation of inorganic far infrared spectra, since many of the compounds for study are not available in solution and have vapour pressures which are too low for gas-phase investigation. Consequently the spectra must be observed with microcrystalline specimens. The spectra of ionic crystals will usually exhibit intermolecular or lattice bands which may be very intense for the reststrahlen kind, or merely quite strong for the remainder. Two hazards arise from this: firstly in the vicinity of a reststrahlen band the crystallites become quite opaque but highly reflecting; and secondly the lattice bands may have comparable frequencies to the intramolecular vibrations of the ions making up the lattice. In the first case, a beam of radiation may traverse the specimen by multiple reflection rather than by transmission, and the observed spectrum will not be the true transmission spectrum. The positions of maximum or minimum reflection are not simply related to the absorption maxima and confusion and misidentification can easily arise†. The second problem is fortunately more readily side-stepped since, by changing the cation, the lattice modes will show large shifts, whereas the intra-molecular modes of the anion will be hardly affected. That the problem is a real one will

---

† It should also be noted that, even if crystals sufficiently thin were available so that transmission methods were feasible, the intense dispersion near the TO mode frequency would shift the observed transmission minimum away from exact coincidence with ν_{TO}.

be seen by noting that the lowest frequency ($\nu_4 F_{1u}$) of the PtI_6^{-2} ion occurs at 46 cm^{-1}, which is well below the region (80–100 cm^{-1}) where the lower frequency lattice modes for K_2PtI_6 are found.[223]

The molecules studied in organic chemistry usually contain light elements held together by relatively strong forces, and as a consequence submillimetre investigations are not particularly relevant to the elucidation of their properties. Nevertheless there are some exceptions, amongst which are those molecules which exhibit rotational isomerism, those exhibiting torsional oscillations about single bonds and those featuring hydrogen bonding in their makeup. Rotational isomerism arises when the barrier to free rotation about a carbon–carbon bond is high. Consider symmetrical tetrabromo-ethane as an example. This molecule is made up of two $CHBr_2$ "tops" in which the bond angles are approximately tetrahedral and the position of one top relative to the other can be defined by the torsional angle τ. Because of the steric repulsions of the substituent atoms in the tops (a factor frequently invoked as the origin of barriers to free rotation), there will be two positions of low potential energy separated by positions of high potential energy. The situation is illustrated in Fig. 5.21 which displays the dependence of potential energy on torsional angle.

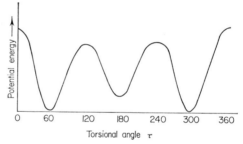

Fig. 5.21. Variation of potential energy with angle of rotation about the C–C bond in $CHBr_2CHBr_2$.

The high potential energy positions occur when the atoms at one end of the molecule eclipse those at the other end when looked at along the molecular axis. The low potential energy positions at 60° and 180° are called the gauche and trans positions respectively. Because of the high barriers, molecules spend relatively long times in the low-energy positions and a liquid sample, therefore, has present two types of molecule—*trans* and *gauche*—and the infrared spectrum is made up of a superposition of the spectra of each component.[224] The assignment of any given band to the one type of molecule or the other is facilitated by the observation that, as the temperature falls, there will be an increase in the proportion of the *gauche* component since this has the lower energy. Assignment is also helped by the different selection rules which apply, since the two types of molecule have different symmetries; in particular the *trans* component has a centre of symmetry and no coincidences are therefore possible between the infrared and Raman spectra. Despite these advantages, unambiguous assignments of the near and mid-infrared have not proved possible so far using data from these regions alone, because there is a considerable degree of band overlapping and there are also present many combination and overtone bands which involve far infrared fundamentals.[225] The far infrared spectrum of liquid tetrabromoethane is shown in Fig. 5.22 from which it

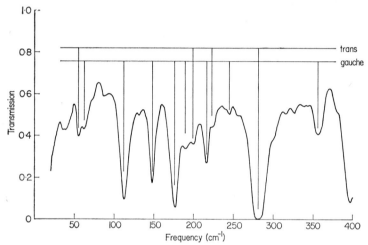

FIG. 5.22. Far infrared transmission spectrum and assignment for 1,1,2,2-tetrabromo-ethane; sample thickness 1 mm.

will be seen that in this region there is very little overlapping. From an examination of both the far infrared and the Raman spectrum it is relatively straightforward to assign[226] all the fundamentals lying below 400 cm⁻¹, and this assignment permits all the complex absorption pattern at higher frequencies to be unravelled. This is particularly important because, with complete assignments for both molecules, the interatomic forces can be deduced and the role of non-bonded interactions in determining barriers to free rotation elucidated.

The two absorption bands at 56 and 62 cm⁻¹ in Fig. 5.22 are assigned to torsional oscillations of the *trans* and the *gauche* molecules respectively. The study of torsional oscillations has interested many workers because the form of the potential energy function can depart radically from the simple quadratic form adopted generally for treatments of the other types of molecular vibration. In the conventional theory of molecular vibrations it is assumed that the potential energy may be expressed as

$$V(x) = V(0) + \tfrac{1}{2} f x^2 \qquad (5.84)$$

and, with this potential function, the wave equation for the vibration can be solved exactly and the energy levels are found to have the simple form

$$E(n) = (n + \tfrac{1}{2}) h c \bar{\nu}, \qquad (5.85)$$

where n is the vibrational quantum number. From this it will be seen that the various transitions $n = 0 \to n = 1$, $n = 1 \to n = 2$ etc. have identically the same frequency and the observed spectrum will consist of exactly superimposed bands. In practice this is not quite the observed situation, since the potential function cannot be pure quadratic in the vibrational coordinate x for indefinitely large x because, for a sufficiently high n, the molecule would have vibrational energy greater than its dissociation energy. To cope with this difficulty, equation (5.84) is continued as a Taylor's series to cubic and quartic terms. The solution of the wave equation now no longer leads to equispaced intervals and the various transitions become separated in the spectrum. The intensities of the higher transitions depend on the population of the lower (N_L) and of the upper (N_u) level via the Boltzmann factor; thus

$$I(n \to n+1) \propto (n+1)(N_L - N_u)$$
$$\propto (n+1) \, N_0 [1 - \exp(-h\nu_{R \to n+1}/kT)] \exp(-E(n)/kT). \quad (5.86)$$

There are, therefore, temperature dependent and upper-level transitions have come to be called "hot" bands for this reason.† High resolution infrared studies frequently show such "hot" bands and, from measurements of their frequencies, the anharmonic parameters x_{ij} in the more general version of equation (5.85), namely

$$(hc)^{-1} E(n_1, n_2 \ldots n_i \ldots) = \sum_i (n_i + \tfrac{1}{2}) \, \bar{\nu}_i + \sum_i x_{ii}(n_i + \tfrac{1}{2})^2$$
$$+ \sum_{i<j} x_{ij}(n_i + \tfrac{1}{2})(n_j + \tfrac{1}{2}), \quad (5.87)$$

can be determined. The effects of anharmonicity are usually small and observed bands only differ in frequency from the values they would have for an ideal quadratic potential function by a few per cent. When we come to consider torsional oscillations, this type of approach can become quite inappropriate, for, if the barrier heights are low, the potential function $V(\theta)$ is very poorly approximated by a quadratic function. The torsional

---

† It should be noted, however, from a summation of equation (5.86), that in the harmonic approximation when all the bands are coincident the overall intensity is *independent* of temperature.

potential function is of necessity periodic in the torsional angle θ, since if we increase this by 2π we arrive at the same configuration. This being the case, we can expand this unknown function as a Fourier series,

$$V(\theta) = V(0) + V_1 \cos\theta + V_2 \cos 2\theta + V_3 \cos 3\theta +, \qquad (5.88)$$

and we can hope to determine the coefficients in this series from an analysis of the observed spectrum. Some of the coefficients in the Fourier expansion may be zero by symmetry, thus for molecules like acetaldehyde, CH_3CHO, an identical potential position occurs after a rotation of the methyl group through an angle of $120°$ and for this reason $V_1 = V_2 =$ zero. In fact the only non-zero terms are the coefficients of $\cos 3\theta$, $\cos 6\theta$, $\cos 9\theta$ etc. The wave equation with a potential function of the form of equation (5.88) is known as a Mathieu equation and analytical solutions are possible in some cases. In the more general situation the equation is solved by numerical methods.

Hydrogen peroxide and deuterium peroxide provide good examples of the complexity introduced into a molecular spectrum when the molecule in question has a low barrier to internal rotation. The potential energy (in cm^{-1}) for D_2O_2 as a function of angle of internal rotation (θ) may be written[227]

$$V(\theta) = 780 + 994 \cos\theta + 641 \cos 2\theta + 55 \cos 3\theta. \qquad (5.89)$$

From this equation it will be seen that there is a high potential barrier in the *cis* position ($\theta = 0$) of 2470 cm^{-1} and a very much smaller barrier in the *trans* position ($\theta = \pi$) of 377 cm^{-1}. The position of minimum energy occurs when $\theta = 110° 8'$ or $249° 52'$ but, since these are equivalent, there are no rotational isomers. Tunnelling through the low *trans* barrier leads to a doubling of the torsional energy levels in much the same way as is found for the "umbrella" mode levels of ammonia; the observed splittings are $n = 0$ ($1\cdot88$ cm^{-1}), $n = 1$ ($42\cdot3$ cm^{-1}), $n = 2$ ($123\cdot5$ cm^{-1}), where n is the torsional vibrational quantum number. H_2O_2 and D_2O_2 are very nearly symmetric tops with the dipole moment perpendicular to the unique (A) axis. The interaction of overall rotation with internal rotation can therefore be discussed in terms of a perturbed symmetric rotor and each level will be labelled by a value of J, K and n. Additionally, and rather analogously to the water-vapour case, the torsional wave functions divide into four orthogonal sets distinguished by their parities with respect to reflection in the two perpendicular planes which define the *cis* and *trans* positions. The four cases may be written $(++)$, $(+-)$, $(-+)$ and $(--)$, and they are associated with K even for the first two and K odd for the second two. Each K state of a given vibrational level consists of doublets separated approximately by the splittings given above. The origin of the rotation spectrum of

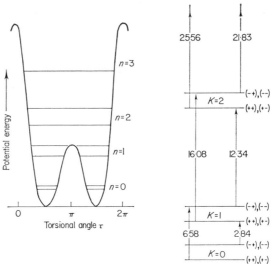

FIG. 5.23. Torsional vibrational potential function, energy levels and origin of the ground state rotational spectrum of D_2O_2 after Hunt and Leacock.[227]

D_2O_2 in the ground vibrational state is shown in Fig. 5.23. Each level in this Figure has associated with it the usual pattern of sublevels due to the quantum number J whose energies to the symmetric rotor approximation will vary as $BJ(J+1)$. The selection rules appropriate for this kind of system are

$$\Delta J = 0 \pm 1, \qquad \Delta K = \pm 1,$$

$$(+\ +) \leftrightarrow (-\ +) \quad \text{and} \quad (+\ -) \leftrightarrow (-\ -).$$

The spectrum of D_2O_2 is dominated by the series of Q branches which arise from the transitions shown in Fig. 5.23, together with the rule $\Delta J = 0$. There is a slight splitting of the lines (≈ 3 GHz) because of small departures from the simple energy formula in terms of B and J, but this has not yet been detected in the far infrared. The effective piling up of lines which occurs accounts for the strong features in the far infrared absorption spectrum and, because of the closeness to the symmetric rotor limiting case, these strong Q branches may be fitted to the simple formula

$$\bar{\nu}(K) = 6 \cdot 58 + 9 \cdot 51\ K - 0 \cdot 01\ K^2 \qquad (5.90)$$

for the left-hand transitions in Fig. 5.23, and

$$\bar{\nu}(K) = 2 \cdot 84 + 9 \cdot 505\ K - 0 \cdot 005\ K^2 \qquad (5.91)$$

for the right-hand transitions. These two equations are not independent and may be combined if desired into a single expression. Q branches with

K as high as nine, in these series, have been observed in the far infrared spectrum and the two branches with $K = 0$ have been resolved in the milli-metre-wave spectrum by Oelfke and Gordy.[228] The frequency precision obtainable in radio-frequency spectroscopy is such that the simple theory given above breaks down, even when full allowance is made for centrifugal distortion. Strictly, one should attempt to solve rigorously the quantum mechanical equations of motion when this is the case, but fortunately for H_2O_2 and D_2O_2 the perturbation treatment can be continued until satisfactory agreement is obtained. Allowance must also be made for the population of excited vibrational states in interpreting the room-tempera-ture spectrum. Some bands in the 70–90 cm^{-1} region arise from rotational transitions in the state $n = 1$, and some further bands in the 150–190 cm^{-1} region arise from rotational transitions in $n = 2$. Vibrational transitions also appear as doublets with each component having its associated rota-tional sub-structure. The region of the spectrum between 150 and 350 cm^{-1} is occupied by the various transitions of the split $n = 0 \rightarrow n = 1$ band. Hunt and Leacock[227] have given a complete assignment of the spectrum and derived many of the molecular parameters. Oelfke and Gordy[228] have obtained some of these to still higher accuracy, and we have the satisfactory situation that the exceedingly complex spectrum is well understood and that a reasonable theory of the molecular motion has been developed.

For most other cases, the observed spectrum yields much less information and consequently the potential function cannot be derived so fully.[229] Commonly, only the $0 \rightarrow 1$ band is observed and all that can be done is to derive the dominant Fourier component. This can be regarded as finding a cosine potential function which has the same curvature (i.e. force constant) as a pure quadratic potential function in the equilibrium position. The barrier heights derived under this limitation are naturally less certain than when we have more extensive experimental information available; as examples, ethyl fluoride has a single torsional band at 243 cm^{-1} from which a barrier height of $1 \cdot 221$ cm^{-1} (3580 K cal mol^{-1}) has been derived, and methyl formate has a band at 130 cm^{-1} from which a barrier height of 412 cm^{-1} (1165 K cal mol^{-1}) can be calculated.[230] Acetaldehyde is a some-what more favourable case since here three bands, $0 \rightarrow 1$ at 150 cm^{-1} and the two components (A and E respectively) of the $0 \rightarrow 2$ band at 262 and 276 cm^{-1}, have been observed. From this data a barrier height of 413 cm^{-1} can be somewhat confidently estimated.[230] Microwave methods have also been used to determine barrier heights.[231] The observed microwave spectrum will consist of a series of lines arising from pure rotational transitions in the vibrational ground state, plus lines arising from rotational transitions in excited states. The intensities of these latter will be temperature dependent because the population of the excited states is given by the Boltzmann factor (equation 6.6) and thus the vibrational frequency can be deduced from studies of the dependence of intensity on temperature. The barrier can then be calculated by the curvature-fitting procedure mentioned above. This method is quite valuable in some cases as torsional bands are often weak and difficult to detect directly in the infrared or Raman spectra, but it really only applies to very simple forms of hindering potential. If the potential is complex, as for D_2O_2, the barrier heights cannot be determined from this type of microwave observation.

Barrier heights and equilibrium positions are now known for quite an array of molecules, and the interpretation of the data in terms of chemical binding theory has made some progress. It is becoming clear that many factors contribute to the phenomenon of a hindering potential. Non-bonded repulsions are significant but not dominant for, if they were, the lowest energy configuration for D_2O_2 would be the *trans* form. Lone-pair interactions clearly play a part, and it has also been suggested that orbital hybridization other than sp^n may be involved. Hybrid orbitals involving d or f electrons would not have the cylindrical symmetry of a sp^n hybrid, and there would be an inherent orbital-following type of force resisting free rotation. Further experiments and attempts at theoretical interpretation are called for, since it would be interesting to know why the barrier to free rotation in nitromethane[232] (CH_3NO_2) is only 2.1 cm^{-1}, whilst that for methylamine[232] (CH_3NH_2) is 685 cm^{-1}.

Another branch of chemical physics in which submillimetre observations play a significant role is the study of hydrogen bonding. Hydrogen bonds are usually very weak with binding energies in the range 5–10 K cal mol^{-1} and, for this reason, and despite the very low mass of the hydrogen atom, the characteristic stretching and deformation frequencies of the hydrogen bond tend to lie in the submillimetre region. A good example of reasonably stable hydrogen bonded structures is found for the aliphatic fatty acids where a large fraction of the molecules in the gas phase are bonded into dimers,[233] i.e.

$$\begin{array}{ccc} & O \ldots H\text{–}O & \\ & \diagup \qquad\quad \diagdown & \\ R\text{–}C & & C\text{–}R \\ & \diagdown \qquad\quad \diagup & \\ & O\text{–}H \ldots O & \end{array}$$

The symmetry of the dimer is described by the point group C_{2h} and from this three infrared-active modes are predicted which can loosely be described as an H-bond stretch, an O–H ... O bend and an H ... O=C–O torsion. The observed frequencies of these modes for formic acid are 248, 164 and 68 cm^{-1}. Studies of this type are very valuable because they give direct information about the potential function in which the hydrogen atom moves, and this may be able to throw some light on the continuing puzzle as to why symmetrical hydrogen bonds with both O–H distances equal are so rare. They are also of value as we may, by implication, be able to deduce some of the properties to be expected of the far less stable hydrogen-bonded entities which must exist in some systems. Of these the most important is water vapour in which it is expected that transient $(H_2O)_2$ dimers must exist. In fact there is now a growing body of evidence that such entities are responsible for some of the submillimetre absorption in the atmosphere.[139, 234] Other systems in which transient dimers[235] are known to form are gaseous HCN, gaseous mixtures of HCN and NH_3 and gaseous mixtures of CO_2 and H_2O. Hydrogen bonding is in many ways the most important phenomenon in chemistry since life would be impossible without it, and submillimetre spectroscopy, which is one of the few methods of directly investigating hydrogen bonding, is therefore clearly a most important weapon in the physical chemist's armoury.

5.10. Submillimetre Waves in Plasmas

A plasma is a very complicated phenomenon; it is an electrically neutral but highly ionized gas consisting of electrons, ions and neutral atoms (or molecules) in the presence of electric or magnetic fields. Plasmas are interesting in their own right as examples of fruitful systems for studying electromagnetic interactions, but they have also become technologically very important because very high temperature plasmas provide the best hope at present of realizing power generation from controlled nuclear fusion. On a much humbler but still very important level they are valuable as sources of broad-band radiation in the submillimetre region. The reason for this is that Kirchoff's law asserts that to radiate effectively at a given wavelength a body must also absorb strongly at that wavelength. Metals are therefore poor radiators of far infrared radiation because they are such good reflectors in this region. Radiators such as the globar and the Nernst filament, which are in widespread use in the mid-infrared, are of very little utility in the far infrared because their radiating coatings become transparent.[236] Quartz is undoubtedly the best material since it remains opaque, especially when hot, to well below $200 \, cm^{-1}$; but even quartz fails for the region below $100 \, cm^{-1}$. Fortunately the radiation from the hot plasma inside the envelope takes over and the medium-pressure quartz lamp may be used down to at least $2 \, cm^{-1}$. The plasma may have an electron temperature of 10^4 K, compared with the envelope temperature of 10^3 K, so there is plenty of sub-millimetre radiation available—relatively speaking!

To see why the plasma is itself "black" at submillimetre wavelengths, we need to consider the propagation of electromagnetic waves in it, and this is treated by magneto-ionic theory.[237] This theory is rather extensive, with several ramifications, but its principal contents can be stated in a relatively simple form. If there are no collisions between the electrons and the ions, a wave travelling in the plasma will not be attenuated but will undergo a shift of phase velocity relative to the vacuum. The electrons in the plasma will oscillate about their equilibrium positions at a characteristic plasma frequency v_p given by

$$v_p = \sqrt{[N_e e^2/(\pi m)]} \qquad (5.92)$$

and in terms of this the refractive index will be given by

$$n = c/v_\phi = [1-(v_p/v)^2]^{1/2}, \qquad (5.93)$$

where v_ϕ is the phase velocity, v the observing frequency, N_e the number of electrons per cm³, e the charge and m the mass of the electron. As a practical example, v_p is 10^{12} Hz for $N_e = 10^{16}$ per cm³. The refractive index of this idealized plasma will always be less than unity (which implies a phase velocity greater than c) but for $v < v_p$ it will be imaginary. This is reminiscent of the situation which was found for idealized ionic crystals and, once again, an imaginary refractive index implies 100 per cent reflection with only evanescent waves allowed inside the medium. These waves do not propagate in any usual sense of the word and their amplitude falls exponentially with depth of penetration into the plasma. The situation is quite akin to the "skin effect" encountered when high-frequency a.c. currents are flowing in metallic conductors, and the free electrons in metals and semiconductors form plasmas in exactly the same way as do those in gases subjected to intense discharges.

In real plasmas, electron–ion collisions do occur and the effect of these is to make the plasma absorptive and to keep the refractive index everywhere real. The complex dielectric constant may be written

$$\hat{\epsilon} = 1 - v_p^2/[v(v-iv_e)], \qquad (5.94)$$

where v_e is the electron–ion collision frequency. From this relation, the refractive index and absorption coefficient may be explicitly derived (see Appendix 3) as follows:

$$n = \left\{ \frac{1}{2}\left(1 - \frac{v_p^2}{v^2+v_e^2}\right) + \frac{1}{2}\left[\left(1 - \frac{v_p^2}{v^2+v_e^2}\right)^2 + \left(\frac{v_p^2}{v^2+v_e^2}\frac{v_e}{v}\right)^2\right]^{1/2}\right\}^{1/2}$$

$$\alpha = \frac{4\pi v}{c}\left\{-\frac{1}{2}\left(1 - \frac{v_p^2}{v^2+v_e^2}\right) + \frac{1}{2}\left[\left(1 - \frac{v_p^2}{v^2+v_e^2}\right)^2 + \left(\frac{v_p^2}{v^2+v_e^2}\frac{v_e}{v}\right)^2\right]^{1/2}\right\}^{1/2}$$

$$(5.95)$$

For most plasmas, ν_e is less than ν_p and, provided this is so, three frequency regions may be distinguished:

1. $\nu < \nu_e$; here n is very high and α is also large and the plasma behaves rather like a conducting metal.

2. $\nu_e < \nu < \nu_p$; here n rapidly plunges to very low values as ν increases past ν_e, and α continues to rise. Electromagnetic waves cannot readily propagate in such a medium and the plasma is said to be "cut-off", the phrase arising from analogy with waveguides.

3. $\nu > \nu_p$; here n approaches its asymptotic value of unity from lower values and α rapidly drops to very low values. The plasma behaves like a low-loss dielectric.

A plasma will therefore be "black" in the far infrared, provided that ν_p is of the order 10^{12} Hz and ν_e is not too small. A full calculation of the optical properties of a plasma from first principles is formidably difficult, but an approximate treatment which will give at least qualitatively correct answers is quite simple. Assume that the vapour inside the mercury lamp is at an effective pressure of 1 atmosphere, that is $0 \cdot 1$ per cent ionized, and its electron temperature is 10^4 K. From 5.92 we have $\nu_p = 2 \times 10^{12}$ Hz. The electron–ion collision frequency, assuming that Coulomb collisions are dominant, is given by

$$\nu_e = 3 \cdot 628 \times N_e \, T^{-3/2} Z \ln \Lambda, \qquad (5.96)$$

where Z is the positive ion charge, $\ln \Lambda$ is a parameter (the Coulomb integral) which in the present case is of the order 5; ν_e by substitution is found to be 8×10^{11} Hz. The plasma will be quite opaque between 20 and 60 cm^{-1} and will therefore radiate strongly. In practice (see Chapter 4), black-body radiation from a medium-pressure mercury arc plasma has been observed down to at least 2 cm^{-1} and up to as high as 100 cm^{-1}, where absorption in the lamp envelope cuts it off.

The determination of N_e and ν_e and other parameters of a plasma is an important practical problem. The art has been called "plasma diagnostics" and is usually carried out by probing the plasma with a beam of electromagnetic radiation of a suitable frequency. Microwaves are extensively used to study rarified plasmas $(N_e \leqslant 10^{13})$, and infrared lasers such as the $3 \cdot 39$ μm He–Ne laser have been used to probe dense plasmas. However, at the He–Ne laser wavelength α is very small for the plasmas currently under study $(N_e \approx 10^{16})$ and n is very insensitive to changes in the plasma conditions. It follows that considerable depths of plasma are necessary to ensure adequate measurement sensitivity. In the present case, where the probing frequency ν will be greater than ν_p, equation (5.95) may be approximated to read

$$\alpha = (2\pi/c)\{\nu_p^2 \nu_e / [\nu(\nu^2 - \nu_p^2)^{1/2}]\} \qquad (5.97)$$

and a characteristic absorption depth d may be written

$$d = \alpha^{-1} = [c/(2\pi\nu_e)](\nu/\nu_p)^2(1 - \nu_p^2/\nu^2)^{1/2}. \qquad (5.98)$$

Clearly d decreases the nearer ν becomes to ν_p and for this reason submillimetre radiation probing is a sensitive method for dense plasmas (N_e, 10^{14}–10^{16}).

The experimental arrangements feature an HCN or an H_2O laser (see Chapter 6) and a Mach–Zehnder interferometer. This latter shares the advantages of the Michelson form in that both the real and the imaginary parts of $\hat{n}$ are available from the Fourier transformation of the interferogram, but additionally it has the further advantage that no radiation returns to the source, which is a very desirable feature when working with highly oscillatory lasers. Using this technique, Chamberlain and his colleagues[238] have studied a potassium-seeded argon plasma at an ambient temperature of 1233 K where the total pressure was 760 torr. The current density was $1\cdot5$ A cm^{-1} and it was found that under these conditions N_e was approximately 10^{14}. Time-resolved studies of the decay of plasmas produced by a pulsed discharge in a fused silica torus have also been carried out using the 337 μm radiation from an HCN laser.[239] Rapid detector responsivity is necessary in this type of experiment, and so the usual Golay cell was replaced by a Putley-type indium antimonide detector. Electron densities of the order 5×10^{15} cm^{-3} were measured and electron temperatures between 10^3 and 10^4 K were estimated.

The optical properties of plasmas are still more complicated in the presence of magnetic fields. Two propagation modes are found, known as the ordinary and extra-ordinary modes; they have different propagation characteristics, depending in a complicated way on the direction of the magnetic field relative to the direction of propagation. When a magnetic field is present, however, it is possible to determine N_e from Faraday rotation measurements, as well as from transmissivity measurements. Dense plasmas in strong magnetic fields are very much to the forefront of thermonuclear research and the power of submillimetre techniques to diagnose the conditions prevailing in the plasma could prove most useful.

5.11. Submillimetre Absorption by Electronic Processes in Insulating Crystals

Atoms or molecules which have a resultant electron spin moment different from zero exhibit the phenomenon of electron paramagnetic resonance (or e.p.r.) absorption. The simplest case to consider is an atom without nuclear spin in an overall Σ state and with one unpaired electron. The two spin states of the odd electron will form a degenerate Kramers doublet in the absence of a magnetic field, but in its presence they will be split and electromagnetic energy of frequency

$$\nu = g\beta H, \tag{5.99}$$

where g is the gyromagnetic ratio of the electron in question, β the Bohr magneton ($1 \cdot 3997$ MHz G^{-1}) and H the field strength, can be absorbed. If radiation at this frequency is passed through a cell containing a sufficient number of the chosen atoms, a sharp dip in transmission will be observed when the applied magnetic field satisfies equation (5.99). Consequently the plot of transmission versus H will show a bell-shaped curve typical of a resonance and therefore experiments of this kind are sometimes called resonance spectroscopy. The resonance frequency can be set, in principle, anywhere in the electromagnetic spectrum, but certain practical considerations point strongly to the microwave, millimetre and submillimetre regions. Firstly, the observed absorption will be the difference between the absorption by ground-state atoms and the stimulated emission from upper-state atoms (cf. equation 5.86), and it follows that ν should be as large as possible so that the combined effect of the favourable Boltzmann factor and the linear dependence of intensity on frequency will maximize the net absorption. Secondly, since the coupling to the electromagnetic field is via a magnetic dipole moment, the process will have an inherently low transition probability and, in the microwave region, high-Q tuned cavities are available which act in essence like multiple reflection long-path cells and these can multiply up enormously the slight absorption per transit. Thirdly, intense mono-chromatic sources are required for this type of spectroscopy, especially if, as is usually the case, the spectra show fine structure arising from nuclear spins or else from the presence of other unpaired electrons. These points influenced the choice of the microwave region for the development of e.p.r. spectroscopy and the spectrometers usually operate at X band ($\lambda = 3$ cm) or Q band ($\lambda = 0 \cdot 8$ cm) with klystrons as sources. The technique is well developed and commercial instruments are available.

The width of an e.p.r. line is determined by many factors, including the rate of relaxation back to thermal equilibrium, but the principal experimental factor is the homogeneity of the magnetic field over the specimen. For many organic free radicals g is approximately 2, so resonance at X-band frequencies occurs when $H = 3 \cdot 6$ kG; a high resolution X-band e.p.r. spectrometer, therefore, requires a large, highly homogeneous magnet capable of delivering up to 4 kG. Magnets of this specification can be readily made with normal technology. The e.p.r. spectra frequently show fine structure for the reasons given above and, since the line-width is independent of magnetic field, whereas the line separation is directly proportional to field strength, it follows that the resolving power of an e.p.r. spectrometer will increase with increasing magnetic field. Submillimetre e.p.r. spectrometers would be very attractive both for this reason and for those given earlier. The submillimetre lasers described in the next chapter are suitable sources but, since for $g = 2$ and $\nu = 890$ GHz, H must be 320 kG, it follows that the experiments would have to be carried out at the limits of even superconducting magnetic technology. For this reason, submillimetre e.p.r. spectrometers have not been deployed so far to study what one might call conventional subjects, such as unstable free radicals produced by irradiation of molecular crystals. However, the g factors for some rare-earth atoms are very large and the e.p.r. spectra of compounds containing these atoms can be investigated rather felicitously with a CW submillimetre laser and a magnet, which is not required to produce more than 100 kG and which can therefore be built to give a reasonably homogeneous field. Cavity methods are not available at such high frequencies, but the increased absorption permits the observation of spectra with an acceptable signal-to-noise ratio, even with the restriction to single-pass methods. As an example, Kotthaus and Dransfeld[240] have observed the e.p.r. spectrum of holmium ethyl sulphate using a CW HCN laser operating at 890·76 GHz. This source is sufficiently stable for the conventional, signal-to-noise improving techniques of field modulation and synchronous detection to be feasible, and the experimentalists produced an excellent spectral record showing an eight-line spectrum centred about a magnetic field of 41 kG. The hyperfine structure arises from interaction with the nuclear spin and, since holmium has only a single isotope, ^{165}Ho, whose nuclear spin $I = 7/2$, one expects eight, i.e. $(2I+1)$, hyperfine components in agreement with experiment. From the location of the centre of the pattern, g is calculated to be 15·5.

The far infrared spectrum of a crystal containing transition or rare-earth metal ions can be quite complex. There will be the usual absorption due to transverse optical phonons but, additionally, there may be low-frequency lines due to electronic transitions in the ion. These latter, arising as they do from essentially two-level systems, have intensities which are strongly temperature dependent and, furthermore, the coupling of electronic and lattice motions virtually vanishes at low temperatures, so the combined effects make the lines sharp and intense at temperatures of 4·2 K or less. The TO absorption bands will usually have their maxima above 100 cm^{-1}, and at cryogenic temperatures these bands also become extremely sharp. As a consequence, most of the crystals of interest become more or less transparent below 100 cm^{-1} when they are cooled to liquid helium temperatures and the lines due to electronic transitions may be readily discerned. These transitions have finite frequency because of the splitting of a given d or f electron configuration into a many-level manifold under the influence of the electrostatic and magnetic fields experienced by the optical electrons. This is best explained by means of some examples. Ions such as Ti^{3+} have a single $3d$ electron and the spectroscopic term nomenclature for the free ion would be ^2D which is ten-fold degenerate (5 orbitals $\times$ 2 spin states). When placed in a crystal and experiencing the electrostatic forces of its neighbours the degeneracy is removed and the level is split. The crystal field splitting can be as much as 20 000 cm^{-1}, and transitions between the split states explain much of the visible colour so commonly observed with transition element chemistry. These transitions are semi-forbidden since they would be $d \rightarrow d$ in character for the unperturbed system and, although the less than spherical symmetry of the field may induce a partly allowed character, the observed absorption bands are weak enough for transition element compounds to appear coloured rather than black to the eye. In a cubic field the ^2D state of Ti^{3+} splits[241] into a $^2E_{2g}$ (upper) and $^2F_{2g}$ (lower) state, but if the field is only approximately cubic (as is often the case) the trigonal component will induce a further splitting of the lower level into $2A_1$ and ^2E components and the gerade–ungerade labels will disappear. For Ti^{3+} in Al$_2$O$_3$ the trigonal splitting is of the order 100 cm^{-1}. Finally, the effects of spin–orbit coupling have to be considered; this leads to a splitting of the ^2E ground state into $_1E_{1/2}$ and $E_{3/2}$ components, separated by 37·8 cm^{-1}, and alters the character of the $^2A_1$ state to $_2E_{1/2}$. At liquid helium temperature a crystalline sample of Al$_2$O$_3$ doped with Ti^{3+} shows[241] absorption bands at 37·8 ($E_{3/2} \rightarrow {}_1E_{1/2}$) and 107 ($E_{3/2} \rightarrow {}_2E_{1/2}$) cm^{-1}. Each level of the Ti^{3+} ion is a doubly degenerate Kramers doublet in the absence of a magnetic field, since an electrostatic field which is even symmetric under time reversal cannot split the degenerate components, each of which is obtained from the other by the application of a time-reversal operator. In the presence of a magnetic field, however, the levels will be split (H is a time-odd operator) and the effect in the spectrum is that each of the two absorption bands splits[241] into four components when the field is parallel to the c-axis of the crystal. The fact that four lines are observed[241] rather than three shows that the g values for the two states are very different and, in fact, the measured values are $g^{\parallel}\, E_{3/2} = 1\cdot11$ and $g^{\parallel}\, {}^1E_{1/2} = 2\cdot00$. No splitting is observed for H $\perp$ c from which it may be deduced that $g_\perp < 0\cdot1$. The isoelectronic V^{4+} ion in Al$_2$O$_3$ shows[241] a similar band at 28·1 cm^{-1} which, however, only splits into three components under the influence of a field. Experiments of this sort, i.e. broad-band spectroscopy at various values of applied field, are quite equivalent to the e.p.r. experiments mentioned earlier; the zero-field resonance gives the magnetic field a "start" and permits e.p.r. absorption to occur at submillimetre frequencies for relatively low H and g. As an example of this the upper frequency component of the split 28·1 cm^{-1} line of V^{4+} would come into coincidence with the 337 μm HCN laser frequency at an applied field of 24 kG.

The V^{3+} ion has two $3d$ electrons and in consequence shows[241] a more complex pattern of level splitting. However, only one transition is observed in the far infrared—at $8 \cdot 25$ cm^{-1}—and this shows interesting behaviour in a magnetic field. The ground state has $M = 0$ and therefore shows no splitting, whilst the upper state is made up of an $M = \pm 1$ pair and therefore does split. As a result, only two components are observed but, whilst the splitting is linear for H $\|$ c, it is quadratic for H $\perp$ c. This difference in behaviour arises because mixing of the three spin states under the perturbing action of the magnetic field is only allowed for H $\perp$ c.

The system Cr^{3+} in Al$_2$O$_3$ gives the precious stone ruby[242] and this doped crystal is remarkable in that it is the basis of two stimulated emission devices—the well-known ruby laser operating at 6943 Å and the ruby maser which is a very valuable low-noise amplifier for the 9 GHz region. The crystalline field experienced by the Cr^{3+} ion is close to cubic in symmetry and this field splits the ^4F state which would prevail for the free ion into three states: the ground state $^4A_2$, a first excited state $^4F_2$, and a still higher state $^4F_1$. These states are labelled according to the irreducible representations of the cubic group T_d and they are quartets because they arise from a manifold in which, obeying Hund's rule, the electrons have the maximum spin multiplicity, i.e. $S = \frac{3}{2}$. There are, however, doublet states as well, and the lowest of these, ^2E, lies below the $^4F_2$ state; the situation is illustrated in Fig. 5.24, which also indicates that the $^4A \rightarrow {}^4F$ bands are very broad. Optical transitions to the excited states shown in Fig. 5.24 are made weakly allowed by the crystal field, but only the band $^4A_2 \rightarrow {}^4F_1$ should appear to the cubic approximation (since $A_2 \times F_1 = F_2 = \Gamma$ (x, y, z)). However, the $^4A_2 \rightarrow {}^4F_2$ band is also observed in absorption, doubtless due to the trigonal symmetry which prevails, and the combined effects of these two bands are responsible for the characteristic red colour of ruby. The line $^4A_2 \rightarrow {}^2E$ is extremely weak[243] in absorption ($\alpha = 0 \cdot 4$ neper cm^{-1} for $0 \cdot 05$ per cent Cr^{3+}) because, to the cubic approximation, it involves a change of multiplicity. The effects of the trigonal component of the crystal field are also shown in Fig. 5.24. The ^2E state splits into an upper $2\bar{A}$ and a lower $\bar{E}$ level separated (at room temperature) by 29 cm^{-1}, and the ground state is split by $0 \cdot 38$ cm^{-1} into two levels of spin $S = \pm \frac{1}{2}$ (upper) and $S = \pm \frac{3}{2}$ (lower); all four levels are Kramers doublets. The ruby laser operates by absorbing pump power (from a Xenon flash tube) in the two broad bands $^4A_2 \rightarrow {}^4F_2$ (green) and $^4A_2 \rightarrow {}^4F_1$ (blue). The excitation is transferred to the sharp ^2E level (by means of processes involving the assistance of lattice phonons) and, provided the flash is sufficiently intense, laser action on the transition $^2E \rightarrow {}^4A_2$ will be possible. This topic will be taken up again in the next chapter as also will the point that, because of the splitting of the ^2E state, the laser can operate at two distinct wavelengths, the R_1 line ($\bar{E} \rightarrow {}^4A_2$) and the R_2 line ($2\bar{A} \rightarrow {}^4A_2$). The splitting and nomenclatural change of the

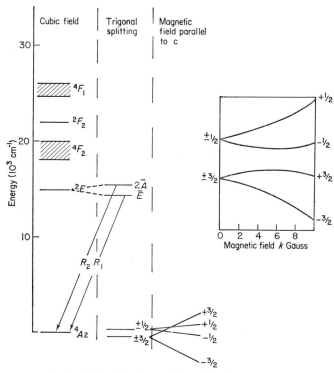

FIG. 5.24. Energy levels of the Cr^{3+} ion in Al_2O_3 (ruby). The splittings of levels under the influence of the trigonal field component or of an external magnetic field are not to scale. The inset shows the Zeeman effect of the ground state for an angle of 54° 44′ between the magnetic field and the c-axis of the crystal.

ground state is usually ignored in this connection since the laser line-width (≈ 0.5 cm^{-1}) is greater than the ground state splitting.

A magnetic field, especially when applied parallel to the ruby optic axis (c), splits the Kramers doublets[244] and this can be detected optically by the observation that the R_1 line develops field-dependent fine structure. It is still more readily detected by microwave e.p.r. experiments, the basis of which is shown on the right of Fig. 5.24. When the field is not parallel to c, the Zeeman effect of the ground state is not linear and there exists a "magic" angle of 54° 44′ for which the splitting of the upper state is a mirrored version of that of the lower state. This particular angle is used to realize the "push–pull" ruby maser—the principles of which are shown schematically in the inset of Fig. 5.24. Because of the symmetry of the diagram, the transition frequencies for $-\frac{3}{2} \rightarrow -\frac{1}{2}$ and $+\frac{3}{2} \rightarrow +\frac{1}{2}$ will be equal; thus, if pump power is applied to the crystal at this frequency the level $-\frac{1}{2}$ will become populated and the level $+\frac{3}{2}$ will be underpopulated so a population inversion will exist and, as shown in Chapter 6, stimulated emission may occur. The maser usually operates with a field of 4 kG and at liquid helium temperature. The pump frequency is 24 GHz and the frequency to be amplified 9 GHz. This type of maser—and there are now many of them—is of great value in applications where noise-free amplification at frequencies of the order 10^{10} Hz is required. The principle unfortunately may not readily be extended to give submillimetre masers because of the requirement for a pumping frequency *higher* than the stimulated emission frequency. However, with the rapid development of intense submillimetre lasers (see Chapter 6), this difficulty may eventually be overcome.

Electronic transitions in the far infrared region for rare-earth ions have been reviewed by Hadni.[245] If the ion has m electrons in the $4f$ shell then the $4f^m$ state will be split by amounts typically of the order 10^4 cm^{-1}, because of the effects of electronic repulsion; each resulting state will be further split by some thousands of cm^{-1} due to spin–orbit coupling. When the ion is placed in a crystal, the effect of the crystal field will be to further split each state into a number of sublevels; transitions between these states—just as was found for the transition metal ions—will usually occur in the far infrared region. As an example, consider ytterbium in ytterbium ethyl sulphate (YES) which has been investigated by Wheeler, Reames and Wachtel.[246] The ion has 13 $4f$ electrons, so $S = \frac{1}{2}$ and L will equal 3 for the ground state (in other words there is one "hole" in the $4f$ shell). The spin-orbit coupling leads to two states, a ground state with $J = L+S$ and an excited state with $J = L-S$ separated by the remarkably large value of 10^4 cm^{-1}. Crystal field splitting of the $^2F_{7/2}$ ground state leads to the observation of absorption bands at 44·0, 108·0 and 265 cm^{-1} for a sample temperature of 4·2 K. The spectrum is very rich since several phonon absorptions occur in the same region, but unambiguous assignment is possible because the crystal-field bands either split or shift under the influence of a magnetic field. Magnetic interactions between the ions in rare-earth compounds can lead to interesting effects. Wright and Moos have shown[247] that below 3·5 K dysprosium phosphate (Dy PO$_4$) has an antiferromagnetic (see p. 217) ground state. Each Dy^{3+} ion (ground state $^6H_{15/2}$) is surrounded by four nearest neighbours at the vertices of a flattened tetrahedron. There are three possible arrangements of the spins of the nearest neighbour ions: they may be all parallel, three may be parallel and one opposed or, finally, two may be parallel with the other two opposed. The resultant magnetic fields will split the Kramers degeneracy of each crystal field level, the splitting being largest for the first arrangement (7·2 cm^{-1}), intermediate (3·6 cm^{-1}) for the second and of course zero for the third. Below the Néel temperature of 3·5 K, the lowest energy state is the antiferromagnetic with the neighbour spins opposing the central ion spin, but above this temperature the stable form is the paramagnetic with the spins parallel. Prinz and Wagner[248] have studied e.p.r. absorption at $4 \cdot 2$ K in Dy PO_4 using a pulsed D_2O laser (see Chapter 6) radiating at $58 \cdot 25$ cm^{-1}. Because the spin flip of the central ion takes it back to the antiferromagnetic configuration which lies $7 \cdot 2$ cm^{-1} *below* the paramagnetic state, the effective frequency of the laser as far as resonance is concerned will be $58 \cdot 25 + 7 \cdot 2$, i.e. $65 \cdot 45$ cm^{-1}. The external field will be augmented by the "built in" or saturation dipolar field which has been measured to be $4 \cdot 1$ kG. Resonance was observed at an applied external field of $67 \cdot 6$ kG which corresponds to an effective field of $H = 71 \cdot 7$ kG. Using the effective frequency and field in equation (5·99) gives $g^{\parallel} = 19 \cdot 55$. Wright and Moos[247] find an essentially similar value but report $g^{\perp}$ to be only $0 \cdot 51$.

The spin vectors of the magnetic atoms in a paramagnetic crystal can be thought of as equivalent to the displacement vectors of the atoms in a vibrating crystal lattice, and one may conceive of a "magnon" in the same way as one is led naturally to define a phonon. Magnon dispersion diagrams may be drawn and one may, of course, have single magnon absorption processes for which the selection rule is $\Delta \bar{k} = 0$ and multiple magnon processes which, provided they satisfy momentum conservation, may occur anywhere in the dispersion diagram. Each branch of the dispersion diagram is doubly degenerate and will break up into two branches under the influence of a magnetic field. Antiferromagnetic resonance by single magnon creation is observed below the characteristic Néel temperature T_N; it corresponds to the production of a wave of paramagnetism from an initially antiferromagnetic† situation. The absorption arises from a magnetic dipole process, since both states have even parity and the band will be expected to show a first-order (linear) Zeeman effect. Two magnon processes will give rise to an observed absorption profile which will tend to reflect the magnon density of states function, and will consequently be strongly peaked near the critical points at the edge of the Brillouin zone. The absorption band will therefore be relatively sharp and will occur at a frequency equal to twice the ordinate of the dispersion diagram at the edge of the zone. Although the usual factors militate against two magnon processes, it must be realized that the $+\bar{k}, -\bar{k}$ system has negative parity and electric dipole transitions are allowed. For this reason, one and two magnon absorption bands are often of comparable intensity. The far infrared absorption spectrum of K_2IrCl_6 at $1 \cdot 3$ K shows[246] two bands, a stronger one at $9 \cdot 5$ cm^{-1} which splits in a magnetic field, and a weaker one at $13 \cdot 0$ cm^{-1} which does not. This failure is typical of a two-

---

† An arrangement of the magnetic atoms on two interpenetrating lattices such that the net moment of one sublattice exactly cancels that of the other.

magnon process and the intensity of this band falls off more slowly with rising temperature than does that of the $9 \cdot 5$ cm^{-1} band, but both disappear at the Néel temperature $T_N = 3 \cdot 0$ K. The magnon dispersion curve for this material shows two branches which intersect the $\bar{k} = 0$ axis at $9 \cdot 5$ and $2 \cdot 0$ cm^{-1} and which meet ($\bar{\nu} = 6 \cdot 75$ cm^{-1}) when $\bar{k} = \pi/2a$. The transition at $\bar{k} = 0$ to the upper branch gives the $9 \cdot 5$ cm^{-1} band and two-magnon absorption from the lower branch gives the $13 \cdot 0$ cm^{-1} band. It is most interesting to observe that the Néel temperature is related to the wavenumber $\bar{\nu}$ of a $\bar{k} = 0$ magnon mode by the relation

$$hc\bar{\nu} = kT_N \qquad\qquad (5.100)$$

and for $T_N = 3 \cdot 0$ K we expect $\bar{\nu}$ to be 2 cm^{-1} in agreement with experiment. Several other antiferromagnets such as MnO, MnF$_2$, FeF$_2$ and CoF$_2$ have been investigated.[249] CoF$_2$ is particularly interesting because of its relatively high Néel temperature ($T_N = 38$ K) and because the far infrared[249] and light scattering experiments[250] have both revealed the two-magnon processes (at $28 \cdot 5$ and 36 cm^{-1}) in this material.[251] Most antiferromagnets have transition metal ions in their make-up but one most interesting exception is α oxygen. Antiferromagnetic resonance absorption occurs[252] as a band near 27 cm^{-1} for crystalline oxygen below the α/β transition temperature of 23 K.

In some ionic crystals, the anisotropy of the crystalline field leads to a slight canting of the nearest neighbour and central ion spins and there is a net magnetic moment. Thus, provided the crystal is below its Néel point, it will behave like a ferromagnet. The presence of a magnetocrystalline anisotropy leads to a zero-field absorption frequency arising from ferrimagnetic resonance. The ferrimagnetic absorption line will show a shift (but no splitting) to higher frequencies as the applied field is increased. The magnetic anisotropy coupling rapidly diminishes with increasing temperature and ferrimagnetic absorption can usually only be observed at very low temperatures (≈ 1 K), and will usually occur below 10 cm^{-1}. Added to this, the absorption intensity is normally very low, so it will be realized that the observation of ferrimagnetic resonance calls for an experimental *tour de force*. Nevertheless, several examples are known, mostly from the work of Richards and his colleagues. Ytterbium iron garnet shows[253] a sharp absorption line at 3 cm^{-1} for a sample temperature of $1 \cdot 2$ K and NiF$_2$ shows[249] a band at $3 \cdot 33$ cm^{-1} for $T \approx 0$ K. Exchange resonances in holmium, samarium and gadolinium iron garnets have been studied by Sievers and Tinkham.[253]

The technique of cyclotron resonance is especially valuable for the elucidation of the electronic structure of semiconductors. This form of resonance comes about because a particle of charge q and effective mass m^* will rotate in a circle with a cyclotron frequency

$$\nu_c = qH/2\pi m^* c \tag{5.101}$$

about the lines of force of a field of strength H. Electromagnetic energy can therefore be absorbed when the radiation frequency equals ν_c. It will be noted that equations (5.99) and (5.101) are identical for $g = 2$, $q = e$ and $m^* = m$ since the Bohr magneton (in frequency units) equals $e/4\pi mc$, where e and m are the charge and mass of a free electron. In semiconductors, however, the resonance can arise not only from electrons but also from "holes" which can be thought of as positively charged entities equivalent to the absence of an electron. For both electrons and holes, the effective mass can differ greatly from m, and it is the power of cyclotron resonance to determine m^* which makes it so valuable a technique.

Just as for e.p.r. absorption, one can locate the resonance frequency anywhere in the spectrum provided one can produce the appropriate magnetic field, but again intensity and resolution considerations point to the use of as high a frequency as possible. The resolution requirement arises because few cyclotron resonance spectra consist of a simple line. For even the simplest elemental semiconductors the structure of the valence band is complex and the spectra will have many components. In contrast to e.p.r. absorption there are some special features of cyclotron resonance absorption which make the use of at least submillimetre frequencies mandatory, if the energy-level structure of the semiconductor is to be determined properly. Principal amongst these is collision of the spiralling electrons with the host lattice. If the resonance line is to be reasonably sharp, the electron must execute a sufficient part of its circular trajectory before collision causes loss of all phase correlation. We must therefore have

$$2\pi \nu \tau \geqslant 1, \tag{5.102}$$

where τ is the electron lattice collision time. For some semiconductors τ is sufficiently long for ν to be a microwave frequency, but for the imperfect compound semiconductors, such as gallium arsenide, which are currently commanding much attention, ν must lie in the submillimetre band. In an investigation of semiconductors it is important to be able to study the temperature dependence of lines as well as to be able to resolve them. On both counts it is necessary that the photon energy be greater than the thermal energy of the electrons; in other words, that $h\nu > kT$. Again, the use of a submillimetre source permits this requirement to be satisfied over a wide range of temperature.

Cyclotron resonance spectra have been observed using infrared spectrometers as the detectors,[254] and Couder[255] has used carcinotron sources in the range 280–740 GHz to study the energy surfaces in tellurium; but the low signal-to-noise performance has handicapped the experimentalists. Now that intense CW lasers (see next chapter) have been developed for the submillimetre region, high-quality spectra can readily be obtained, and studies of the quantum effects in the degenerate valence band of germanium, for example, have been accomplished.[256] This topic will be taken up again in Chapter 6.

5.12. Submillimetre Aspects of Superconductivity

Many metals and alloys at a sufficiently low temperature exhibit the phenomenon of superconductivity; that is, a current can flow with no potential difference across the conductor. In terms of Ohm's law, one could say that the resistance was identically zero. The accepted theory of this effect, due to Bardeen, Cooper and Schrieffer,[257] has as its central theme the concept of the formation of electron pairs. The so-called "Cooper pairs" are coupled together by means of the exchange of virtual lattice phonons and this, together with the Pauli exclusion principle which favours electron doublets of opposite spin, enables the cohesive energy of the pair to exceed the repulsive Coulombic energy. Not unexpectedly, the full theory is quite complicated, but a simple phenomenological outline is possible. One could imagine that, below a certain temperature, the electron "gas" in the metal could condense in rather the same way as an ordinary vapour can turn into a liquid. Above this critical temperature T_c there are no Cooper pairs, whilst at absolute zero there would be no normal electrons. The electron pairs behave like bosons rather than fermions, and this feature is the origin of their remarkable properties.

The critical temperature T_c is related, as are several other characteristic temperatures, to the existence of an energy gap E_g and we may write

$$E_g = 3 \cdot 5 \, kT_c, \tag{5.103}$$

which is an essential result of the BCS theory. It follows further from the theory that, at absolute zero, a superconductor will be transparent up to a frequency

$$\nu = 3 \cdot 5 \, kT_c/h, \tag{5.104}$$

after which it will behave as a normal metal (see Section 5.13). Critical temperatures tend to be of the order 10 K, from which one expects the frequencies of the absorption edges to be of the order 20 cm^{-1}; they therefore lie in the submillimetre band. Thin films of superconducting metals have been shown[92] to transmit radiation of frequency less than that of the absorption edge, and the existence of this transparency has also been inferred from the electrical properties of superconducting microwave cavities.[92] The absorption-edge frequencies are not well defined experimentally, since the onset of heavy absorption is gradual rather than instantaneous, but, making judicious assignments. Richards and Tinkham found[92] values for v ranging between $2 \cdot 5 \, kT_c/h$ and $4 \cdot 5 \, kT_c/h$, in fair agreement with the theory. Some typical examples are tantalum with $T_c = 4 \cdot 39$ K, $\bar{v} = 10$ cm^{-1}, and lead with $T_c = 7 \cdot 15$ K, $\bar{v} = 25$ cm^{-1}.

Another basic result of the BCS theory is that the wave functions describing the various Cooper pairs have perfect phase correlation in the bulk of the superconductor. The phase is not of course a physically observable quantity and it may be given any arbitrary value at a given point, but once this is fixed the phase everywhere else is determined. This notion led Josephson[258] to consider what would happen if two pieces of superconductor, originally widely separated, were brought into electrical contact. Initially there would be zero phase correlation, and finally there would be perfect correlation; it is natural, therefore, to imagine that there is a smooth increase of correlation as the separation diminishes. A mechanism for this smooth change can be found in the fact that quantum waves can penetrate physical edges or potential barriers and, when the evanescent waves from one piece overlap those from the approaching piece, phase correlation will be induced. The sort of separation at which this correlation would be significant is a distance of the order 10 Å. At separations of this order or less, the overlap of wave functions permits an electron pair originally in one piece to appear in the other by the familiar process of "tunnelling". A supercurrent will therefore flow across the gap and, if the phase shift across the gap is ϕ, this current will be given by

$$i = i_0 \sin \phi. \tag{5.105}$$

For currents greater than i_0, there is no real solution for ϕ, and the superconductor–insulator–superconductor combination switches to normal operation as a junction diode.

When we say "normal" operation, this is not to imply that all phase coherence across the junction is lost; what happens is that there is still phase coherence but it is now time dependent and given by the equation

$$d\phi/dt = 4\pi eV/h, \tag{5.106}$$

where V is the voltage across the gap. Equations (5.105) and (5.106) are the basic relations which describe the operation of Josephson junctions.[258] The extra factor of two on the right-hand side of equation (5.106) comes from the fact that an electron *pair* has to be broken up to provide the "normal" carriers. If V is constant, equation (5.106) may be immediately integrated to give

$$\phi = (4\pi eV/h)t = 2\pi v_0 t + \phi_0, \tag{5.107}$$

which indicates that, in addition to the "normal" current, there is an oscillatory supercurrent of frequency ν_0 flowing across the gap. The junction will therefore radiate electromagnetic waves of this frequency. In numerical terms a voltage of 1 mV corresponds to a frequency of $483 \cdot 6$ GHz, that is $16 \cdot 12$ cm^{-1}.

If a junction with a current i_B and a corresponding voltage V_B is exposed to radiation of frequency ν and effective electric field strength V, we then have

$$\phi = 2\pi\nu_B t + (2eV/h\nu) \sin 2\pi\nu t + \phi_0, \tag{5.108}$$

which, upon substitution into equation (5.105), gives

$$i = i_0 \sin [2\pi\nu_B t + (2eV/h\nu) \sin 2\pi\nu t + \phi_0]. \tag{5.109}$$

This is the familiar equation for frequency modulation and one can say that the radiation field frequency modulates the Josephson currents. Equation (5.109) is quite analogous to equation (4.32), and once again the amplitudes of the Fourier components are Bessel functions. The current at frequency ν_B (cf. equation 4.33 and following) is given by

$$i = i_0 J_0(2eV/h\nu) \sin [2\pi\nu_B t + \phi_0] \tag{5.110}$$

and, since $J_0(x)$ falls as x increases from zero, it follows that the current flowing will diminish as the radiation intensity rises. This is the basis of the use of Josephson junctions as broad-band detectors, which is illustrated in Fig. 5.25.

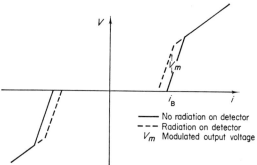

FIG. 5.25. Direct current Josephson effect in the presence and absence of a suitable far infrared radiation field (from the work of Grimes, Richards and Shapiro[259]).

It will be seen that for $\nu_B = 0$ the current falls to $i_0 J_0(2eV/h\nu) \sin \phi_0$; that is to say, the zero voltage step is reduced in amplitude as the radiation field increases. The reduction is very non-linear for large radiation intensity, but for small V we may expand $J_0(2eV/h\nu)$ in powers of its argument and find

$$J_0(2eV/h\nu) = 1 - \tfrac{1}{4}(2eV/h\nu)^2 + \ldots \tag{5.111}$$

The reduction is linearly dependent on the intensity of the radiation field, and Josephson junctions form square-law or power detectors, just as do most other detectors in common use. In operation it is not usual to monitor the zero-voltage step, but rather the practice is to drive the junction from a constant current source when, as will be seen from Fig. 5.25, the voltage across the junction will vary with the radiation intensity. In particular, if the radiation is amplitude modulated, a voltage at the modulation frequency will appear which may be amplified and rectified in the usual fashion. It is interesting to note that the sensitivity of a Josephson broad-band detector is expected to vary inversely as the square of the frequency, whereas the emission of black-body sources (equation 1.18) varies *directly* with the square of the frequency. The response of a spectroscopic system featuring a black-body source, a "grey" spectrometer and a Josephson detector should therefore be "flat", i.e. be independent of frequency up to the frequency of the energy gap and zero thereafter.

Grimes, Richards and Shapiro[259] set up a Michelson interferometer with Josephson junctions made up from various combinations of superconducting wires as the detectors. They found, somewhat surprisingly, that the junctions responded to frequencies higher than the energy gap. Thus for In–In ($E_g = 7 \cdot 2$ cm^{-1}), although the detector had a maximum response at $5 \cdot 4$ cm^{-1}, it extended in usefulness as far as 15 cm^{-1}. The Nb–Nb combination is attractive because of the high ($E_g = 22$ cm^{-1}) energy gap and, as expected, detectivity is maintained as far out as 40 cm^{-1}. The actual response curve is, however, quite complex in shape with a minimum at E_g and the details of this are still not fully understood. The detectors are quite easy to make: one wire is cut off with a flat section and the other is sharpened to a point. They are brought into contact and the natural oxide film provides the insulating gap. As is common with junction diodes (see Chapter 2), the response depends critically on the pressure applied to hold the two elements together. In the case of Josephson diodes one has the experimental complication that one has to carefully adjust this pressure and then immerse the junction in liquid helium without any change occurring in the adjustment! Grimes and his colleagues successfully achieved this and reported the remarkably high detectivity of their junctions. They found noise-equivalent powers of 5×10^{-13} for 1 Hz bandwidth and further showed that the rise-time of the detector was as short as 10 nanoseconds.

The modification of the zero-voltage step, called the d.c. Josephson effect, is but a special case of a more general phenomenon, usually called the a.c. Josephson effect. Whenever the voltage across the junction is such that the corresponding Josephson frequency is a harmonic of the radiation field frequency, a current step at constant voltage will occur in the V/I

characteristic. This is because when $\nu_B = l\nu$, there will be a term of the form $\sin^2(2\pi l\nu t)$ in the series expansion of equation (5.109), and this of course produces a constant, i.e. d.c. current increment. The step will therefore occur when

$$l\,h\nu = 2eV_B, \qquad l = 1, 2, 3 \text{ etc.} \tag{5.112}$$

If the incident radiation contains more than one frequency component, there will be steps at voltages corresponding to frequencies which are any sum or difference of any of the harmonics of all the fundamental frequencies present. Clearly in the general case the V/i characteristic will have very many steps and in the limit of broad-band radiation the steps will merge into the displaced but smooth broken line curve in Fig. 5.25.

The a.c. Josephson effect has so far been used for two types of experiment: the construction of narrow-band ultrasensitive detectors and the generation of harmonics and difference beats in the submillimetre region. In the narrow-band detector arrangement, the practice is reversed and it is usual to keep V constant and to monitor the width of the current step. Richards and Stirling[260] coupled a Josephson junction to a microwave cavity when, of course, only values of ν which are also cavity-mode frequencies may satisfy equation (5.112). They found that this combination acted like a regenerative radio receiver with high sensitivity (10^{-14} noise-equivalent power) and with a very narrow range of spectral response ($<0\cdot01$ cm^{-1}). The frequency of maximum response can be altered by changing V and choosing a different resonant cavity should this be necessary. The mixing and harmonic generation experiments have been mostly carried out at the National Bureau of Standards, Boulder, Colorado, by Evenson and his colleagues. Their interest has been in using Josephson devices as links in a harmonic multiplication chain, which is to be used to make new determinations of the velocity of electromagnetic radiation. Naturally, the upper frequency limit of usefulness is of paramount importance in this connection. Steps were observed[261] from various laser and klystron sources up to a voltage of 17 mV, which corresponds to an oscillation frequency of 274 cm^{-1}. Very high harmonics can be observed[262] with Josephson junctions which makes them superior to normal frequency multipliers in frequency counting applications. Thus the group at The National Bureau of Standards have observed the 103rd harmonic of a 70 GHz signal. Difference beats between the radiation of an HCN laser (891 GHz) and the very high harmonics of a 10 GHz fundamental have been observed, and the experimentalists remark with some justification that this is unprecedented. Coherent detection of the radiation at 118 μm (2·5 THz) from a water-vapour laser has also been reported.[263] So far no explanation is forthcoming of the extraordinary power of these detectors to work well, at frequencies much above that corresponding to break up of the Cooper pairs.

A most interesting experiment has been reported by Grimes, Richards and Shapiro[259] in which the radiation from one Josephson junction is detected by another. At the moment this is merely a curio, but it may have considerable significance in the future. It is intriguing to note that this system realizes, at submillimetre frequencies, the type of direct spectroscopy discussed in Chapter 1.

5.13. Properties of Metals and Semiconductors at Submillimetre Wavelengths

The optical behaviour of metals and semiconductors is governed by the possible energy states available for the electrons in the bulk of the material. A calculation of the energy levels for even the simplest possible system would clearly be impracticable, but it is fortunately possible to develop a theory which produces results in broad agreement with experience, starting from quite simple concepts. It is usual to consider a perfect crystalline lattice as the development point of the theory, even though such a structure is obviously not essential for a material to be metallic (q.v. mercury) and amorphous semiconductors, such as selenium glasses, are in widespread use and are attracting a great deal of theoretical attention.

Taking lithium as our example, we can imagine the crystal to be formed by bringing isolated atoms together from virtually infinite separation to the effective interatomic spacing in the crystal. At large distances each atom will have the sharp energy levels (1s, 2s, 2p etc.) appropriate to an isolated atom but, as they approach one another, the electronic interaction will lead to the spreading out of the energy levels into a band. This is shown schematically in Fig. 5.26.

The Pauli exclusion principle permits two electrons (of opposite spin) to occupy each energy level, and it follows therefore that the 2s band for lithium will be half filled with electrons. An energy level will always be available to accommodate an electron which has been accelerated even by an

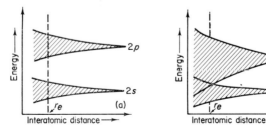

FIG. 5.26. Energy band structure for (a) lithium and (b) beryllium. The lower lying 1s band is ignored since it is relatively insensitive to interatomic separation.

arbitrarily small amount and consequently the electrons can move under the influence of an external field; in other words, metals conduct electricity. It might be thought that, by the same argument, materials such as beryllium would be non-conductors since the $2s$ band is exactly filled, but here the $2p$ band overlaps the $2s$ band at the equilibrium inter-nuclear separation and once more an electron is permitted to receive an arbitrarily small increment of energy.

The spreading out of electronic energy levels into bands is quite analogous to the spreading out of the vibration frequencies of molecular oscillators into branches when the oscillators are strongly coupled to each other, as in a crystal. Once more the solutions of the wave equation must demonstrate the periodicity of the lattice. The treatment of electrons moving in a periodic field of force was developed principally by Bloch and the wave functions are often referred to as Bloch waves. Each wave is characterized by a value of the wave vector $\bar{k}$ and once more we may plot dispersion diagrams relating the energy and the momentum of the electrons. The simplest model is that of free electrons for which

$$E = \tfrac{1}{2}mv^2 = p^2/2m = (h^2/8\pi^2 m) \, | \, \bar{k} \, |^{\,2}, \qquad (5.113)$$

where E is the energy, m the mass and p the momentum of the electron The dispersion diagram is therefore a parabola. When we now introduce the periodic field of force due to the nuclei and the corresponding wave vector $\bar{k}$ (restricted of course to the first Brillouin zone), the effect is to fold the parabola back on itself into sections and to separate the intersections of parabola portions at $\bar{k} = 0$ and $\bar{k} = \pi/a$. This is illustrated in Fig. 5.27.

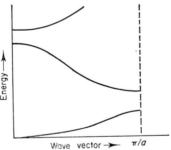

FIG. 5.27. Dispersion diagram for free electrons in a metal.

We have thus reproduced the energy band spectrum with the forbidden gap shown in Fig. 5.26(a). The electrons are distributed between the possible energy levels according to the Fermi–Dirac distribution function

$$f = [1 + e^{(E-F)/T}]^{-1}, \qquad (5.114)$$

where F, the energy of the so-called Fermi level, can be thought of as an energy parameter which normalizes the distribution under the condition that each level can be occupied by two and only two electrons. At absolute zero f is unity for all E less than F and zero for all E greater than F.

The qualitative features of the optical behaviour of metals follow quite simply from this. At radio and infrared frequencies, where the photon energy is less than the width of the partly filled conduction band, the absorption coefficient will be large and the reflection close to 100 per cent. At some higher frequency, typically in the ultraviolet, the photon energy will correspond to promotion of an electron into the forbidden gap; the process will not be allowed and the metal will become more or less transparent. A familiar illustration is the transmission of visible light through extremely thin gold sheets. Rather surprisingly, a quantitative treatment of the optical behaviour of metals can be developed within the framework of simple classical dielectric theory. The electrons in the metal form a plasma and their equation of motion may be written[264]

$$m(d^2x/dt^2)+mv_e(dx/dt) = eE_0 \exp (2\pi i v t). \qquad (5.115)$$

The solution of this equation for x, followed by the evaluation of $\hat{\epsilon}$, leads to equation (5.94) for the complex dielectric constant of a plasma. From this equation it follows that ϵ' is negative below a critical frequency v_{cr} given by

$$v_{cr}^2 = v_p^2 - v_e^2. \qquad (5.116)$$

In the absence of an absorptive term, a negative ϵ' would imply 100 per cent reflection but, even in its presence, the reflectivity will approach this value for $v \ll v_{cr}$. If it is assumed that all the electrons in the metal are free, N_e will be typically 10^{22} and v_p will lie in the near ultraviolet; assuming v_e to lie at most in the mid-infrared, it will be seen that v_{cr} is an optical frequency. It follows by substitution in equation (5.95) that in the submillimetre region all normal (i.e. not superconducting) metals will be virtually perfectly reflecting and totally opaque for the thinnest available films.

Semiconductors are very similar to metals from a theoretical point of view. The principal difference is that the lower bands are all full and there is no overlapping of the top filled band by an empty band. As a result, a semiconductor at absolute zero cannot conduct electricity for there are no levels available to accommodate an electron which has received a small increase in energy. Similarly, if a photon of energy less than the band gap (i.e. the energy difference between the top of the last full band and the bottom of the nearest empty band) is incident on the semiconductor, it must either be reflected or transmitted since it cannot be absorbed. As a consequence, semiconductors such as silicon are transparent in the infrared up to a frequency corresponding to a transition across the band gap; at higher frequencies they behave much like metals as is evident from the metallic sheen of a piece of polished silicon observed by eye. The Fermi level for a semiconductor lies usually halfway between the valence band (i.e. the top filled band) and the conduction band (i.e. the next empty band), so that at temperatures above absolute zero there will always be some electrons promoted thermally into the conduction band. This is the explanation for the phenomenon of semiconductivity, i.e. low conductivity which rapidly rises with increase of temperature. The current is carried both by the electrons in the conduction band and by the "holes" in the valence band. A "hole" is the absence of an electron and behaves as a positive particle. The dispersion diagram will again feature branches which are roughly sections of parabolae and which, near the centre of the Brillouin zone, take the form

$$E(\bar{k}) = E(0) \pm (h^2/8\pi^2 m^*) \mid \bar{k} \mid^2. \qquad (5.117)$$

The positive sign applies to the conduction band (i.e. for electrons) and the negative sign to the valence band (i.e. for holes). The quantity m^* is the "effective mass" of the particle, and the fact that this quantity is often very different from the electron mass reflects the approximations used in building up the theory. An idealized dispersion diagram for a semiconductor is shown in Fig. 5.28. The magnitude of the energy gap is crucial to the classification of a solid; if it is zero the solid is a metal, if of the order 1 eV ($8 \cdot 60 \times 10^3$ cm^{-1}) or less the solid is a semiconductor, and if much greater than 1 eV it is an insulator.

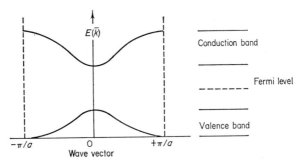

FIG. 5.28. Schematic representation of the dispersion diagram for a simple, elemental, pure semiconductor.

If a semiconductor is irradiated by radiation whose photon energy is greater than the band gap, electrons will be promoted to the conduction band leaving holes in the valence band. The net effect will be that the conductivity of the material will increase at a rate proportional to the radiation intensity, and because of this semiconductors can be used as photo-conductive detectors. As examples, silicon, for which the energy gap is $1 \cdot 12$ eV

$(9 \cdot 04 \times 10^3 \text{ cm}^{-1})$, can be used as a photoconductor in the very near infrared; germanium ($E_g = 0 \cdot 7$ eV, $5 \cdot 65 \times 10^3 \text{ cm}^{-1}$) can be used to somewhat longer wavelengths and indium antimonide ($E_g = 0 \cdot 18$ eV, $1 \cdot 45 \times 10^3 \text{ cm}^{-1}$) can be used as far as 70 μm. Very recently semiconductors and semimetals have been developed with still smaller energy gaps and they offer good prospects as photoconductive detectors at even longer wavelengths.[265]

So far the discussion has been limited to the physics of pure semi-conductors—the so-called intrinsic processes. Many properties of semi-conductors are, however, strongly influenced by the presence of impurities; these are called extrinsic properties. Even the purest materials available contain up to 10^{13} impurity atoms per cm^3 and this sometimes complicates the interpretation of the properties of the material. As an example, lead sulphide has an energy gap of $1 \cdot 04$ eV, yet it performs well as a photo-conductor out as far as 4 μm. There is still debate as to the origin of this peculiarity but certainly the presence of impurity atoms (principally oxygen) has a great deal to do with it. Of course, many semiconductors are deliberately doped with impurities to improve their properties or to make the p- and n-type material necessary for the construction of electronic devices such as transistors. From the viewpoint of their submillimetre properties, the presence of impurities, either inadvertent or deliberate, is crucial. At low concentration, impurities contribute sharp levels lying in between the valence band and the conduction band. Transitions from the valence band to low-lying acceptor levels can give absorption features for a material which should otherwise be transparent over the whole far infrared. Similar absorption bands may appear due to transitions from donor levels into the conduction band. Increased absorption due to these processes tends to limit the usefulness of semiconductors as submillimetre materials and experi-mentalists are always trying to get purer and still purer material. However, the self-same effects have been turned to advantage in the construction of extremely sensitive submillimetre detectors. The impurity levels in germanium doped with antimony, boron or gallium are only of the order of 100 cm^{-1} away from the band edges so that, if a suitable piece is cooled to liquid helium temperature, it will display extrinsic photoconductivity right out into the far infrared. Experimental results have indicated good sensitivity down to 80 cm^{-1}. Unfortunately there is a lower limit to the frequency range accessible with this type of detector because of the phenomenon of overlap. To illustrate this, imagine that we have a semiconductor of lattice constant 3 Å and dielectric constant 10, and that it contains 2 per cent of impurities. The mean distance between impurity atoms will be 10^{-7} cm and the radius of a Bohr orbit will be about the same since it has the value $\epsilon' a_0$. As a result, strong overlap will occur and the sharp impurity levels will smear out into an impurity band which may overlap either the valence or the conduction band. If this occurs, once more an electron may receive an arbitrarily small acceleration and the material will display a metallic type of conductivity. The conduction electrons or holes are usually referred to as free carriers and there will be strong absorption below the plasma frequency of these electrons. The dielectric constant of the material is mostly determined by other factors, such as the strong absorption above the band gap, so it is a fair approximation to set the refractive index n constant. With this assumption equation (5.95) may be simplified to read

$$\alpha = 2\pi v_p^2 v_e / [cn(v^2 + v_e^2)]. \tag{5.118}$$

It will be seen that this satisfies equation (42) of Appendix 3 in the d.c. limit.

Free carrier absorption is observed in many semiconductors but is particularly significant for germanium ($v_{cr} = 1$ cm^{-1}) and n-type indium antimonide ($v_{cr} = 10$ cm^{-1}). In the latter case, the extension of absorption into the submillimetre band is due to the very low effective mass ($m^* = 0 \cdot 014$ m). The Bohr orbits therefore have large radii (10^{-5} cm) and overlap of the conduction band occurs even for impurity concentrations of the order 10^{-13} atoms per cm^3. Now, although extrinsic photoconductivity is not feasible under these circumstances, Putley has shown[23, 266] that a detector can nevertheless be made which depends on free carrier absorption. Kinch and Rollin[267] have also described a detector of this type. The detectors have to work at liquid helium temperature to reduce thermal excitation to a minimum and, at this temperature, the coupling of the electrons to the host lattice becomes very weak. The electron mobility can therefore increase rapidly when energy is absorbed due to heating up of the electron gas. The increased mobility is manifest as an increased current and the radiation may therefore be detected. Because of the mode of operation this type of detector is sometimes called a "hot electron" photoconductive detector. The version produced by Kinch and Rollin[267] is very sensitive (noise equivalent power $= 3 \times 10^{-13}$ W for 1 Hz bandwidth), but the spectral range is limited by the width of the free carrier absorption which, as stated above, does not extend significantly above 10 cm^{-1} for InSb. The Putley version usually features a magnet wound round the absorbing crystal and, for economy of operation, this magnet is made of superconducting wire.† In the presence of a magnetic field, the continua of levels in the valence and conduction bands break up into a set of sharp levels, the Landau levels, with forbidden gaps between. In fact, the allowed levels are given by

$$E_i = hv_c(n_i + \tfrac{1}{2}), \tag{5.119}$$

† The sensitivity can be improved at the expense of the response time by using a super-conducting step-up transformer immediately after the crystal.

which is the usual result for a parabolic potential energy function. The effect of the magnetic field is to separate the donor levels from the allowed levels of the conduction band and thus to make photoconductivity of the usual extrinsic type possible once more. The stronger the magnetic field is, up to values of 10 kG the broader is the frequency response and the more sensitive at peak is the detector. The peak response tends to occur at 1 mm (10 m^{-1}) but there is still usable responsivity as far out as 50 cm^{-1}. The overall sensitivity (noise-equivalent power = 10^{-12} W in 1 Hz bandwidth) is less than that of the Kinch–Rollin version, but the extra bandwidth makes the Putley detector the favoured form for low frequency spectroscopy. It is important to realize that two processes are taking place in the Putley detector—hot electron photoconductivity and cyclotron resonance induced photoconductivity. At magnetic fields in excess of 10 kG, the cyclotron resonance part tends to dominate and the bandwidth is reduced. The peak response now occurs near ν_c. The responsivity is still lower (5×10^{-11} noise-equivalent power) but the tunability is a very attractive feature for certain experiments involving the diagnosis of rapidly changing plasmas.[268] All InSb detectors have relatively rapid response times ($\approx 1 \mu$s) and this, coupled with their high sensitivities, makes them essential for much submillimetre work, despite the inconvenience of liquid helium technology.

Gallium arsenide far infrared detectors have recently been described by Stillman, Wolfe, Melngailis, Parker, Tannenwald and Dimmock (*Appl. Phys. Lett.* **13**, 83, 1968). The detector element was an epitaxial layer 40 μm thick of n-type GaAs which was grown on a chromium-doped GaAs substrate. The detector operated at 4·2 K and was used to observe the radiation from a DCN (195 μm) and an HCN (337 μm) laser and also from a 902 μm carcinotron. The noise equivalent power values were $1 \cdot 2 \times 10^{-11}$ W at 195 μm, $1 \cdot 4 \times 10^{-12}$ W at 337 μm and 6×10^{-11} W at 902 μm. It is concluded that extrinsic photoconductivity due to shallow impurity (concentration $6 \cdot 8 \times 10^{14}$ cm^{-3}) levels is responsible for the detectivity at 337 μm and below, whilst the onset of "hot" electron photoconductivity is responsible for that at 902 μm. The detecting element has a high innate resistance, so there is no need for the "step-up" transformer or preamplifier which is necessary for InSb detectors. The response time of GaAs detectors was found to be less than 1 μs using a germanium avalanche modulator to chop the incident radiation.

Photoconductive detectors all have relatively short response times because the speed of response of the detector is set in practice by the capacities of the leads to the detecting element and, since with good construction these can be made very small, the response times can readily be made less than 1 μs. However, if the ultimate in detectivity is required, longer response times are unavoidable and bulk material bolometers must be used. The most sensitive detector for the far infrared yet made has been described by

Drew and Sievers (*Appl. Optics*, **8**, 2067, 1969) who used a heavily doped germanium crystal cooled to $0 \cdot 37$ K by liquid ^{3}He. The germanium was *p*-type material doped with indium (6×10^{16} cm^{-3}) and antimony ($2 \cdot 4 \times 10^{16}$ cm^{-3}), and the noise-equivalent power found was 3×10^{-14} W for a one second integrating time. The response time was of the order 10^{-2} s. Drew and Sievers claim that their detector comes within a factor of four of being photon-noise limited and of realizing therefore in the far infrared the detectivity of photo multipliers in the visible region!

The absorption spectrum of a semiconductor will usually feature a plasma absorption at low frequencies and absorption by transverse optical lattice modes at somewhat higher frequencies. Additionally, there will be absorption bands due to cyclotron resonance if the specimen is in a magnetic field, and there may be features due to localized phonons at impurity lattice sites or else to the breakdown of the $\bar{k} = 0$ selection rule because of an-harmonicity etc. Quite clearly the spectrum can be complex, but it is important to know it over a wide frequency range because from it the three important parameters, N_e, m^* and ν_e, may be deduced. These can be derived by other means, principally from Hall-effect measurements, but the non-contact aspect of the spectroscopic method makes it more attractive. If the material is reasonably transparent, the absorption spectrum may be observed directly and Stolen,[269] for example, has shown that the submillimetre absorption in high-resistivity gallium arsenide is dominated by a band due to the excitation of the transverse optic mode at $268 \cdot 2$ cm^{-1}, and that there are some much weaker bands arising from two-phonon processes in the 60–180 cm^{-1} region. Impurity induced absorption in germanium is illustrated in Fig. 4.27.

When the crystal is strongly absorbing, it will be difficult to observe the transmission spectrum and recourse must be had to reflection measurements. Birch[270] at NPL has devised a special module (shown in Fig. 5.29) which, together with a Michelson interferometer, permits normal incidence reflection spectra of quite small specimens to be observed. The reflectivity of an absorbing dielectric plate at normal incidence is given by

$$R = \hat{r}\hat{r}^* = [(n-1)^2 + n^2\kappa^2]/[(n+1)^2 + n^2\kappa^2]. \qquad (5.120)$$

This is a somewhat cumbersome equation to work with, but fortunately κ is nearly always very much smaller than n and, to reasonable accuracy, one may set $\kappa = 0$ in equation (5.120) and arrive at equation (3.47). Writing down the real and imaginary parts of equation (5.94) for the case of a semiconductor where there is a lattice dielectric constant ϵ_L one has

$$\epsilon' = \epsilon_L[1 - \nu_p^2/(\nu^2 + \nu_e^2)], \qquad \epsilon'' = \epsilon_L \nu_p^2 \nu_e/[\nu(\nu^2 + \nu_e^2)], \qquad (5.121)$$

where ν_p, the plasma frequency, is given by

$$\nu_p^2 = (N_e e^2/\pi m^* \epsilon_L). \qquad (5.122)$$

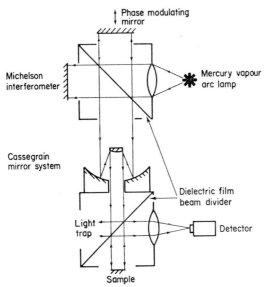

FIG. 5.29. Apparatus used by J. R. Birch at NPL to observe submillimetre reflection spectra at normal incidence.

In the region of the plasma edge, ν will be greater than ν_e and in the spectrum a minimum of reflectivity would be expected when

$$\nu = \nu_p(1 - 1/\epsilon_L)^{-1/2}. \tag{5.123}$$

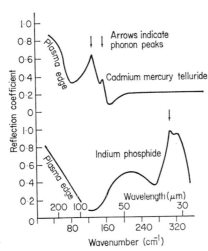

FIG. 5.30. Reflection spectra of CdHgTe and InP in the far infrared (J. R. Birch and C. C. Bradley—to be published).

From the measured spectrum, the minimum of reflection can be identified and the plasma frequency calculated. Knowing m^* from cyclotron resonance experiments, N_e may be deduced. Some results obtained by Birch and his colleagues are shown in Fig. 5.30. In less approximate work, in which the absorption by the specimen is also included, there is no simple equivalent of equation (5.123) and the best procedure is to use a computer to find the set of N_e, m^* and v_e which gives the best fit to the data. Even using the approximate method, care must be taken that the displacement of the reflection minimum frequency due to the reststrahlen dispersion is corrected for.

SUMMARY

The account of the application of submillimetre spectroscopy to physical problems, which has been developed in this chapter, has necessarily been brief and eclectic. Nevertheless, from it some idea should emerge of the wealth of information to be gleaned in this once virtually unknown region. Now that reliable and easily operated submillimetre equipment is readily available, one can look forward to further discoveries being made in what is effectively only the second decade of spectroscopy in the submillimetre region.

CHAPTER 6

Submillimetre Masers and Lasers and Submillimetre Aspects of Non-linear Phenomena

6.1. Theory of Lasers

The word Maser is an acronym derived from the initial letters of the phrase "Microwave Amplification by the Stimulated Emission of Radiation". The devices which produce stimulated emission at optical frequencies are now called Lasers (where the initial letter stands for Light) although they were originally called optical masers. There is still some confusion of terms, but in this book the convention will be adopted that anything which looks like a laser and which acts like a laser will be called a laser, regardless of the wavelength of its output.

The phenomenon of stimulated emission was shown to exist by Einstein in his celebrated synthesis of classical thermodynamics and quantum radiation physics. To follow his argument in outline, imagine that a very large number of molecules are confined in an isolated cavity at a temperature T and that they can exist in two states—a ground state and an excited state separated by an energy E. Molecules will be rapidly changing from one state to the other by the emission and absorption of radiation of wavenumber $\bar{\nu} = E/hc$. In thermal equilibrium these two processes must be going at appropriate rates to produce the classical result, based on the equipartition principle that

$$N_E = N_0 \exp\left(-E/kT\right) \qquad (6.1)$$

where N_E is the equilibrium population of the excited state and N_0 that of the ground state. The loss of molecules from the ground state by absorption of radiation will take place at a rate

$$-\mathrm{d}N_0/\mathrm{d}t = N_0 U(\bar{\nu}) \, \mathrm{d}\bar{\nu} \, B_{OE} \qquad (6.2)$$

where $U(\bar{\nu})\mathrm{d}\bar{\nu}$ is the density of radiation in the cavity, having frequencies between $\bar{\nu}$ and $\bar{\nu}+\mathrm{d}\bar{\nu}$, and B_{OE} is the Einstein coefficient for stimulated absorption. Einstein showed that the loss of molecules from the excited state must occur by *two* processes: firstly spontaneous emission which can be regarded as arising from the random (zero-point) fluctuations of the vacuum field, and secondly stimulated emission due to the thermal radiation field. It follows therefore that

$$-\mathrm{d}N_E/\mathrm{d}t = N_E[A_{EO} + U(\bar{\nu})\,\mathrm{d}\bar{\nu}\,B_{EO}] \qquad (6.3)$$

where A_{EO} is the Einstein coefficient for spontaneous emission and B_{EO} that for stimulated emission. The radiation density in the cavity can be derived from equation (1.16) by noting that if a small hole were cut through the walls of the cavity the power radiated through the hole would be $\frac{1}{4}c\,U(\bar{\nu})\,\mathrm{d}\bar{\nu}$ which must equal $F(\bar{\nu}T)\,\mathrm{d}\bar{\nu}$; therefore

$$U(\bar{\nu})\,\mathrm{d}\bar{\nu} = 8\pi h c\bar{\nu}^3\,\mathrm{d}\bar{\nu}\,[\exp(hc\bar{\nu}/kT) - 1]^{-1}. \qquad (6.4)$$

At equilibrium, $\mathrm{d}N_0/\mathrm{d}t$ must equal $\mathrm{d}N_E/\mathrm{d}t$ and if equation (6.1) is to be satisfied it follows that

$$B_{OE} = B_{EO} = B \quad \text{and} \quad A_{EO} = 8\pi h c\bar{\nu}^3 B. \qquad (6.5)$$

The dependence of the ratio of the spontaneous to the stimulated coefficients on the cube of the frequency is most important for this implies that as one goes to lower and lower frequency, spontaneous emission becomes less and less probable. It therefore becomes progressively easier to make stimulated emission devices because the competing spontaneous process rapidly becomes negligible. By the converse argument, severe experimental difficulties are expected in the development of lasers for the far ultraviolet[†] and, so far, there are no X-ray lasers at all.

A molecular system in thermal equilibrium is characterized as outlined above by the distribution of the molecules amongst the available energy levels according to the Boltzmann distribution function,

$$N_i = N_0 \exp(-E_i/kT). \qquad (6.6)$$

Non-Boltzmann distributions can be brought about in several ways. One might, for example, apply a sudden disturbance to the system, but the effect will be transitory and after the disturbance is over the system will relax back to the equilibrium distribution at a rate determined by the magnitudes of the various A and B coefficients. If these are large the relaxation is rapid but if they are small it can be quite slow. A famous example occurs with helium gas. The ground state of the helium atom has both electrons in the $1s$ orbital with opposed spins. The first excited state of the atom has one electron in the $1s$ orbital and one electron in the $2s$ orbital with the electron spins parallel. Radiative transitions between these two states are absolutely forbidden and the Einstein coefficients are zero. If an electric current is passed through helium gas, atoms will be formed in the $1s\,2s\,(^3S)$ state and, after the current is

† One successful example is the development[271] of the molecular hydrogen laser $[B\,^1\Sigma^+ \to X\,^1\Sigma_g^+]$ at 1600 Å.

switched off, a very non-Boltzmann distribution will exist for some seconds since the excited atoms can only relax down to the ground state by collision with the walls of the containing vessel. Such a distribution has come to be known as a population inversion and is an essential prerequisite for laser action.

The Einstein coefficients can be related quite easily to more familiar concepts such as integrated band strengths. To do this we must consider a parallel beam of monochromatic radiation travelling through the two-level molecular system discussed above. The rate of loss of intensity from the beam can be written

$$dI(\bar{\nu})/dx = -h\bar{\nu}B(N_0 - N_E) I(\bar{\nu}) \tag{6.7}$$

where N_0 and N_E are the numbers of molecules per cubic centimetre in the two levels. Assuming that the absorption line is sharp, and recalling Lambert's law,

$$dI(\bar{\nu})/dx = \alpha(\bar{\nu}) I(\bar{\nu}), \tag{6.8}$$

we may write

$$\int_{\text{band}} \alpha(\bar{\nu}) \, d\bar{\nu} = h\bar{\nu}_0 B(N_0 - N_E) \tag{6.9}$$

where $\bar{\nu}_0$ is the centre frequency of the absorption band. In this derivation we have ignored the gain in intensity of the beam due to spontaneous emission since this, being incoherent and non-collimated, will contribute only negligibly. The important thing to notice is that the stimulated emission *is* coherent with the travelling wave and that the loss of energy is less than would be expected if only the absorption from the ground state were being considered. If N_E could somehow be made larger than N_0, then from equation (6.7) the wave, instead of being attenuated, would be amplified and therefore grow in amplitude as it passed further into the medium. This is the mechanism by which masers and lasers operate. The rate of amplification depends on B and therefore on the integrated intensity of the corresponding absorption band. It is for this reason that, although several systems exist in which population inversion is readily achieved, these do not provide bases for laser action; the ease of inversion comes about because of the zero value of B for the transition between the two states in question.

We must, therefore, consider how a population inversion can be brought about between two levels which are connected by a finite transition probability. The first method which might suggest itself is to apply an intense and exceedingly short flash of radiation to the system. If the spectral range of the flash includes the absorption frequency of the transition we might hope to get a population inversion, momentarily at any rate. A two-level laser of this type would, however, be very inefficient, for if the absorption line is (in reverse) to act as the basis of a laser it must of necessity be very sharp and only a minute fraction of the incident power could be absorbed. A second point is that, if a population inversion relative to the ground state is to be brought about, over 50 per cent of the atoms have to be taken up to the upper state during the flash, and this, as will be shown later (Section 6.7), is impossible due to the phenomenon of saturation. For these reasons, flash-pumped lasers are based either on three-level systems (q.v. ruby) or else on four-level systems (q.v. uranium in calcium fluoride). The ruby laser operates (see Fig. 5.24) by absorbing energy from the flash in a broad band ($^4A_2 \rightarrow {}^4F_2$) and funnelling a good fraction of this energy down to a sharp lower level (^2E) from which stimulated emission to the ground state occurs. The uranium laser operates similarly but with the variation that the lower state of the stimulated transition is *not* the ground state and is thus normally virtually unpopulated.

A second method of bringing about a population inversion, illustrated by the helium–neon laser, is to invoke selective energy transfer by collision. In a gaseous discharge through helium, as remarked earlier, a high concentration of the 2^3S metastable helium atoms will form. When these collide with neon atoms in their ground state a very efficient transfer of the 160 000 cm^{-1} of energy occurs, giving neon atoms in $2s$ levels. However, unlike helium, neon has lower levels ($2p$) to which radiative transitions are possible and these will not be significantly populated by collision. As a consequence a considerable $2s - 2p$ population inversion will exist and laser action will be possible leading to a series of lines between 1·0 and 1·5 μm. Collisions of ground-state neon atoms with 2^1S excited helium atoms give selective population of the neon $3s$ levels leading to laser action at 0·6328 μm ($3s_2 \rightarrow 2p_4$) and at 3·39 μm ($3s_2 \rightarrow 3p_4$). Higher analogues may also appear if the excitation conditions are correct and their use for providing submillimetre lasers will be discussed later in the chapter. At microwave and millimetre wavelengths, where spontaneous emission can be neglected, a third method is available in that it is possible to physically separate upper state from lower state molecules and thus, by allowing only the former to enter the resonant cavity, produce a high degree of population inversion in the active medium. The separation is brought about, using the Stark effect, by allowing the molecules to flow through an arrangement of electrodes which produce a quadrupolar field. In such a field, a molecule in a state which increases in energy in an electric field (i.e. a positive Stark effect) will be focussed into the beam, since there the field is zero. Conversely, a molecule in a state which decreases in energy in a field will be deflected out of the beam. An excellent example was found by De Lucia and Gordy[70] for HCN where the $J = 2$, $F = 1$ state is strongly focussed into the beam and the $J = 1$, $F = 1$ is strongly deflected out of it. They were able therefore, by allowing the beam to continue into a Fabry–Perot resonator, to observe stimulated emission at 117·2 GHz from the

$J = 2$, $F = 1 \rightarrow J = 1$, $F = 1$ transition. Stimulated fluorescence, in which molecules are pumped into a particular rotational level of an upper vibrational state by the action of the intense radiation from a mid-infrared laser, provides a valuable source of submillimetre laser action. The transitions involved will be pure rotational ones in the upper state or else in the lower state after a cascade. This topic is discussed later in this chapter. The principal submillimetre lasers, however, owe their operation to none of these processes but instead depend upon the phenomenon of rotational perturbation with its resultant effect of resonance transfer. This occurs whenever quantum mechanical mixing permits a molecule in a given stationary state to behave as though it had the character of a nearby stationary state. This subject will now be developed in some detail.

The energy levels of a polyatomic molecule in its ground electronic state may be described by a set of quantum numbers which specify the degree of vibrational excitation and another set which specify the rotational motion. To a very good approximation, the actual energy of a given level may be regarded as the sum of the vibrational and the rotational energy. To be exact, there is some interaction between rotation and vibration which manifests itself as a slight dependence of the rotational constants (see Chapter 5) on the vibrational quantum numbers, but if the rotational energy is calculated, using the constants appropriate to the vibrational level under consideration, splendid agreement with observation is usually obtained. Sometimes, however, levels are observed which are not at the expected position; when this occurs a perturbation is said to exist. Perturbations can be of several kinds: a quite common phenomenon is to observe two bands when only one would be expected. This is called Fermi resonance and arises whenever two vibrational levels (not both fundamentals) have the same symmetry and closely similar energies. The quantum mechanical treatment of molecular vibration is commonly developed in what is known as the harmonic oscillator approximation; that is we regard the molecular potential energy as depending only on quadratic terms in the atomic displacement coordinates (equation 5.84). Within this approximation the problem is said to be separable and we can regard the molecule as made up of $3N-6$ independent oscillators where N is the number of atoms in the molecule. Taking carbon dioxide as an example we can label any given vibrational level as $(n_1 n_2^l n_3)$ where the three modes are the symmetric stretch, the bending motion and the asymmetric stretch respectively, the n's are the vibrational quantum numbers and l is a number indicating the degree of vibrational angular momentum induced by the simultaneous excitation of both components of the degenerate ν_2 mode. Now the levels $(10^\circ 0)$ and $(02^\circ 0)$ both have symmetry A_{1g} and agree almost exactly in frequency ($1337 \, \text{cm}^{-1}$). To the harmonic oscillator approximation this coincidence has no significance and the two levels would retain their identity.

The Raman spectrum would therefore be expected to feature just a single intense band at 1337 cm^{-1} corresponding to the transition $(00°0) \rightarrow (10°0)$. The transition $(00°0) \rightarrow (02°0)$ would be very feeble because overtone and combination modes are always very weak in the Raman effect. When cubic, quartic, etc. terms are included in the potential energy expression (leading to the anharmonic potential of (5.87) separability no longer applies and interaction of levels is observed. The magnitude of the perturbation is inversely proportional to the unperturbed frequency separation and so the two states of CO_2 interact strongly to give the two observed levels at 1285·6 and 1388·3 cm^{-1} and the Raman spectrum shows two intense bands—not one. Each of the observed states is an intimate mixture of the two unperturbed states and the strength of the interaction can be gauged by the extent to which they repel each other—one up and one down—from the unperturbed position. It is clearly not possible to label these states in any simple fashion. Each of them can behave as either of the original unperturbed states would be expected to behave. In particular the level $(10°0)$, if it were to exist in a pure form, would be metastable because radiative transitions to the ground state are forbidden; but since both the observed levels have the character of $(02°0)$ they can both be rapidly depopulated by means of the cascade

$$(0\ 2°\ 0) \rightarrow (0\ 1^1\ 0)$$

$$(0\ 1^1\ 0) \rightarrow (0\ 0°\ 0) \tag{6.10}$$

each component of which is strongly allowed. This depopulation is involved in the operation of the CO_2 laser in which molecules undergo transitions from $(0\ 0°\ 1)$ to the two perturbed levels. The laser gives a series of rotational lines (Fig. 6.17) in two bands centred at 961 cm^{-1} and 1064 cm^{-1}. This is only an illustration in the present context since the principal mechanism for the CO_2 laser is energy transfer from nitrogen molecules in their first excited vibrational level. It does, however, bring out the point that population inversions can be brought about either by overpopulating the upper level or depopulating the lower level.

Fermi resonance is a form of quantum mechanical mixing involving entire vibrational states with a consequent shifting of all the rotational states of the two vibrational levels. Another form of perturbation called Coriolis interaction is much more specific to particular rotational levels. Coriolis interaction arises whenever the net effect of rotation plus vibration of a given type can be thought of as equivalent to exciting a vibration of another type. The selection rule for Coriolis interaction is that the direct product of the symmetry types of the two normal modes should contain the species of a rotation. The interaction can only occur between levels of the same J and its magnitude decreases with increasing energy separation of the two interacting levels.

Not surprisingly the most obvious manifestation of Coriolis effects is observed when the interaction occurs between two components of a degenerate level, for here all the perturbing levels would have identical energies in the absence of interaction. Taking CO_2 again as an example, the effect of Coriolis interaction between the two components of the degenerate bending mode $(0\ 1^1\ 0)$ is to remove the degeneracy and each J level now consists of two close levels, the separation of which increases with J. This is called l-type doubling. In the case of methane, Coriolis interaction between the triply degenerate components of the F_2 type vibrations, ν_3 and ν_4, removes the degeneracy and leads to modified rotational constants. With methane, however, we come across what has been called second-order Coriolis perturbation; that is mixing of distinct vibrational levels, a phenomenon most relevant to laser action. The ν_2 level (species E) of methane is not connected to the ground level, species A_1, by an allowed transition and ν_2 should therefore not appear in the infrared absorption spectrum of gaseous methane. However, Coriolis interaction between ν_2 and ν_4 is allowed since

$$E \times F_2 = F_1 + F_2, \qquad (6.11)$$

and F_1 contains the three rotations R_x, R_y and R_z. The rotational wave functions of ν_2 consequently become mixed with those of ν_4 and, as a result, ν_2 appears weakly in the infrared spectrum.[272] The observed spectrum indicates clearly the origin of the forbidden intensity because the intensity distribution as a function of J is highly anomalous; in particular, transitions to the $J = 0$ level do not occur. We will now go on to show how perturbations between levels can explain the operation of some important submillimetre lasers.

6.2. The HCN Laser

When an electric current is passed through a vapour at low pressure containing hydrogen, carbon and nitrogen, HCN is formed at a low concentration in various excited vibrational levels. The level $(1\ 0°\ 0)$ is connected to the ground state by a very weak transition probability[273] and is therefore essentially metastable. As a consequence levels such as $(1\ 1^1\ 0)$, which are members of a "stack" built upon $(1\ 0°\ 0)$, will have much higher populations in the discharge conditions than would be expected from straightforward application of equation (6.6). The level $(0\ 4°\ 0)$ occurs at nearly the same energy but is normally not significantly populated because it is connected to the ground state by the strongly allowed cascade

$$(0\ 4°\ 0) \rightarrow (0\ 3^1\ 0) \rightarrow (0\ 2°\ 0) \rightarrow (0\ 1^1\ 0) \rightarrow (0\ 0°\ 0).$$

The theoretical energy levels for the states $(0\ 0°\ 0)$, $(1\ 1^1\ 0)$ and $(0\ 4°\ 0)$ are

K

TABLE 6.1. Energy levels of the $(0\,0°\,0)$, $(1\,1^1\,0)$ and $(0\,4°\,0)$ states of HCN (from the data of Maki and Blaine[274])

J	$(0\,0°\,0)$	$(1\,1^1\,0)$	$(0\,4°\,0)$
0	—	2805·58	2803·07
1	2·95	2808·52	2806·05
2	8·87	2814·39	2812·02
3	17·74	2823·20	2820·97
4	29·57	2834·93	2832·90
5	44·35	2849·59	2847·86
6	62·09	2867·22	2865·72
7	82·78	2887·79	2886·60
8	106·42	2911·25	2910·47
9	133·01	2937·68	2937·29
10	162·56	2967·00	2967·12
11	195·07	2999·30	2999·91
12	230·53	3034·48	3035·22
	$B'' = 1\cdot4784\ \mathrm{cm}^{-1}$	$B' = 1\cdot468\ \mathrm{cm}^{-1}$	$B' = 1\cdot4916\ \mathrm{cm}^{-1}$
	$D'' = 3\cdot3 \times 10^{-6}\ \mathrm{cm}^{-1}$	$D' = 4\cdot4 \times 10^{-6}\ \mathrm{cm}^{-1}$	$D' = 2\cdot2 \times 10^{-5}\ \mathrm{cm}^{-1}$

given in Table 6.1. In the 2800–2900 cm^{-1} region, only one absorption band is observed[274] for HCN gas—that corresponding to the transition $(0\,0°\,0) \rightarrow (1\,1^1\,0)$. The individual lines in the P $(\Delta J = -1)$, Q $(\Delta J = 0)$ and R $(\Delta J = +1)$ branches are in nearly every case at exactly the frequency calculated from the data in Table 6.1; the ground state pure rotational lines shown in Fig. 5.3 may also be found correctly from this data. When, however, the $(0\,0°\,0) \rightarrow (1\,1^1\,0)$ band is studied closely, some small discrepancies appear. The lines $R(8)$, $R(9)$, $R(10)$, $P(10)$, $P(11)$ and $P(12)$ occur at slightly different frequencies than expected, from which it is concluded that the levels $J = 9$, 10 and 11 of the upper state are perturbed. The $R(9)$ line under high resolution breaks up into a doublet. To explain the perturbation, Maki and Blaine[274] pointed out that, whereas the $J(0)$ level of $(0\,4°\,0)$ is some $2\cdot51\ \mathrm{cm}^{-1}$ below that for $(1\,1^1\,0)$, the B value for $(0\,4°\,0)$ is greater and eventually corresponding rotational levels must cross. This crossing occurs at $J = 10$ and, since we have two levels of virtually the same energy and the same J and the symmetry properties are right, a strong Coriolis perturbation should occur. A weaker perturbation affects the $J(9)$ and $J(11)$ levels. The doubling of the $R(9)$ line comes about because the transition $(0\,0°\,0)\,J(9) \rightarrow (1\,1^1\,0)\,J(10)$ is accompanied by $(0\,0°\,0)\,J(9) \rightarrow (0\,4°\,0)\,J(10)$. All other transitions to levels in $(0\,4°\,0)$ are unmeasurably weak and this particular one is made active because the mixing of levels, caused by the perturbation, gives $(0\,4°\,0)\,J(10)$ some of the character of $(1\,1^1\,0)\,J(10)$.

In 1964, Gebbie, Stone and Findlay[275] at the National Physical Laboratory discovered that when a pulsed discharge was passed through HCN gas at a pressure of about 1 torr, stimulated emission occurred at a wavelength of 337 μm provided the discharge occurred in a glass tube terminated at each end by a mirror; i.e. in an optical cavity. This arrangement is the familiar Fabry–Perot type of resonator used for most gas lasers. It was at first thought that the emitting species was the CN radical since the visible radiation from the discharge was mostly made up of the familiar red and violet band systems of this radical. A plausible mechanism involving some well characterized perturbations in the level scheme of CN (Appendix 5) was then proposed.[75] Subsequently Maki and Lide gave[276] strong evidence that the emitter was in fact HCN and this was proved by Hocker and Javan[277] who made very accurate frequency measurements not only of the 337 μm radiation but also of several other emissions which could be obtained from the system. It is now established that the system of six laser emission lines between 284 and 373 μm is associated with the Coriolis perturbation between (1 1^1 0) and (0 4° 0) near $J = 10$. The transitions are shown schematically in Fig. 6.1.

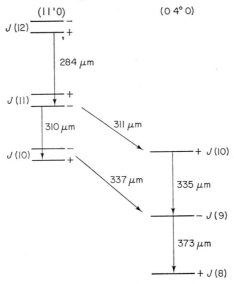

FIG. 6.1. Rotation-vibration energy levels of HCN near 2900 cm^{-1} and the origin of laser action in HCN vapour.[277] The l-type doubling for the (11^1 0) state is shown greatly exaggerated.

The levels of (1 1^1 0) are shown as doublets in this Figure because of the splitting into levels of even and odd parity by the l-type doubling. The rotational levels of (0 4° 0) have even parity for J even and odd for J odd. Intense lines must satisfy the selection rules $\Delta J = \pm 1$ and $+ \leftrightarrow -$, $- \leftrightarrow +$, but $+ \leftarrow\!\!\!|\!\!\!\rightarrow +$ and $- \leftarrow\!\!\!|\!\!\!\rightarrow -$, which are appropriate for electric dipole transitions. The two strong laser emissions at 311 and 337 μm are intersystem transitions made allowed by taking on the character of the pure rotational transitions $J(11) \rightarrow J(10)$ and $J(10) \rightarrow J(9)$ within $(1\ 1^1\ 0)$. HCN has a large dipole moment, so pure rotational transitions are intense. It is to be noted that we have no reason to suspect anything but strict Boltzmann distribution amongst the rotational levels of both vibrational states. The laser action comes about because of the perturbation and the population inversion between $(1\ 1^1\ 0)$ and $(0\ 4°\ 0)$. The transition moment for $(1\ 1^1\ 0) \leftrightarrow (0\ 4°\ 0)$ should be extremely small and a population inversion in a discharge is therefore unremarkable.† However, because of the mixing of character by the perturbation, the transition moment becomes large for two transitions only and laser action is possible. When these two transitions are being fiercely operated by the high stimulating fields in the cavity, the distribution of population amongst the rotational levels of both vibrational states can become highly non-Boltzmann. Thus, if the laser radiates at 337 μm, the $J(10)$ level of $(1\ 1^1\ 0)$ is rapidly depopulated and a population inversion between $J(11)$ and $J(10)$ can be brought about, leading to stimulated emission at 310 μm. Likewise we can expect radiation at 373 μm due to stimulated emission of the transition $J(9) \rightarrow J(8)$ within $(0\ 4°\ 0)$. Similar remarks apply to the pumping action of the 311 μm radiation.

There is no longer any doubt that all the transitions indicated in Fig. 6.1 are correctly assigned. Hocker and Javan[277] have measured the time frequencies of these transitions, using a method of heterodyne beating, of the radiation from a CW (continuous-wave) version of the laser with that from a harmonic of a klystron in a crystal diode detector. Their results are

$$
\left.
\begin{array}{lll}
311\ \mu\text{m} & \nu = 964 \cdot 3134\ \text{GHz} \\
335\ \mu\text{m} & \nu = 894 \cdot 4142\ \text{GHz} \\
310\ \mu\text{m} & \nu = 967 \cdot 9658\ \text{GHz} \\
337\ \mu\text{m} & \nu = 890 \cdot 7607\ \text{GHz}
\end{array}
\right\} \text{estimated error } \pm 0 \cdot 001\ \text{GHz}
$$

From these figures $\Delta\nu$ values between $J(11)$ of $(1\ 1^1\ 0)$ and $J(9)$ of $(0\ 4°\ 0)$ obtained by the two paths are $1858 \cdot 7276 \pm 0 \cdot 001$ GHz and $1858 \cdot 7265 \pm 0 \cdot 001$ GHz: a most elegant demonstration of the Ritz combination principle. There is likewise little doubt that the population inversion mechanism is substantially correct. However, one difficulty not so far fully explained is that HCN is not stable to electron impact and the concentration of HCN in the discharge will be extremely low (estimated partial pressure 1 μm). Infrared studies on the discharge, confined in a multi-reflection long-path cell, have failed to

† Collisions between molecules will tend to restore thermal equilibrium and this process will be extremely efficient for the $(1\ 1^1\ 0)$, $(0\ 4°\ 0)$ case since the two states have virtually identical energies. The lifetime of the inversion will therefore be a very sensitive function of pressure and gas composition. Pollack has shown, however, that emission is still possible with little or no vibrational population inversion.[278]

reveal its presence, and only by means of microwave spectroscopy (where the peak absorption is independent of concentration) in the region of the $J = 0 \rightarrow J = 1$ transition at $88 \cdot 63$ GHz has it been possible to show that it is there at all.[279] The low concentration of HCN, dispersed in a mixture of starting materials and reaction products, implies that collisions between HCN molecules will be relatively rare, which is fortunate for the operation of the laser since, as mentioned earlier, such collisions would involve a nearly resonant, and therefore highly probable, transfer of energy, leading to a rapid restoration of thermal equilibrium. Collisions with foreign molecules will also bring this about eventually, but at a much slower rate. Nevertheless we are faced with the difficulty that a very small number of molecules, presumably distributed amongst a large number of possible energy levels, is radiating a great deal of power. The laser must therefore be remarkably efficient and somehow or other a very large fraction of the HCN molecules must go through the $(1\ 1^1\ 0)$ level and emit. The fact that just about any starting mixture containing H, C and N will do for satisfactory operation, combined with the observation that there is always a delay ($\approx 5\ \mu s$) between the onset of the current pulse and the beginning of stimulated emission, leads to the suspicion that the CN radical is involved in the mechanism even if it is not the emitter itself. It is possible that some selective chemical reaction of the type

$$R - H + CN \rightarrow R' + HCN \qquad (6.12)$$

tends to favour cascade routes to the ground state via $(1\ 1^1\ 0)$. If this is so then a large fraction of the molecules formed in the discharge will pass through the emitting states. This is very much a conjecture, and some of the evidence is suspect since purely physical theories of the time-dependent refractive index of the plasma could explain the time-delay characteristics.[280]

Very shortly after the discovery of stimulated emission at 337 μm, it was shown in many laboratories that the system would in fact oscillate at a large number of wavelengths. Some of these are indicated as the primary and cascade processes in Fig. 6.1, but others are observed which do not belong to this system.[281] A set of emission lines near 130 μm has been attributed[282] to transitions from $J(27)$ and $J(26)$ of $(1\ 2^2\ 0)$ to $J(26)$ and $J(25)$ of $(0\ 5^1\ 0)$ and from $J(26)$ and $J(25)$ of $(1\ 2^\circ\ 0)$ to $J(25)$ and $J(24)$ of $(0\ 5^1\ 0)$. The observed wavenumbers are $79 \cdot 262$, $77 \cdot 743$, $76 \cdot 430$ and $74 \cdot 111$ cm^{-1}. The resonance responsible for the laser action is of the same type as that for the lower frequency emissions but, because of the slight differences in anharmonicity, the crossing of levels occurs further up at $J = 26$. Another group of emission lines between 200 and 223 μm may[283] arise from a still higher resonance— possibly that between $(1\ 3^1\ 0)$ and $(0\ 6^2\ 0)$; the transitions involved would be $J(17)\ (1\ 3^1\ 0) \rightarrow J(16)\ (1\ 3^1\ 0) = 49 \cdot 7$ cm^{-1}, $J(16)\ (1\ 3^1\ 0) \rightarrow J(15)\ (0\ 6^2\ 0) = 47 \cdot 4$ cm^{-1} and $J(15)\ (1\ 3^1\ 0) \rightarrow J(14)\ (0\ 6^2\ 0) = 45$ cm^{-1}.

The delicate balance of vibrational parameters which ensures so many resonances for ^{1}H^{12}C^{14}N will be destroyed by isotopic substitution. It was the failure to observe emission at 337 μm† from ^{1}H^{12}C^{15}N which indicated that resonance between vibrationally excited states was important in the laser mechanism. With D^{12}C^{14}N, for example, very few near coincidences occur; the only one significant for laser action is that between (2 2° 0) and (0 9^1 0). These states cross near $J(21)$ and the resulting perturbation leads to four emission lines:[282]

$$(2\,2°\,0)\,J(23) \rightarrow (2\,2°\,0)\,J(22) = 55\cdot009 \text{ cm}^{-1} \text{ (182 } \mu\text{m)}$$

$$(2\,2°\,0)\,J(22) \rightarrow (0\,9^1_-\,0)\,J(21) = 52\cdot6457 \text{ cm}^{-1} \text{ (190 } \mu\text{m)}$$

$$(2\,2°\,0)\,J(21) \rightarrow (0\,9^1_+\,0)\,J(20) = 51\cdot3607 \text{ cm}^{-1} \text{ (195 } \mu\text{m)}$$

$$(0\,9^1_+\,0)\,J(20) \rightarrow (0\,9^1_-\,0)\,J(19) = 48\cdot927 \text{ cm}^{-1} \text{ (204 } \mu\text{m)}$$

Two weaker cascade lines have also been obtained more recently from this system; they are the $J(22) \rightarrow J(21)$ transition in (2 2° 0) at 190 μm and the $J(21) \rightarrow J(20)$ transition in (0 9^1 0) at 195 μm. They can be distinguished[284] from the stronger lines by accurate frequency measurement.

6.3. The Water-vapour Laser

The water-vapour system was the very first from which far infrared stimulated emission was obtained. Late in 1963, Gebbie, Kimmitt and Mathias,[285] working in collaboration at the Services Electronics Research Laboratory at Baldock in England, passed short (≈ 1 μs) pulses of peak height 46 kV and peak current 13 A through water vapour at a pressure near 1 torr contained in a tube 2·5 cm internal diameter and 4·8 m long. One mirror of the Fabry–Perot system was provided at the end of the tube remote from the analysing interferometer. Stimulated emission was observed at several wavelengths between 23 and 79 μm, and because there was no obvious second mirror in the cavity it was suggested that the gain was so great that the system was essentially super-radiant. Subsequently it was shown that external mirrors such as those in the interferometer or even the window of the Golay cell itself could act as the second mirror of the cavity. This brings to light a considerable difficulty of interpretation with laser systems, for ideally one should have totally passive analysing arrangements to avoid the problems introduced by feedback into the highly oscillatory laser. It is always difficult to be absolutely sure that none of the radiation removed from the system is subsequently, in part, returned to it.

Further work at NPL and other laboratories led to the discovery of many more emission wavelengths and at the time of writing over sixty

---

† Under vigorous excitation conditions, emission *can* be obtained from ^{1}H^{12}C^{15}N. The observed[281] wavelengths are 110, 113, 139 and 165 μm.

emission lines are known ranging from 2 μm to beyond 200 μm. Later, several of these were successfully obtained under CW excitation conditions[286] and it was shown that cascade and competitive transitions were involved.[287] Zeeman effect studies showed that the magnetic moment of the emitter was very small, i.e. of the order of a nuclear magneton. This strongly suggested that the emitter was a saturated molecule rather than a free radical, and combining this conclusion with the previous evidence led three groups to simultaneous identifications of the emitter as the water molecule itself.[288] Once again, rotational perturbation between close-lying states is involved. A comprehensive account of the analysis has been given by Benedict and his colleagues.[289] Their work will be illustrated by choosing from it the assignments for some of the more powerful (and hence more technologically useful) lines. The fundamental origin of the laser action lies in perturbation of rotational levels of the states (100) and (001) by the overtone of (010), namely (020). The reason for the strong interaction is that the bending fundamental has almost half the frequency of either the symmetric stretching mode (100) or the antisymmetric stretching mode (001) which are themselves virtually degenerate. It follows that (020) will be almost equal in energy to either (100) or (001) and, since the potential energy function is markedly anharmonic, vigorous perturbation will occur. The perturbation involves both Fermi resonance and Coriolis coupling, but the former is probably the most significant for the (100)–(020) interaction whilst only the latter is possible in the (020)–(001) perturbation. Each vibrational energy level has associated with it a complex set of rotational levels similar to those shown for the ground state in Fig. 5.1. Many close coincidences occur with corresponding perturbation; from these we may, for example, select (010) 6_{61} (i.e. $J = 6$, $K_a = 6$, $K_c = 1$) = 4407·045 cm^{-1}, (001) 6_{33} = 4408·024 cm^{-1} and (100) 6_{43} = 4394·45 cm^{-1}. The parameters of the resonance (i.e. the coefficients of the wave function mixing) have been worked out by Benedict and his colleagues[289] who deduced that perturbation between the first two is very strong. The origin of some laser emissions from H_2O in terms of this and another nearby resonance is shown in Fig. 6.2.

The definition of parity used in this Figure is essentially that of Herzberg and it is therefore at variance with the definition in Benedict's original paper. Benedict prefers a labelling in terms of the behaviour of K_a and τ, so $(+ +)$ and $(+ -)$ remain unchanged but $(- -)$ and $(- +)$ are interchanged. It must also be noticed that the parities of levels involving an odd number of quanta of ν_3 are not the same as (K_a, K_c) but mirror $(K_a + 1, K_c)$. The reasons for the population inversions have been discussed by Pollack[278] who has shown that the perturbation of one rovibrational state by another can lead to laser action even when there is little or no vibrational population inversion, and the initial rotational populations are strictly Boltzmann. These conditions would of course normally apply, because the near degeneracy of the two states would lead to a rapid collisional cross relaxation. Thus, although for HCN there is a plausible reason for a vibrational inversion, this is not essential for the laser to operate, and the working of the water vapour laser can be understood even though there is no reason to expect anything but equal populations for the three vibrational states.

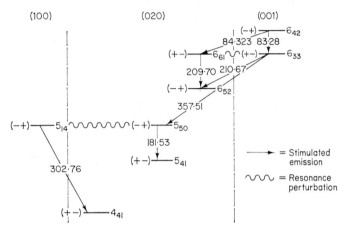

FIG. 6.2. Resonance perturbations and laser action in water vapour; the numbers in the arrows are the observed wavenumbers of the stimulated emission lines.

The effect of the resonance is to transform a transition probability of the type (001) $6_{33} \rightarrow$ (020) 5_{50}, which would be vanishingly small, into one of the type (020) $6_{61} \rightarrow$ (020) 5_{50}, which is a pure rotational transition and therefore very intense. The net result is the powerful emission at $357 \cdot 51$ cm^{-1} ($27 \cdot 972$ μm) which dominates the radiant output from the water-vapour laser. The very valuable far infrared emission at $84 \cdot 323$ cm^{-1} ($118 \cdot 591$ μm) owes its origin to a similar phenomenon. The effect of these two transitions when strongly excited is to alter the population of their upper and lower levels and then further population inversions may exist leading to other transitions such as that at $83 \cdot 28$ cm^{-1}.

Laser action has also been observed[289] with $H_2^{18}O$ but the number of emission lines is much less. The slight shifts of levels due to the isotopic substitution are sufficient to upset the delicate balance and resonances are far fewer. The strongest emission occurs at $353 \cdot 42$ cm^{-1} ($28 \cdot 295$ μm) and owes its origin to perturbation between (100) 6_{43} and (020) 6_{61}, the actual transition being (100) $6_{43} \rightarrow$ (020) 5_{50}. With D_2O, we are back to the situation where there are many resonances but, rather surprisingly, this fact has been deduced from the observation of plentiful laser action rather than by prior study of the absorption spectrum.[289] The behaviour of the D_2O system is quite different from the H_2O system in that, although the $\Delta J = \pm 1$ lines are the strongest in pulsed operation, it is mostly $\Delta J = 0$ lines which occur in CW operation. The available emission lines from the D_2O laser do, however, span the range from 58–380 cm^{-1} and many of them fall nicely into large gaps in the H_2O laser spectrum and the device is therefore most valuable in the laboratory. There is, for example, no line in the H_2O spectrum between 45 and 83 cm^{-1} or between 87 and 100 cm^{-1}, but from D_2O CW operation is possible at $58 \cdot 25$ cm^{-1} and $92 \cdot 823$ cm^{-1}. These two lines are attributed to the transitions $(100)\,11_{0,\,11} \rightarrow (020)\,11_{38}$ and $(100)\,11_{66} \rightarrow (020)\,11_{75}$ made active by resonance between $(100)\,11_{0,\,11}$ and $(020)\,11_{47}$ and between $(100)\,11_{57}$ and $(020)\,11_{75}$ respectively.[289]

Absolute frequencies on the time scale have been reported for some of the H_2O emissions.[290] As examples we have

$$118 \cdot 591 \ \mu\text{m} = 2\ 527\ 952 \cdot 8 \ \text{MHz} = 84 \cdot 323 \ \text{cm}^{-1}$$

and

$$220 \cdot 228 \ \mu\text{m} = 1\ 361\ 282 \cdot 6 \ \text{MHz} = 45 \cdot 407 \ \text{cm}^{-1}.$$

These frequencies are determined to a precision which is an order of magnitude better than those reported for HCN, a technical advance made possible because the "cavity fringe" pattern exhibited a "Lamb dip".[291] This phenomenon will be explained in the next section, but briefly its existence permits the cavity length to be servo-controlled so that the laser frequency remains constant. It is thus possible to determine some transitions in the excited states of H_2O to eight significant figures and the ultra-high resolution of microwave spectroscopy has been reproduced in the infrared. Unfortunately this is of little value (quite unlike normal microwave spectroscopy) for determining accurate molecular parameters of H_2O or HCN, since of necessity at least one of the levels involved has to be perturbed for emission to be observed at all. If enough transitions are measured it is in principle possible to work out the parameters of the perturbation and thus indirectly to determine the rotational constants, but this is unlikely to yield much better values than already obtained from conventional infrared studies. These remarks do not apply necessarily to higher-frequency lasers such as the CO_2 laser radiating at $10 \cdot 6 \ \mu$m where the inversion mechanism involves selective collision, nor to the molecular lasers operating by stimulated fluorescence. In fact, difference frequency measurements of some of the CO_2 laser lines have given very accurate upper-state constants.[292] This is a most interesting development and it will be touched upon again later, but another intriguing prospect from submillimetre high precision frequency measurements is the possibility of determining the velocity of light to an accuracy where tests of fundamental physical theories will be possible. This topic will now be developed.

6.4. Mode Patterns, Frequency Locking and the Determination of the Velocity of Light

The cavity mirrors of a laser form the familiar Fabry–Perot type of resonator. Three types have been used at one time or another: both mirrors plane (now obsolescent), one plane and one spherical (folded *confocal*), and finally both spherical with equal radii of curvature (confocal). The classical theory of Fabry–Perot cavities cannot be taken over directly and used to interpret the properties of lasers because, whereas in the normal case the amplitude of the wave is diminished at each reflection and we can safely replace a summation over a finite number of terms with one over an infinite number, in the laser the amplitude is *rising* with each pass and such a sum would diverge. Likewise the theory of cylindrical perfectly conducting waveguides ending in plane parallel conducting reflectors is of little use, since the glass walls of a laser are very poor reflectors and are certainly not conductors. The laser system is a quite complex one to analyse. Fox and Li have developed[293] a satisfactory account based on Huyghens diffraction, although their treatment was only practicable through having computers available to numerically evaluate some of the rather difficult functions which arose. The problem essentially is that of studying the diffraction losses around the mirrors and the field distributions (i.e. mode patterns) which correspond to propagation with low diffraction loss. The word "mode" is in common use in describing the operation of masers and lasers, although it has to be admitted that the practical devices do not have modes as well defined as those of a microwave cavity. A Fabry–Perot resonator with infinite end mirrors can propagate with resonance any wavelength satisfying the relation

$$L/\cos \theta = m \frac{\lambda}{2} \qquad (6.13)$$

where L is the length of the resonator, θ the angle between the normal to the end reflectors and the direction of propagation, and m an integer. From the continuum of modes, only a small number will possess a high Q and therefore be significant in laser action. Fox and Li have shown[293] that the highest Q is possessed by the even symmetric quasi-modes and the next highest Q by the quasi-modes of odd radial symmetry. The meaning of these terms is as follows: in an even symmetric mode the electric field strength is a maximum at the centre of the mirror and falls to a low value at the edge, whilst the relative phase difference across the mirror is nearly zero almost to the edge of the mirror; in a mode of odd radial symmetry the electric field is zero along a nodal line through the mirror centre and the amplitude is a maximum (of opposite phase on opposite sides of the nodal line) at a distance half way to the mirror edge along a line perpendicular to the nodal line. There are still higher modes and the whole set of mode functions bears a strong resemblance to the familiar s, p, d etc. atomic orbital functions and like them forms a basis set in terms of which any arbitrary function may be expressed. In particular, although plane waves do not normally propagate in the resonator, such a wavefront can be synthesized by taking a suitable linear combination of modes. The power loss by diffraction per transit is determined by the mode pattern and by the dimensionless parameter (Fresnel Number) $N = a^2/L\lambda$, where a is the radius of the mirror. It is important to realize that, whereas for visible region lasers N is of the order of 10 and the diffraction loss negligible, in submillimetre lasers N is frequently of the order of unity and diffraction losses can be as high as 20 per cent for plane mirror resonators. The situation can be considerably improved by employing a confocal system or the type of resonator with one mirror plane and the other spherical. The confocal system with $N = 1 \cdot 0$ has a diffraction loss[293] of less than $0 \cdot 1$ per cent.

We are now in a position to interpret the behaviour of the power output from a laser as a function of cavity length. The high Q modes are obtained from equation (6.13) by making θ equal to zero. If λ is constant, i.e. if the natural spontaneous line-width is extremely narrow, then every time L is an integral number of multiples of $\frac{1}{2}\lambda$, resonance will be achieved and high power output observed. Behaviour of this type is shown in Fig. 6.3 which illustrates the power output from a CW HCN laser as a function of cavity length. The large peaks marked A are due to emission at 337 μm and the peaks marked D are due to emission at 311 μm; the different spacing is clear from the diagram. The peaks marked B and C arise from odd symmetry axial modes for which θ is not zero but still very small. The spacing of these modes is therefore very slightly different from the dominant A modes and, although this is not measurable over the range illustrated in the Figure, it is sufficient over the total range L to ensure that these modes occur displaced from the A modes. Similar remarks apply to the weak E modes. Despite the different spacing, the time frequencies of the various modes are in principle identical, the difference in position arising purely from geometrical factors. There are some analogies with the wavenumber contraction and resolution limitations of Michelson interferometers illuminated by non-parallel radiation.

We must now go on to consider the behaviour of the laser when the natural fluorescence line-shape has a finite width. The theory of line-shapes has been outlined in Chapter 5 and it is important to realize (via equation 5.10) that, whereas a Doppler-broadened line in the visible region for a light molecule like H_2O might have a width of 1000 MHz, a similar line occurring in the far infrared near 100 cm^{-1} would have a width of only 8 MHz. The frequencies at which the cavity is resonant for axial modes with θ zero are

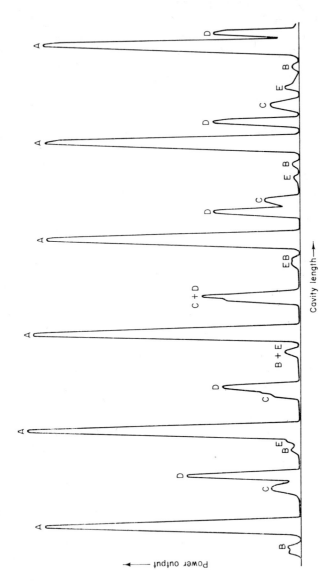

FIG. 6.3. Cavity fringe pattern of an HCN laser. The peaks marked A are dominant mode emission at 337 μm; those marked B and C are other 337 μm modes, whilst D and E correspond to 311 μm modes. (From unpublished work of C. C. Bradley.)

separated by increments

$$\Delta \bar{\nu} = (2L)^{-1} \qquad (6.14)$$

so that if we assume that the velocity of light is not much different in the plasma from its value in vacuum (weak dispersion) it follows that these modes for a 3 m tube are separated by 50 MHz in frequency. We see therefore that while for an optical laser there will be many cavity resonances across the natural profile, for a submillimetre laser there can be at most only one resonance within the significant region. It is for this reason that the output of a submillimetre laser plotted as a function of cavity length shows the characteristic "cavity fringes" (Fig. 6.3). The argument remains valid when pressure broadening is considered, for this is found to amount to only some 10 MHz per torr whilst the natural, or radiation-damped, line-width is quite negligible. The width of the cavity resonances is set by the finesse of the resonator (analogous to the Q factor) which is defined as the ratio of fringe separation to half-width. Typical values for this quantity are of the order 10, so the cavity resonances will be approximately 5 MHz wide. The line-width of a CW laser emission is determined by various factors such as mechanical imperfections and thermal drifts, as well as more fundamental phenomena like spontaneous emission into the mode. If this latter is the determining factor then the line-width is given by[294]

$$\Delta \nu = 4\pi h (\Delta \nu)^2 \, \nu / P \qquad (6.15)$$

where $\Delta \nu$ is the natural line-width, ν the laser frequency and P the power. Spontaneous emission is hardly relevant even for optical lasers where application of the above formula indicates a line-width of $3 \cdot 6$ Hz for an operating power of 1 watt, but in submillimetre lasers it can be completely neglected and the effective line-width (and therefore the coherence) is determined by experimental instabilities. It is believed that the line-widths of CW HCN lasers may range between 10^5 and 10^3 Hz, depending on the degree of experimental precaution taken. It is naturally rather difficult to measure such narrow lines. Interference methods[295] have been tried using a Michelson type of interferometer with one arm introducing a path difference of approximately 10^3 metres. Strong interference was still manifest, from which one can conclude that the line-width is less than 3×10^5 Hz.

Although the line-width of individual emissions from the laser is very small, the frequency itself can vary over wide limits. The set of very sharp resonances given by equation (6.14) goes over into a virtually identical set when L is increased by $\frac{1}{2}\lambda$, so any individually marked resonance sweeps over a range of 50 MHz (for the 3 m tube) to get to the next position down. At any time when the frequency of a resonance corresponds to a point on the natural line profile where the gain is sufficient for oscillation, stimulated emission will be observed. In practice the laser frequency can be varied by up to ± 5 MHz merely by altering the length of the cavity. If the radiation from two lasers is simultaneously detected by a square-law (or power) detector such as a crystal diode, beat frequencies may be observed in the output of the detector. Difference frequencies of this type of up to 5 MHz have been observed when one laser was deliberately off-tuned.[296] In passing it should be noticed that the equivalent experiment with optical lasers, using a photo-cathode as the square-law element, is complicated by the large number of axial modes which can exist within the line-width. Beat frequencies of up to 300 MHz have been detected from He–Ne lasers mixed in this way.[297] The output from a square-law detector can show beats even when the detector is receiving radiation from a single laser, provided that the excitation conditions are sufficiently high for the laser to be operating in more than one mode. Of course only one of these can ever be truly axial, but it is always possible for a non-axial mode to be oscillating at another point on the natural line profile. Two modes like this do not compete for the available power in the same way as modes of other types of oscillator, because they arise essentially from different molecular populations. The distinguishing label is the velocity component along the axis of the laser and each point on the Doppler-broadened profile corresponds to a distinct set of molecules having velocity components in a narrow range. On reflection, it will be seen that this is also true for a pressure-broadened line profile. The output of a spectrum analyser fed by the signal from a crystal diode observing one high-power CW HCN laser is shown in Fig. 6.4. This sort of record is precisely the type of direct spectroscopy discussed in Chapter 1.

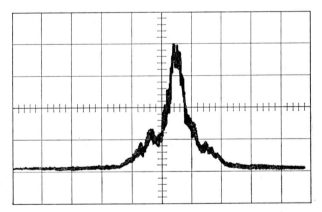

Fig. 6.4. Spectrum of beat oscillations between two modes of a single CW HCN laser. Centre frequency 260 kHz, spacing 2·5 kHz per division. (From unpublished work of D. W. E. Fuller at NPL.)

A strong beat note at 260 kHz is observed with a width of 2·5 kHz. This latter may be a measure of the spectral width of each emission since random fluctuations of cavity length might be expected to affect each mode similarly. Beat notes have been obtained between the radiation from a laser and that from a klystron after suitable harmonic multiplication. As the klystron fundamental frequency is swept over the region corresponding (after multiplication) to the laser frequency, beat notes with a width of up to 20 kHz are obtained. This too is thought to be an upper bound to the line-width of the emission.[298]

We will consider now the problem of frequency stabilization of lasers. This can be achieved ideally by operating in one mode and rigidly fixing the cavity length so that a cavity resonance coincides with the centre of the line profile. The latter is important not only because the gain is the highest at the line centre but because the phenomenon of frequency pulling has zero effect there. Frequency pulling is a consequence of the anomalous dispersion in the region of the emission line. In a laser, because the absorption coefficient is negative, the optical properties are the reverse of the typical behaviour of absorptive systems shown in Fig. 4.19. The refractive index *increases* as the frequency rises through $\bar{\nu}_i$. The phase shift per transit, therefore, depends on frequency and the net effect is that the cavity modes are no longer exactly equispaced. The observed frequency of a mode tends to be nearer the molecular resonance frequency than one would expect and because of this is said to be "pulled". With HCN lasers good experimental practice, designed to hold the output frequency constant, is to stabilize the cavity length by using invar rods, to stabilize the discharge by careful choice of electrodes, starting materials and pumping conditions, and to keep the fine adjustment of cavity length so arranged either manually or by means of a servo arrangement that the output power is a maximum. This was the regimen used for the absolute frequency measurements quoted earlier which were accurate to 1 MHz or 1 part in 10^6. With the CW H_2O laser it is possible to do rather better. Lamb,[299] in the course of an extensive analysis of the theory of lasers, has considered the expected power output as a function of detuning of the cavity resonances from the molecular frequency. The power saturation of the Doppler-broadened line will lead to a sharp dip at the exact centre of the line, provided that other line-broadening processes such as collision broadening or natural radiative broadening, are small compared to the Doppler broadening. The effect occurs because a molecule with zero velocity component along the laser axis can interact with waves travelling in either direction along the axis. Absorption effects are therefore twice as great at the line centre as they are in the wings. The width of the Lamb dip will be defined by the subsidiary broadening processes and the depth of the dip will be determined by the relative excitation conditions. The power output of the laser as a function of detuning will therefore be given by

$$P(\Delta\nu) \propto \{-\eta^{-1} + \exp - (c\Delta\nu/\nu_0\bar{u})^2\}\{1 + c^2(\Delta\bar{\nu})^2/[c^2(\Delta\bar{\nu})^2 + (\Delta\nu)^2]\}^{-1} \quad (6.16)$$

where $\Delta\nu$ is the frequency displacement from the line-centre frequency ν_0: $\bar{u}$ the Doppler-broadening parameter and $\Delta\bar{\nu}$ the collision-broadening parameter have been defined in Section 5.2. The numerator of this equation includes, in addition to the Doppler line-shape function, a parameter η which indicates the ratio of actual laser excitation to the minimal excitation required to maintain oscillation with exact tuning, i.e. with $\Delta\nu$ zero. The denominator involves a Lorentzian line-shape function including the collisional line-width $\Delta\bar{\nu}$. Oscillation is only possible if the numerator is positive and it will be seen that the larger η is, the larger can $\Delta\nu$ be with oscillation maintained. This reflects the experimental fact that the number of modes which can oscillate increases with excitation. The denominator also reaches a maximum when $\Delta\nu$ is zero and, depending on the relative values of the natural line-width and the Doppler line-width, the shape of the $P(\Delta\nu)$ versus $\Delta\nu$ curve can become quite interesting. Some calculated results for the H_2O laser at low pressures (where collisional broadening is small) are shown in Fig. 6.5. The response curve shows a central tuning minimum or "Lamb dip".

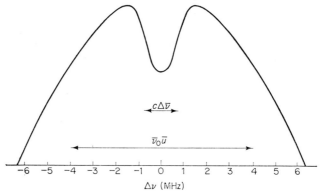

Fig. 6.5. Power output from an H_2O laser as a function of detuning (relative excitation) = 2·0.

This dip when it is observed is a very easy thing to tune onto by means of servomechanisms and, by locking their laser in this way, Pollack and his colleagues were able to achieve the frequency accuracy mentioned earlier.[290] In principle, still higher accuracy is possible. In order to achieve this it will be necessary to start with a laser locked to the Lamb dip and with a klystron phase locked to a time standard. The beat note from a suitable harmonic of the klystron mixing in a crystal diode with the output of the laser can be used to provide a control voltage which can be used to alter the laser current. In this way a frequency accuracy of 1 part in 10^9 may be feasible.

In passing, it should be remarked that the Lamb dip is not unique to masers and lasers. A central minimum can be observed whenever high power levels are involved and the dominant broadening mechanism is the Doppler effect. At millimetre or shorter wavelengths, the Doppler broadening is usually much larger than the collisional broadening for low-pressure gases and vapours and the use of the Lamb dip provides an alternative to the molecular-beam methods when it is desired to resolve detail finer than the width of the Doppler-broadened line. Winton and Gordy[300] have observed Lamb dips for the $J''(8)$ to $J''(20)$ pure rotational lines of OCS in the frequency range 100–256 GHz; that is 3 to $1 \cdot 2$ mm. The line frequencies were determined to a precision of ± 1 kHz and from them rotational constants were calculated which are two orders of magnitude more accurate than the previously known values. Thus for OCS $B_0 = 6 \cdot 081\ 492\ 05$ GHz and $D_J = 1 \cdot 3$ kHz. The K-splittings of the $J''(1)$, $J''(2)$ and $J''(3)$ lines of CH_3F have been readily observed using this technique and very accurate values of B_0, D_J and D_{JK} have been obtained. These are $B_0 = 25 \cdot 536\ 146\ 6$ GHz, $D_J = 0 \cdot 059\ 87$ MHz and $D_{JK} = 0 \cdot 440\ 27$ MHz. Hyperfine structure in the $J(15) \rightarrow (16)$ transition of $^{35}ClCN$ has been comfortably resolved and altogether the method is very promising. The experimental arrangements are straightforward. The gas is contained in a high Q Fabry–Perot cavity which is tuned to resonance at the centre of the absorption line to be studied. Microwave power is fed in through a small coupling hole at one end and led out again either through the same hole or else through a similar hole at the other end. The output from the detector, as the source frequency is swept through a cavity fringe, will therefore show the absorption line and, provided the power is high enough, will also show the Lamb dip. Winton and Gordy[300] were able to demonstrate that they had sufficient power to saturate the relatively weak pure rotation lines of CO ($\mu = 0 \cdot 11$ D).

Now that it is possible to measure the time frequencies of stimulated emission lines, physicists have turned their attention to the problem of using infrared lasers for a more accurate determination of the velocity of electromagnetic radiation. The old methods which involved the measurement of the time taken for a pulse of light to travel a fixed and known distance have long since been superseded by methods based on determining simultaneously the wavelength and frequency of a highly monochromatic emission in a suitable region of the spectrum. If ν is the frequency and λ the vacuum wavelength of such radiation then we have, from equation (5.47),

$$\nu\lambda = c \tag{6.17}$$

where c is the velocity of light *in vacuo*. This equation can also be written

$$\nu = c\bar{\nu} \tag{6.18}$$

which was the basis of the "band spectrum" method mentioned in Chapter 2.

L

The standard of length is defined in terms of the wavelength of a visible emission line; in fact 1 metre is defined to be 1650 763·73 wavelengths of the unperturbed transition $2p_{10} \rightarrow 5d_5$ in ^{86}Kr. The standard of time is now set by the so-called "caesium clock" and 1 second is defined to be 9192 631 770 cycles of the hyperfine transition $(4, 0) \rightarrow (3, 0)$ in the ground state of ^{133}Cs under zero external field.[301] Unfortunately one may not determine c directly by either measuring the time frequency of the ^{86}Kr line or the wavelength of the Cs transition, because experimental techniques do not exist for absolute measurements at optical frequencies and diffraction effects limit the accuracy attainable in wavelength measurements in the radio region. Froome in 1958 chose[302] the high microwave (4 mm) region as a compromise where diffraction effects are within bounds yet time frequencies are still measurable by making use of a chain of harmonic multiplication. His value for c ($2 \cdot 997\ 925 \pm 0 \cdot 000\ 001) \times 10^{10}$ cm s^{-1}, is one of the experimental determinations which led to the present accepted value,

$$c = (2 \cdot 997\ 926\ 6 \pm 0 \cdot 000\ 000\ 9) \times 10^{10} \text{ cm s}^{-1}.$$

Submillimetre or infrared determinations of c would be still better, since the diffraction uncertainties would be even smaller. The availability of a large number of CW intense laser sources spanning the infrared region makes possible the establishment of a chain of frequency standards extending upwards towards optical frequencies. Knowing therefore the frequency of, say, a CO_2 laser line near $10 \cdot 6$ μm or a He–Ne laser line near $3 \cdot 39$ μm, it will be possible to determine c to high accuracy by measuring the wavelength of the laser line, relative to the fundamental length standard, in a suitable interferometer. An experiment of this sort has been reported by Daneu, Hocker, Javan, Rao and Szöke[303] who determined accurately the wavelengths of some submillimetre laser lines. In their interferometer, the mirror movement was measured by counting fringes generated by the radiation from a 6328 Å He–Ne laser. The laser itself was stabilized by locking on to the Lamb dip, and its wavelength was determined to be 6329·915 Å in a separate experiment in which it was directly compared to the ^{86}Kr standard in a Fabry–Perot interferometer. The wavelength of the $118 \cdot 6$ μm line of H_2O was found to be $118 \cdot 590\ 85 \pm 0 \cdot 000\ 2$ μm, from which, with the time frequency given earlier, the value of c was found to be

$$c = [2 \cdot 997\ 922 \pm 0 \cdot 000\ 006] \times 10^{10} \text{ cm s}^{-1}.$$

This agrees with the accepted value.

Direct frequency measurement by detecting the difference beat between a laser and a harmonic of a klystron, becomes very difficult for frequencies greater than 3 THz (i.e. 3×10^{12} Hz). In 1969, Hocker, Small and Javan[305] succeeded in mixing the 84 μm radiation from a D_2O laser with the combination of the fourth harmonic of 337 μm HCN laser radiation and a $5 \cdot 9$ GHz signal from a klystron. From the measured beat note they were able to calculate the D_2O laser frequency as $3 \cdot 557\ 143$ THz ± 2 MHz. This method of using the harmonics of a previously determined laser frequency is essential for measurements in the mid- and near infrared regions. Another prerequisite is the availability of a suitable detector and fortunately the metal-oxide-metal (MOM) detector[58] has been shown to be usable to at least 60 THz. Josephson detectors are also of value in this connection[262, 263] and may be usable as far as 8 THz. Many laser frequencies have been measured using various techniques and some of the results are given in Table 6.2.

TABLE 6.2.

Source	Frequency	Wavelength or wavenumber	Calculated c $\times 10^{10}$ cm s^{-1}	Refer- ence
HCN	$804 \cdot 7509$ GHz	$372 \cdot 547\ \mu$m	$2 \cdot 998\ 075$	277, 281
	$\Big\{ 890 \cdot 7607$ GHz	$336 \cdot 579\ \mu$m	$2 \cdot 998\ 113$	277, 281
	$890 \cdot 7602$ GHz	—	—	304
H_2O	$\Big\{ 2 \cdot 527\ 9528$ THz	$118 \cdot 590\ 85\ \mu$m	$2 \cdot 997\ 921$	290, 303
	$2 \cdot 527\ 9525$ THz	—	—	304
D_2O	$3 \cdot 557\ 143$ THz	$84 \cdot 279\ 07\ \mu$m	$2 \cdot 997\ 927$	305, 303
H_2O	$3 \cdot 821\ 775$ THz	—	—	306
	—	$47 \cdot 463\ 16\ \mu$m	—	303
	$10 \cdot 718\ 073$ THz	$27 \cdot 970\ 80\ \mu$m	$2 \cdot 997\ 931$	306, 303
CO_2				
$P(18)$	$28 \cdot 359\ 800$ THz	—	—	307
$P(20)$	$28 \cdot 306\ 251$ THz	—	—	307
$R(10)$	$32 \cdot 132\ 353$ THz	$1071 \cdot 877$ cm^{-1}	$2 \cdot 997\ 765$	58, 309
$R(12)$	$32 \cdot 174\ 169$ THz	$1073 \cdot 271$ cm^{-1}	$2 \cdot 997\ 767$	58, 309
CO	$58 \cdot 024\ 341$ THz	—	—	308
($P(13)$ of $n = 7$ $\rightarrow n = 6$)				

It will be seen from this Table that the precision of determination of c is no better at the moment than the standard error of the accepted value. A great deal of the uncertainty arises from the wavelength measurements, but most of the frequencies are only known at present to an accuracy of 1 part in 10^6. However, there does not seem to be any reason why both frequency and wavelength should not be determined to at least 1 part in 10^7 and possibly even to 1 part in 10^8. If this could be achieved it would be unnecessary to maintain separate standards of length and time. In this connection it is interesting to observe, as noted by Javan and his colleagues,[308] that the CO $5 \cdot 2\ \mu$m emission is sufficiently high in frequency for the methods of harmonic generation, using bulk non-linearity (see Section 6.8) to be feasible. It is thus possible in principle to build a chain of harmonic multiplication which will extend from the radio-frequency region up to the optical region. Evenson and his colleagues[307] have suggested that the 3·39 μm line of the He–Ne laser near 88 THz, locked to a saturated methane device, might provide a good candidate for a combined length–time standard. It is a requirement of a satisfactory international standard that there be a laid-down procedure which enables the standard to be reproduced anywhere in the world. Lasers are normally notoriously bad in this respect and have, for this reason, not had the immediate acceptance which their high monochromaticity would suggest. However, in the case of the He–Ne 3·39 μm emission, it is possible to lock the laser to the peak of the $P(7)$ line of the ν_3 band of methane and thus to obtain a frequency reproducibility of 1 part in 10^{11} and a stability of better than 5 parts in 10^{14} for averaging times of 10^3 seconds.[310] When this locked frequency has been determined to high accuracy in terms of the caesium standard it may well be accepted along with the velocity of light as a universal standard.

6.5. Practical Details of Submillimetre Laser Systems

The engineering and optical details of submillimetre lasers are really quite simple and it has to be admitted that there is nothing in their construction which would have been beyond the technology of fifty years ago. This is in marked contrast to the sophistication of visible lasers—an illustration of the general principle that, for all optical systems, operational problems get progressively easier as the wavelength increases.

A schematic diagram of suitable equipment is presented as Fig. 6.6. A discharge, either continuous or pulsed, is passed from a suitably ballasted source to appropriate electrodes and thence through the gas mixture flowing in a glass tube. The glass tube is vacuum sealed and contains within it the two

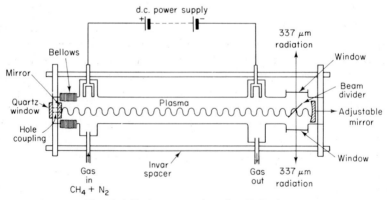

FIG. 6.6. Basic construction of an HCN laser.

front-surfaced mirrors which form the Fabry–Perot resonator. Aluminium mirrors are suitable for the lower frequency lasers, but reststrahlen absorption in the ever-present aluminium oxide film makes them less appropriate for lasers operating at wavenumbers above 50 cm^{-1}. For these latter, mirrors made by evaporating gold onto an aluminium blank have proved highly successful. One mirror is mounted on the spindle of a micrometer in order that the cavity length may be adjusted; the other features screw adjustments so that the two mirrors can be made sufficiently parallel to one another. Radiation can be coupled out of the cavity either by means of a dielectric film beam divider or else via a small coupling hole drilled through the fixed mirror. A practical laser constructed out of standard modular hardware is shown in Fig. 6.7. This particular instrument has the distinction of being the shortest

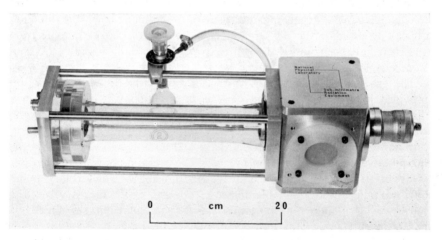

FIG. 6.7. Modular submillimetre laser.

laser[311] ever to emit at 337 μm; in practice the lasers are made somewhat longer. Pulsed lasers have been constructed up to 5 m in length and CW lasers (where the gain per metre is inherently less) are usually at least 1 m in length. The power output goes up quite rapidly with increase in length, since the gain per pass is higher, but there is a practical limit to how long a laser can be, set by the difficulty of establishing a stable discharge over a distance of more than a few metres. The losses in the cavity arise principally from diffraction and are therefore determined by the Fresnel number. If N is increased—by, for example, using a larger tube diameter—then the losses are reduced and the power output increases. For this reason, high-power lasers are more usually made from 4 in. diameter tube rather than from the 2 in. diameter tube which is compatible with NPL modular hardware. Absolute power measurements are difficult to make on the radiation from most submillimetre lasers because the power levels are usually rather low. Radiometers can give only approximate values and because of this it is more usual to attempt a calibration of a Golay cell. A rule of thumb used at NPL is that a Unicam Golay cell in good order gives 200 V output for 1 mW input power. Golay cells cannot possibly give outputs of 100 V and remain linear and the cell might even be damaged by exposure to such levels of input power. What is done in practice is to mount attenuators (generally thick polyethylene impregnated with carbon black) of known attenuation in front of the cell window and to infer the incident power by scaling up the Golay reading. Using this type of technique it is concluded that 1 m CW HCN lasers with hole coupling give power outputs of the order of 1 mW. The largest lasers so far constructed—8 m—have given power outputs varying from $\sim$100 mW[304] to over 500 mW,[312] depending on the size of the coupling hole. It is still more difficult to estimate the peak power of pulsed lasers; values ranging from 1 to 10 W have been quoted at one time or another as being possible at 337 μm from very long (5 m) HCN pulsed lasers.

The gas mixture in an HCN laser can have virtually any composition provided it contains H, C and N. The laser action was discovered in a discharge in HCN but this was soon superseded by acetonitrile (CH_3CN) and propionitrile (C_2H_5CN). These latter compounds are liquids at room temperature and can be stored in the small flask and admitted to the laser via the needle valve shown combined in Fig. 6.7. The operating pressure in the laser is about 0·2 torr—a value readily achieved using a small rotary pump (30 litres min^{-1}) and a suitable degree of opening of the needle valve. The most popular mixture at the moment is a 50/50 by volume mixture of methane and nitrogen. This mixture forms HCN in the discharge by a very complex reaction[313] involving many unstable intermediaries, but the reaction can be written down at least formally as

$$CH_4 + N_2 \rightarrow HCN + NH_3. \qquad (6.19)$$

Permanent gases are preferable to vapours in that the pressure in the reservoir is not so temperature sensitive and this particular mixture is less troublesome in the matter of polymer deposition. It was noticed in the very first experiments with cyanic discharges that a brownish polymeric material formed on the walls of the discharge tube. A similar material is always found to form in any HCN laser regardless of the starting materials. Its chemical nature is unknown but it certainly contains carbon and nitrogen for it is apparently able to supply these elements to a discharge through hydrogen or water vapour in a heavily coated laser[314] leading to emission at 337 μm. The polymer probably contains hydrogen as well, for infrared evidence suggests the presence of CH groups. HCN lasers have been operated successfully for up to

30 hours sealed off and, presumably, here one of the sources of the necessary HCN is the thermal decomposition of the deposits of polymer on the walls of the laser.[315] This polymer is certainly an interesting material in its own right and biochemists have even suggested that it might have been an essential link in the evolution of life on Earth ;[316] but as far as submillimetre lasers are concerned it is an unmitigated nuisance. The polymer is heavily absorbing at 337 μm and thin layers of it formed on the beam divider or on the mirrors of the cavity seriously depress the power output from the laser. Rather surprisingly, the deposits on the glass walls have a similar effect for plane parallel cavities. The reason for this is that the walls are partly reflecting and do take part in the cavity operation and for this reason the simple theory of Fox and Li[293] needs modification.[317] When the walls become coated with an absorbing layer, the Q of the cavity goes down and the power output falls. The effect is much less noticeable for confocal cavities where reflection from the walls is much less significant. The result of increasing polymer deposition is that eventually the laser has to be dismantled and cleaned. With CH_3CN as the operating material the power output falls typically by a factor of ten over a period of 30 hours : with $CH_4 + N_2$ the same result occurs in a period of 100 hours. The rate of deposition can be slowed down by allowing the walls of the tube to get very hot or by reducing the amount of CH_4 in the mixture. If this latter choice is adopted then one can obtain extended operational life at the expense of reduced initial output power. The longest lifetimes come from confocal hole-coupled lasers where periods up to 300 hours have been achieved.[315]

Water vapour lasers are not affected by polymer deposition but even so it has not proved feasible to operate them in a sealed-off configuration. The commonest fuel for the laser is simply water vapour bled in through a needle valve. However, many other starting materials work just as well, including such compounds as nitromethane (CH_3NO_2). This fact, coupled with the observation that a discharge through a mixture of $NO_2 + NH_3$ is particularly good[318] and that this mixture is one of the best sources of OH radicals,[319] leads us to doubt that the laser operates by directly exciting H_2O molecules. Probably, as in the case of the HCN laser, free radical reactions are involved. A possibility would be

$$R - H + OH \rightarrow R + H_2O^*. \qquad (6.20)$$

By ultraviolet measurements on the discharge it might be possible to determine the most likely vibrational and rotational state of H_2O^* formed and thus gain some insight into the laser mechanism. Certainly the reverse reaction,

$$H_2O \rightarrow OH + H, \qquad (6.21)$$

leads to a highly anomalous distribution of molecules in the various rotational states of OH.[320]

Various types of electrode have been employed in the course of laser development.[321] The original system used solid brass electrodes with an arc discharge between them. This type was superseded by one featuring a barium zirconate coating on a directly heated platinum cathode. This cathode, operating at 1200° C, gives similar thermionic emission to the triple (Ba, Sr, Ca) carbonate-coated cathodes which would have a life of only minutes in the highly "poisonous" atmosphere inside the laser. In this respect barium zirconate is virtually unique. Because the electrons are leaving the hot cathode with energies lying in a narrow band, the discharge is much more stable than is the arc discharge and fluctuations in the time range $0 \cdot 1$–$0 \cdot 001$ s are very much less. A disadvantage of hot cathodes is that they have a lifetime of only about one day, so each day's work has to begin with the coating and activation of a new cathode. For this reason they have now been replaced by hollow cathodes made from brass or stainless steel which have lifetimes in excess of 100 hours and are much easier to fabricate. Many designs have been used ranging from a flat sealing plate featuring a central drilled-out stub to sophisticated contrivances internally water cooled. The anode is relatively unimportant and can be just a metal rod except when the highest frequency stability is desired, in which case a design similar to that of the cathode may be used. The power supplies for CW lasers can be very simple, consisting of a bridge rectifier with minimum smoothing and ballast resistors made from electric fire elements. The power pack has to provide a voltage of several kV to initially break down the discharge path. When the discharge is established, the voltage across the laser falls to a lower value, ~ 800 V for a 1 m laser[322] and up to $4 \cdot 5$ kV for an 8 m laser.[304] The current through the tube can be as high as 1 A and a great deal of heat is dissipated in the discharge and the walls of the laser tend to get very hot. Cooling by means of fans or occasionally a water jacket is desirable to eliminate any danger of the walls cracking. Pulsed lasers run quite cool because of the long duty cycle but, although they are of great historical importance, they are seldom used nowadays except when searching for new lasing systems and in the time-resolved study of pulsed plasmas.

The frequency stability of a laser depends rather critically on the stability of the discharge.[315] If two lasers are set up and adjusted so that the striations in the discharges are stationary and have sharply defined leading edges, when the radiation from the pair is detected by a crystal detector beat notes of up to 30 KHz may be observed. If, however, the discharge in either laser becomes unstable or if the striations develop a visible shimmer then the beat notes may range up to 100 kHz.[296] These phenomena are probably connected with the change of refractive index which must accompany a striation. An oscillating or unstable striation will induce a degree of mode "pulling" leading to a shift of frequency of the unsteady laser compared with the stable laser.

Mechanical instabilities can also affect the apparent width of the emission line. Strauch[323] has shown that either the 337 μm line or the 311 μm line of HCN can have measured widths of up to 10^5 Hz, but that the beat note from the pair is only 5 kHz wide. This shows, in agreement with what was said earlier, that the "true" line-width is less than 5 kHz and that any experimental factor which shifts the frequency of one line will shift that of another by approximately the same amount.

The choice of output coupling method depends on the particular application desired. If a good approximation to a plane wavefront is required, as for example in experiments where the radiation is to be sent over a long distance, then beam-divider coupling, together with suitable lenses, is mandatory. If, on the other hand, maximum power is required, hole coupling is preferable. The beam divider is generally a 6 μm film of polyethylene terephthalate. This has a low reflectivity and low absorption at 337 μm, so losses in the beam divider are small. Nevertheless, it is interesting to observe that the radiation coupled out of the cavity is polarized in the plane of Fig. 6.6. The reflectivity is much lower for radiation polarized in this plane than for that in the perpendicular plane because the beam divider is not far away from the Brewster angle. Apparently the losses by reflection for perpendicularly polarized radiation are sufficient to suppress the operation of the laser to a large extent. Hole coupling is particularly appropriate to submillimetre lasers, where diffraction is the principal source of loss and where it is virtually impossible to make mirrors with the very high reflectivity and small lossless transmission so much a feature of visible-region lasers. If a small hole were drilled in one of the mirrors of a He–Ne visible laser, the effect would be to suppress the even symmetric (TEM_{00}) dominant mode, which has a high intensity at the mirror centre, and to transfer operation to an odd mode (TEM_{01}) which has zero intensity at the mirror centre. Little power would therefore be coupled out. For a 337 μm HCN laser, on the other hand, the diffraction losses in the TEM_{01} mode can still be higher than the combined, diffraction and hole-coupled, losses in the TEM_{00} mode, if the hole is reasonably small. For this reason it is possible to couple out power at 337 μm in the dominant TEM_{00} mode. The loss per transit is proportional to the area of the hole divided by the area of the so-called "spot". The "spot" size is defined by the distance from the mirror centre at which the intensity of an even symmetric mode has reached $1/e$ times its maximum value. The larger the Fresnel number, the smaller is the "spot" and the smaller therefore must the coupling hole be. Most submillimetre lasers have N lying between 1 and 10, so the "spot" size is somewhere near $0 \cdot 6$ times the mirror radius. If, therefore, we have 2 in. diameter mirrors for the cavity, a 2 mm coupling hole will give a power loss per transit of 2 per cent. The laser system has a gain of ~ 10 per cent per metre[324] so that a 1 metre confocal laser will operate well with such a coupling hole since the diffraction losses will also be about 2 per cent. A detailed treatment of hole coupling has been given by McNice and Derr.[325]

Beam divider and hole coupling are the two usual means of extracting power from the laser cavity, but on occasion, and for special purposes, other techniques may be used. The three principal alternatives are (1) diffraction coupling round the edge of one of the mirrors, (2) the use of a metal mesh beam divider or metal mesh cavity mirror, and (3) the use of a zero-order reflection grating as one of the cavity mirrors. Diffraction coupling gives a wavefront whose profile is very undesirable for subsequent experiments, but the fact that this method does not introduce any additional losses into the cavity gives the laser the best chance of oscillating on lines which have very low gain coefficients. For this reason diffraction coupling is of value for the observation of very weak lines and was used for this purpose by Mathias and his colleagues[281] in their investigation of some of the weaker HCN lines.

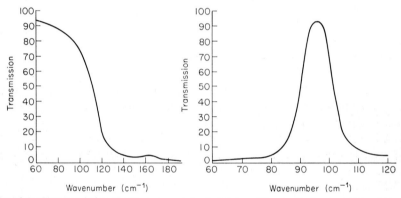

FIG. 6.8. Characteristics of a low-pass and a band-pass filter made from combinations of metal mesh grids by Sir Howard Grubb Parsons and Co. Ltd.

The increasing use of metal meshes in submillimetre technology has been mentioned in Chapters 2 and 4. These elements can be thought of as artificial dielectrics[326] and they can perform at submillimetre frequencies the functions which waveguide irises or interference filters perform at microwave or optical frequencies respectively.[326] Some typical characteristics of commercial low-pass and band-pass filters are shown in Fig. 6.8. A metal mesh can replace the 45° dielectric beam divider of a conventional laser, but the most intriguing application is their use to replace one of the mirrors of the cavity. Ulrich, Bridges and Pollack[327] have described a semi-confocal HCN laser in which the plane mirror was replaced by a pair of metal meshes which together constituted a Fabry–Perot interferometer. The reflectance of a Fabry–Perot interferometer, looked at from the outside, is a critical function of the interferometer spacing and therefore, by using a pair of meshes in place of the plane mirror, it is possible to vary the effective reflectance of the end element of the laser cavity. This provides a means of varying the degree of output coupling whilst still having a reasonably plane wavefront. This is a distinct advantage over hole coupling. Variable coupling is possible with a conventional beam divider laser[328] if a third mirror is used as shown in Fig. 6.9(a).

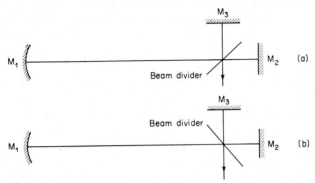

FIG. 6.9. Output coupling from three-mirror beam divider lasers.

The combination of the beam divider and mirrors M_2 and M_3 makes up a Michelson interferometer and, by varying the position of M_3, the power output can be varied from zero to twice what it would be if M_3 were not there; this assumes of course that the amount of power extracted is negligible in comparison with the total power in the cavity. The arrangement shown in Fig. 6.9(b) is essentially a double cavity sharing a common mirror. The gain is high because of the length of the main cavity, whilst the spacing of the cavity modes is much increased because of the presence of the short cavity (see equation 6.15). This situation is very desirable if a near infrared or visible laser is to be operated on a single longitudinal mode, for to achieve this it would be necessary to have the mode spacing greater than the Doppler width of the natural line.[329]

Zero-order coupling, from a diffraction grating serving as one of the cavity mirrors, is normally only used to provide a monitor beam whilst the main beam is coupled out conventionally at the other end of the laser.

Diffraction gratings used as cavity mirrors were introduced by Moeller and Dane Rigden[330] for the CO_2 laser. The cavity can only be resonant for wavelengths which satisfy both the cavity-length condition and also the grating equation for the chosen angle between the optic axis and the normal to the grating. In general there will only be one such wavelength and the laser will radiate at this wavelength or not at all. In the CO_2 case, the laser normally gives out only P branch lines because these have an inherently higher gain. They compete, therefore, successfully with the R branch lines which are consequently suppressed. However, by using the frequency-selective cavity, which can suppress the P branch lines, the R branch emission can be observed. Frequency-selective cavities have been used by Jeffers[331] to study competitive processes in the H_2O laser and the technique was adopted by Brannen and his colleagues[332] to extend observation as far out as the 118·6 μm line of H_2O. An echellette grating introduces a high degree of polarization into the diffracted beam, the component polarized parallel to the grooves frequently being only half as intense as that polarized perpendicular to the grooves. Brannen, Hoeksema and Sarjeant[332] have shown that the radiation at 118·6 μm from a hole-coupled frequency-selective laser is virtually 100 per cent polarized with the electric vector perpendicular to the grooves. This is an interesting observation, for the line corresponds (see Fig. 6.2) to a $\Delta J = 0$ with $J > 1$ type of transition which should be bistable circularly polarized. The strong cavity anisotropy introduced by the grating is apparently able to uncouple the two polarization senses giving the observed linear polarization. A magnetic field can separate the two circularly polarized conditions leading to a splitting of the gain curve into two components. The laser therefore shows a "polarization switch" as the cavity is tuned through resonance. This was part of the evidence which helped identify the emitting molecule in the water-vapour laser. All the transitions in the HCN laser are $\Delta J = \pm 1$ type and are therefore[333] linearly polarized. The electric vector may lie anywhere in a plane normal to the laser axis but any cavity feature which emphasizes a given direction may serve to lock the polarization parallel to this unique direction. In particular, it has been shown[334] that a series of fine parallel scratches on the plane mirror of a confocal cavity can ensure virtually 100 per cent polarization parallel to the scratches. This is a convenient way of getting a highly polarized output from a hole-coupled laser.

6.6. Spectroscopy Using Submillimetre Lasers

6.6.1. *Spot-frequency Determinations of Optical Constants*

The principal difficulty facing the experimentalist who wishes to use submillimetre lasers as sources for spectroscopic systems is that they are fixed frequency devices. It is true that by altering the cavity length, or else by employing high-speed amplitude modulators,[335] it is possible to shift the frequency by a few megahertz but this is only 1 part in 10^5 of the centre frequency. This should be compared with the 10 per cent frequency sweep of klystrons. There are various suggestions, ranging from non-linear mixing with microwave radiation in a suitable crystal to the use of ultra-fast (10^9 Hz) modulators, which may ultimately improve the frequency sweep but at the moment these are still speculative and we must face the fact that for all intents and purposes the laser gives out fixed frequency monochromatic radiation.

Two distinct types of experiment suggest themselves: firstly, one can take advantage of the high power and high monochromaticity of the available lasers to determine definitive optical constants of materials at a series of fixed wavelengths; secondly, one can investigate those systems where the absorption coefficient may be varied by the application of an external influence such as high pressure, change of temperature or electric and magnetic fields. The first type of experiment has been discussed in Chapter 4 where it was shown that the relative refractive indices obtained from Fourier refractometry could be placed on an absolute scale if a laser measurement could be made at a frequency within the range of the interferometric observations. A modern apparatus for determining the refractive index of a liquid at the frequency of a far infrared laser is shown in Fig. 6.10. This apparatus,

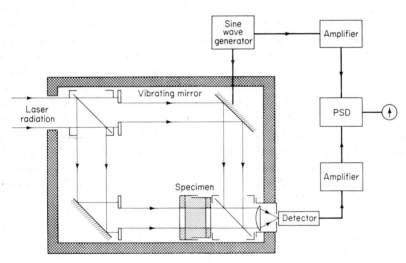

Mach–Zehnder interferometer

FIG. 6.10. Apparatus used by Chamberlain[336] at NPL to measure the refractive indices of liquids at the frequencies of submillimetre lasers.

developed at NPL by Chamberlain,[336] features a phase-modulated Mach–Zehnder interferometer. The plot of detector output as a function of sample thickness will consist of a set of damped oscillations: from the "pitch" of the oscillations the refractive index may be calculated, and from the rate of attenuation with distance the absorption coefficient may be derived.[115] There are now several suitable laser sources spanning the far infrared and it may be possible in special cases to infer the form of continuous and slowly varying absorption profiles from a series of spot measurements. This is, however, obviously done more economically using an interferometer and so the principal interest in laser spectroscopy has been found in experiments of the second type.

6.6.2. *Cyclotron Resonance Measurements*

Electron spin resonance (e.s.r.) experiments using submillimetre lasers were discussed in Section 5.11 where it was shown that the very high frequency was advantageous for the study of some atoms with high g factors but that magnetic field strength and homogeneity problems prevented the technique from coming into general use. Cyclotron resonance experiments are rather different, for here a high analysing frequency is essential if the spectrum is to be resolved and analysed. The basic requirements have been spelled out in Section 5.11 but another practical point is that ν_c must be greater than the frequency of the plasma edge if transmission methods are to be feasible. The experimental arrangements can be quite simple. The radiation from a hole-coupled laser is led along one arm of a T-shaped light pipe. At the intersection it encounters a beam divider and some of the radiation proceeds to a reference detector. The remainder is led to the crystalline semiconductor specimen mounted in a cryostat between the pole pieces of a magnet. The transmitted radiation proceeds to a second detector and then, by means of suitable electronics (applying the amplified and rectified reference voltage across the slide-wire of a potentiometer is a good way), the ratio of the two signals is drawn out as a function of magnetic field. The effective masses of the electrons and holes (equation 5.101) can be much less than the electron mass; for example, m^* for the conduction electrons in n-InSb is of the order $0 \cdot 014\, m_e$ and the cyclotron resonance which, for a field of 68 kG, would be expected at $6 \cdot 3$ cm^{-1} is found[337] in practice at 357 cm^{-1} which is the wavenumber of the very strong 28 μm line of the H_2O laser. The simple theory given earlier, in terms of which the continuum of states in a band breaks up into a discrete set of equispaced levels under the influence of an external magnetic field, applies only to the conduction band. The states within the valence band of even the simplest elemental semiconductors such as germanium are far more complex. The valence band of germanium is to zero order six-fold degenerate at $\bar{k} = 0$, but the effect of spin-orbit coupling is to split the degeneracy leading to a four-fold degenerate state at the top of the band and a doubly degenerate state which is sufficiently far below the top to be ignored. The levels of the four-fold degenerate state interact with each other to lift the degeneracy for low quantum numbers. The result is that at high temperatures, where states with high n are involved, the cyclotron resonance spectrum is made up of lines due to conduction band electrons together with two broad resonances which are ascribed to the "light" and "heavy" hole respectively. The energy of a hole decreases with increasing n but this implies that its separation from the acceptor levels increases. Thus a higher temperature is necessary to ionize a higher n state. This is sometimes expressed by saying that the acceptor levels are the sources of the holes. At temperatures such that $h\nu_c > kT$, a fine structure appears in the cyclotron resonance spectrum of the holes. The lines of this fine structure are called "quantum effects" and for their observation the conditions given before are necessary. The quantum effects arise [338] for $n \leqslant 6$ roughly speaking and the energies have been calculated, using quantum mechanical perturbation theory by Stickler, Zeiger and Heller,[339] for the simplest case which is H perpendicular to the (111) direction of the crystal. Each level is labelled by two numbers, a harmonic oscillator-type quantum number n and a parameter ρ. There are four "stacks" corresponding to $\rho = 1, 2, 3$ or 4 but all values of n are not allowed indiscriminately; n may have any value for $\rho = 1$, must be 2 or greater for $\rho = 2$ or 3 and must be 4 or larger for $\rho = 4$. The selection rule to a first approximation is

$$n = \pm 1 \quad \text{for} \quad H \perp E \quad \text{and} \quad n = \pm 3 \quad \text{for} \quad H \| E.$$

Transitions between stacks are governed by these rules and the additional rule

$$\rho(1) \leftrightarrow \rho(3) \leftrightarrow \rho(2) \leftrightarrow \rho(4).$$

Stickler, Zeiger and Heller[339] plot their energy-level diagram in terms of a dimensionless parameter $\epsilon_{n\rho}$ such that m^*, the effective mass for the transition, is given by

$$m^* = m/[\epsilon_{n\rho} - \epsilon_{n'\rho'}] \tag{6.22}$$

The smaller ϵ becomes, the closer is the level to the top of the valence band.

Stickler and his colleagues[339] observed cyclotron resonance in germanium for $H \| [111]$ and at sample temperatures between $4 \cdot 2$ and $1 \cdot 2$ K. They used cavity-resonance methods and for sources employed either a $68 \cdot 3$ GHz klystron, frequency doubled by an Ohl type silicon crystal, or else a 2 mm CSF carcinotron. At $1 \cdot 2$ K, $h\nu$ is six times kT when ν is $136 \cdot 6$ GHz. Quantum effects were clearly observed and a convincing assignment was presented. As an example, the highest field line that they observed, corresponding to $m^*/m = 0 \cdot 331$, was ascribed to the transition $(4, 4) \rightarrow (5, 4)$ and therefore involved levels near the top of the band. Their assignment was broadly confirmed by the 337 μm observations of Bradley et al.[337] but in detail there were discrepancies. The origin of these discrepancies has been revealed by the work of Button, Brecher, Lax and Bradley[340] who studied p-type indium antimonide and germanium using both the 337 μm HCN and the $118 \cdot 6$ μm H_2O lasers. They have shown that the perturbation of the degenerate valence

bands by both the split-off valence band and the conduction band is significant in affecting the cyclotron resonance levels. The 8×8 matrix Hamiltonian
formalism introduced by Pidgeon and Brown[341] was found to provide a
useful basis for treating the problem and energy levels have been calculated
and assignments made. Some of their results are shown in Fig. 6.11. An
interesting physical point from their treatment is that, because of the perturbation, cyclotron resonance, which is usually thought of as an intraband
phenomenon, takes on partly the character of an interband transition. There
are strong parallels here with the perturbations responsible for gas-laser
action in the submillimetre region. For particular directions of H, it is still
possible to label levels with a value of n and a ladder index and this is shown
in the middle inset of Fig. 6.10. The stack a^+ is called the anomalous light
hole and transitions within it contribute to the peaks 1, 2 and 3 in the left-
hand inset. The stack a^- is called the anomalous heavy hole and transitions
within it give the quantum effect line 7, together with a continuum stretching
between line 4 and line 5. Line 6 is due to cyclotron resonance of the impurity
levels. Line 8 is the heavy hole resonance due to transitions in b^-. The stack
b^+ is the light hole stack and contributes to 1 and 2. The observed profile
shown in Fig. 6.10 is therefore made up of very many individual lines and,
since the non-parabolicity is very pronounced, the transitions of a given type
will not in general lie on top of each other; in other words, the energy levels
are extremely anharmonic. Since this is the case, each line arises essentially
from a two-level system and so there will be marked dependences of intensity
on temperature. The energy of a level *below* the top of the valence band is
plotted in the central inset of Fig. 6.11 and so it will be realized from an
inspection of this diagram that lines will first increase in intensity as the
temperature rises from 0 K—due to creation of holes by promotion of electrons to the impurity levels—and that they will finally fade away as near
equality of population of the upper and lower levels is attained. From the
temperature scaling of this phenomenon for each line a very good estimate of
the upper- and lower-state energies may be deduced and the assignment may
thereby be checked. Because of the seven-fold increase in observing frequency
it was possible to observe the quantum effects with sample temperatures as
high as 56 K and a very thorough check was possible from the temperature
dependence of the line intensities. Another advantage of relatively high
temperature work is that there will be plenty of holes produced thermally
and it is unnecessary to use the methods of optical excitation which Stickler
et al.[339] found desirable for germanium and essential for silicon when the
sample temperature was $1 \cdot 2$ K.

Submillimetre cyclotron resonance is a field of physics which is developing
rapidly and already studies have been published of n- and p-type InSb,[342]
p-type tellurium[343] and p-type germanium,[337] which was discussed above.

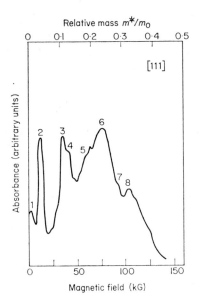

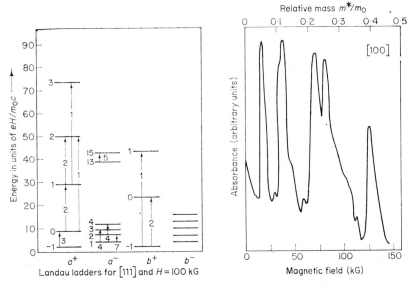

FIG. 6.11. Cyclotron resonance in p-type germanium after Button, Brecher, Lax and Bradley[340] for a sample temperature of 25 K. Note the strong dependence of spectrum on direction in the crystal. The relative mass for each transition can be found from the energy-level diagram using the equation $m^*/m_0 = (\Delta E)^{-1}$.

M

The availability of high-power CW lasers to provide the analysing radiation has enabled experimentalists to observe departures from the simple theory, especially when the cyclotron resonance frequency approaches the transverse optical or longitudinal optical-mode frequencies of a compound semiconductor. The conduction-band electrons will tend to polarize the surrounding lattice and each moving charge will be surrounded therefore by an induced "halo", and the effective mass of the carrier will increase. Such a combination is called a polaron and the extent of the lattice–electron interaction will be governed by the lattice polarizability which, from equation (28) of Appendix 3, is directly proportional to the dielectric constant. The dielectric constant of an ionic lattice varies rapidly in the vicinity of the optical modes (equation 5.52) and it is expected therefore that the effective mass of the carriers will not be constant but will vary with ν_c as ν_c approaches the reststrahlen region. This has been observed by Dickey, Johnson and Larsen[344] for InSb where an anomalous dispersion type of behaviour was observed as the cyclotron resonance frequency moved through the reststrahlen frequency 198 cm^{-1}. The increase of m^* with ν_c is somewhat analogous to the effects of anharmonicity in molecular vibration spectra and it is therefore often said to arise from band "non-parabolicity". The polaron effect is not the only cause of a departure from a simple quadratic dependence of E on $\bar{k}$, but the strong interaction between the electrons and the lattice is reflected in such phenomena as "phonon-assisted" cyclotron resonance where lines are observed at a frequency $\nu_c + \nu_{LO}$. Indium antimonide is only weakly polar and studies of it have not been able to provide a rigorous test of polaron theory. Waldman et al.[345] have therefore investigated the much more polar semiconductor cadmium telluride and have shown that the increase of m^*, as ν_c approaches the reststrahlen region, accords well with large polaron theory based on the Fröhlich Hamiltonian. The curvature of the energy versus magnetic field strength plots is, however, small and requires a spectrally pure source if it is to be properly measured. Waldman and his colleagues used a 337 μm (29·7 cm^{-1}) HCN laser, a 195 μm (51·3 cm^{-1}) DCN laser, a 172 μm (58·1 cm^{-1}) D$_2$O laser and a 118·6 μm (84·3 cm^{-1}) H$_2$O laser as they approached $\nu_{LO} = 181·5$ cm^{-1}.

Bound polarons can also be observed, a good example being found in the work of Brandt and Brown[346] on AgBr. At cryogenic temperatures, AgBr develops complex far infrared absorption during and immediately after irradiation by ultraviolet light of frequency greater than the indirect band gap. This is ascribed to the trapping of a conduction band polaron at some positively charged site. A sharp line is found at 168 cm^{-1} which is assigned to the $1s - 2p$ (i.e. *Lyman* α) transition in the resulting "hydrogenic atom". Alternatively, this could be assigned as an F-centre absorption appearing in the far infrared. On either interpretation, the occurrence of this band is a most remarkable phenomenon. Another band is observed at 192 cm^{-1} which is attributed to the Rydberg head, i.e. $1s \rightarrow \infty$ or ionization of the bound state. At a still higher frequency (292 cm^{-1}), a third band is observed which is thought to be due to the $1s \rightarrow 2p$ transition plus one quantum of the longitudinal optic mode. This combination should appear at 307 cm^{-1}, since $\nu_{LO} = 139$ cm^{-1}, but the factors which lead to the frequency contraction are not yet completely understood.

6.6.3. *Near Coincidence Spectroscopy and the Stark Effect*

Another type of spectroscopy capable of yielding valuable information even with the restriction to the use of fixed frequency sources, is the study of near coincidences with pure rotational lines of gases. The best example of this is found for the $6_{15} \rightarrow 6_{24}$ pure rotational line of D_2O which Bradley *et al.*[347] find to lie at $29 \cdot 714 \pm 0 \cdot 008$ cm^{-1} by interferometric spectroscopy. As will be seen, this is coincident within the experimental error with the HCN laser emission at $29 \cdot 7125$ cm^{-1}. D_2O vapour does indeed absorb the 337 μm radiation with an absorption coefficient of $1 \cdot 48 \times 10^{-3}$ neper cm^{-1} for a pressure of 1 torr, but since this is only a small fraction of the expected α_{max}, namely $0 \cdot 187$ neper cm^{-1}, it is concluded that the centre frequency of the transition is some 10 line-widths away from the laser frequency. At such a separation, the absorption coefficient is a parabolic function of gas pressure (see equation 5.28) and this has been confirmed experimentally. When considerable pressures of foreign gas (nitrogen) are added, the absorption coefficient varies in an interesting way. Clearly at zero foreign gas pressure the absorption is low and at very high foreign gas pressure, when the absorption is completely smeared out, the value will also be low. It follows (and can be proved by differentiation of equation 5.32) that, at an intermediate pressure, the absorption reaches a maximum. The pressure corresponding to this maximum absorption is related to the frequency separation between the line centre (ν_0) and the laser (ν_L) by the equation

$$| \nu_0 - \nu_L | = \sigma_0 P_0 + \sigma_N P_N \qquad (6.23)$$

where σ_0 and σ_N are the pressure-broadening parameters for self and nitrogen broadening respectively and P_0 and P_N are the corresponding pressures. Experimentally, with $P_0 = 2 \cdot 5$ torr and $P_N = 50$ torr, a maximum absorption occurred. From this observation, combined with reasonable estimates of σ_0 and σ_N, a value for $| \nu_0 - \nu_L |$ equal to 234 ± 24 MHz was calculated.[347] It is not possible by this method to determine the value of ν_0 since there is no way of knowing which side of the line the laser frequency occurs. The absorption profile and its changes with pressure are virtually symmetrical about ν_0. The refraction changes about ν_0 are, however, antisymmetrical and by measuring refractive indices Strauch and his colleagues[348] have shown that the line frequency lies below the laser frequency. This has been confirmed by the calculations of Frenkel, Sullivan, Clough and Benedict[349] who conclude that the line frequency lies 369 MHz below the laser frequency. The discrepancy between this value and that deduced from the pressure-scanning method was thought to arise from the failure of the simple line-shape theory to describe adequately the absorption far out in the wings of a line. However, Duxbury and Jones[350] have shown that the pressure-broadening data on D_2O may be reinterpreted to give $\sigma_0 = 26\cdot8$ MHz torr^{-1} and $\sigma_N = 6$ MHz torr^{-1}, from which $| \nu_0 - \nu_L |$ is found to be 367 MHz, in excellent agreement with the calculated value. Several other examples of near coincidence absorption have been discussed by Duxbury and Burroughs ;[351] amongst the substances studied was 1 : 1 difluoroethylene ($CF_2 = CH_2$) which has a line less than 2 MHz away from the 337 μm line of the HCN laser.

The topic of near coincidence has been taken up by Duxbury and Jones[350] who have investigated the Stark effect. It was remarked in Chapter 5 that each level of an asymmetric rotor is $(2J+1)$-fold degenerate. Each degenerate component may be labelled by the magnetic quantum number M which can have the values $M = 0, \pm 1 \ldots \pm J$. The degeneracy arises from the isotropy of space, for each value of M corresponds to a projection of J onto a fixed direction and clearly all directions are equivalent. When, however, an electric field is applied, the isotropy disappears because the electric field "labels" directions in space and lifts the degeneracy. The shift of the levels of an asymmetric rotor away from their zero-field position is given just as for the linear rotor by equation (2.11). In the particular case of the $6_{15} \rightarrow 6_{24}$ of D_2O, the numerical frequency shifts are given by

$$\Delta\nu \,(\text{MHz}) = \mu^2 E^2 \times 10^{-9} \,[5\cdot312 + 0\cdot439 \,(M')^2 + 1\cdot886 \,(M'')^2] \quad (6.24)$$

where μ is in Debyes and E is in V cm^{-1}. It will be seen, therefore, that as the field increases each Stark component sweeps over the laser frequency and if the transition is allowed an absorption of energy will result. The selection rules for Stark spectra are $\Delta M = 0$ if the electric vector of the radiation is parallel to the field and $\Delta M = \pm 1$ if it is perpendicular. The beam divider coupled radiation from a 337 μm HCN laser is highly polarized so the two types of spectra are obtained by rotating the Stark cell about its axis through 90°. The experimental arrangements are not, however completely straightforward, for in order to obtain the high field strengths it is necessary to have the two electrodes rather close together. Not only are there the usual difficulties involving electrical breakdown of the gas but at these wavelengths the Stark cell can behave as a cut-off waveguide for the perpendicular polarization. For these reasons it has proved possible so far to observe only the higher M transitions in D_2O. Some spectra obtained with a 300 μm spacer are shown in Fig. 6.12. By the use of a 185 μm spacer, it was possible to continue observation down to $3'' \to 3'$ in the $\Delta M = 0$ series and to $4'' \to 3'$ in the $\Delta M = \pm 1$ series. From the observed resonant fields and the known dipole moment ($1 \cdot 88_8$ Debye) and from equation (6.24), the frequency separation of the zero-field line from the laser can be inferred. The value found is 376 ± 12 MHz below the frequency of the laser. This compares well with the two values quoted earlier.

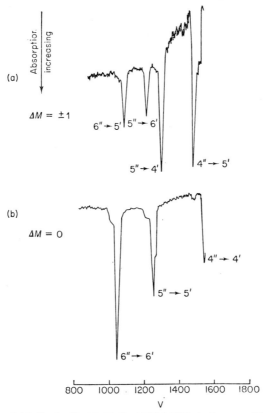

FIG. 6.12. Stark effect in D_2O at $890 \cdot 8$ GHz (cell spacer 300 μm).

There are some close coincidences between lines of the D_2O laser and some rotation-inversion transitions of NH_3. The structure of the rotation spectrum of ammonia was discussed in Chapter 5 where it was shown that the "lines" consist of widely (≈ 40 GHz) spaced doublets each member of which shows K fine structure. The D_2O line at $171 \cdot 6$ μm ($1 \cdot 747$ THz) lies some $16 \cdot 3$ GHz below the lower frequency component of the $J(2) \to J(3)$ line of NH_3; the D_2O laser lines at $84 \cdot 1$ μm ($3 \cdot 564$ THz) and $84 \cdot 29$ μm ($3 \cdot 557$ THz) lie in between the two components of the $J(5) \to J(6)$ line.

Uehara, Shimizu and Shimoda[352] observed the Stark effect for all three lines but the need to use relatively high (20 torr) pressures and pulsed lasers limited their resolving power. Duxbury and Jones[353] have studied the Stark effect of the $J(4) \rightarrow J(5)$ line of ND_3 using a $1 \cdot 540$ THz DCN laser. Despite these successes, it must be admitted that Stark-effect studies in the submillimetre region are, in comparison with those at microwave frequencies, handicapped by the much larger Doppler widths which prevail in this higher-frequency region. Perhaps it may prove possible in future to use Lamb dip techniques, already applied at $10 \cdot 6$ μm, in the submillimetre region and by this means be able to resolve hyperfine structure. Brewer, Kelly and Javan[354] used a CO_2 laser to study the Stark effect in NH_2D and were able to overcome the Doppler broadening by invoking the Lamb dip, so that their observations were confined to a narrow region of the Doppler-broadened profile. Brewer[355] has found another way round this difficulty by making use of the high power of the CO_2 laser to produce non-linear effects. He studied CH_3F for which there is a very close coincidence of the $Q(12)$ line of the ν_3 band with the $P(20)$ line of the laser. By using two lasers slightly off-tuned from each other he was able to observe a sharp Stark resonance. The reason for this is that a molecule will only interact strongly with *two* radiant fields when it Doppler shifts them equally. It follows that a sharp resonance will be observed when the Stark splitting in *one* of the two states involved in the transition exactly equals the frequency separation of the two lasers. This sort of experiment is therefore unique in that one can observe the Stark effect of *levels* rather than of *transitions*. Brewer was able therefore to measure μ for each level and to observe a difference. His results were $\mu(\text{ground}) = 1 \cdot 8549 \pm 0 \cdot 0010$ D and $\mu(\text{excited}) = 1 \cdot 9009 \pm 0 \cdot 0010$ D. So far this type of measurement cannot be made at longer wavelengths because of the absence of sufficiently intense sources, but there are good auguries for the future.

6.6.4. *Zeeman Effects in Rotational Spectra*

Magnetic fields can also lead to a removal of the M-degeneracy of rotational lines and one expects therefore to observe Zeeman effects in pure rotational spectra. However, just as an electric dipole moment is essential for an observable Stark effect, a magnetic dipole moment is essential for a Zeeman effect. Large magnetic dipole moments can only occur if the molecule contains unpaired electrons and for this reason Zeeman spectra are much less common than Stark spectra. The best known example is found for oxygen where the molecule contains two unpaired electrons and is therefore a diradical. The two ^{16}O nuclei in the common form of O_2 have zero spin and it follows therefore (see G. Herzberg, "Diatomic Molecules", p. 135ff.) that only the symmetric rotational levels will occur. The ground state of O_2 is $^3\Sigma_g^-$ (approximately Hund's case (b)) and for this state the symmetric rotational levels have N odd. The overriding rule in quantum mechanics is that J, the total angular momentum, is always fixed in magnitude and direction, a fact that is often expressed in the remark that J is a "good" quantum number. Most of the cases of rotational motion so far discussed have involved molecules for which rotation about a molecular axis is the only form of angular momentum present. When this is the case J and N are identical, but for O_2, where there are two unpaired electron spins, J is the resultant of N and $S = \pm 1$. If the coupling is strictly case (b), N is a good quantum number, but even if there are departures—and in fact O_2 lies somewhere between cases (a) and (b)—it is still useful to think in terms of levels characterized by a value of N and a value of J. The great majority of the rotational energy comes from the motion about the axis perpendicular to the internuclear axis (i.e. N) and therefore we envisage levels $(N, J = N)$ given by the usual rotation formula

$$E(N = J) = B_0 N(N+1) + D_0 N^2(N+1)^2 + \text{higher terms}, \quad N = 1, 3, 5 \text{ etc.}$$
(6.25)

Each of these levels is accompanied by two more, $J = N+1$ and $J = N-1$, at lower energy. For all N except $N = 1$, the two states $J = N \pm 1$ are closely similar in energy and lie approximately 60 GHz below the $J = N$ level. The actual displacement does, however, vary with N and a full theoretical treatment has been given by Tinkham and Strandberg.[356] The situation for $N = 1$, 3, 5 is shown in Fig. 6.13. The selection rules for pure magnetic dipole absorption are

$$\Delta J = 0 \pm 1 \quad \text{and} \quad \Delta N = 0 \pm 2,$$
(6.26)

the latter being a quantum mechanical reflection of the classical result that, since a rotation through 180° gives an identical configuration, the magnetic dipole is rotating twice as fast as the molecule. Applying these rules to the energy-level diagram (Fig. 6.13) it will be seen that a complex absorption band will be expected near 60 GHz, there will be an isolated absorption line at $118 \cdot 76$ GHz, and the next absorption system will not be expected until the 400 GHz region. All these features have been observed by microwave methods.[357, 358]

It is possible to extract B_0 values from the measurements of the fine structure of the 60 GHz band and this has been done by Mizushima and his colleagues[359] who find $B_0 = 43 \cdot 1003$ GHz. This gives a good value for c when combined with the B_0 value (from ultraviolet measurements) of Babcock and Herzberg,[360] namely $B_0 = 1 \cdot 437\ 77$ cm^{-1}. Unfortunately this agreement is quite illusory for McKnight and Gordy[358] have measured directly the $N(1) \rightarrow N(3)$ triplet frequencies (see Fig. 4.14 for a very much lower resolution study) and found from an analysis of their data $B_0 = 43 \cdot 100\ 589$ GHz. Wilheit and Barrett[361] have located an error in the theory of Mizushima[359] and have shown that when this is removed Mizushima's measured 60 GHz frequencies are consistent with the B_0 value of McKnight and Gordy.[358] From this it would appear that the B_0 value given by Babcock and Herzberg[360] is not determined to quite the precision given in their paper and should in fact be $1 \cdot 437\ 68$ cm^{-1}. The numerical version of equation (6.25) is therefore

$$E(\text{cm}^{-1}) = 1 \cdot 43768\ N(N+1) - 4 \cdot 91 \times 10^{-6}\ N^2(N+1)^2$$
$$+ 3 \cdot 0 \times 10^{-10} N^3(N+1)^3. \quad (6.27)$$

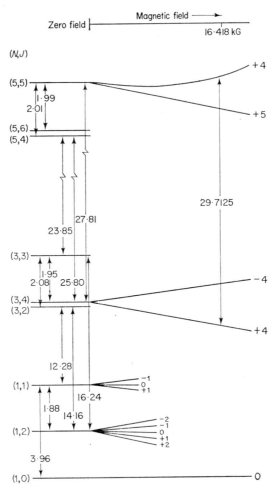

FIG. 6.13. Pure rotational and spin reorientation absorption in oxygen. The Zeeman effect is shown to the right of the diagram and for clarity most of the M-levels have been omitted. The transition frequencies are in cm^{-1}.

The absorption frequencies may not be found directly from this equation, since the $\Delta J = \pm 2$ transitions are forbidden, but the central component of the observed triplet is always close to this in practice because of the approximate equality of the fine-structure splittings. As far as lower resolution delay-type experiments are concerned, lines will be expected at

$$N(1) \rightarrow N(3) \quad 12 \cdot 28 \text{ cm}^{-1}, \quad 14 \cdot 16 \text{ cm}^{-1}, \quad 16 \cdot 24 \text{ cm}^{-1}$$

$$N(3) \rightarrow N(5) \quad 23 \cdot 85 \text{ cm}^{-1}, \quad 25 \cdot 80 \text{ cm}^{-1}, \quad 27 \cdot 81 \text{ cm}^{-1}$$

etc. These, and their higher analogues, have been observed by interferometric methods (see Chapter 4) but the extreme feebleness of magnetic dipole absorption made the use of very long path lengths and moderate pressures essential for a successful observation. McKnight and Gordy[358] found that, even with microwave methods, a path length of 20 ft was necessary with cooling to 77 K to clearly observe the $N(1) \rightarrow N(3)$ triplet.

Paramagnetic resonance absorption in oxygen at X-band (3 cm) wavelengths has been reported by Beringer and Castle.[362] These authors point out that at fields which would correspond, via equation (5.99), to absorption frequencies much less than the spin-coupling frequency (≈ 60 GHz), simple Zeeman effect theory holds. However, even at X-band (10 GHz), the onset of the Paschen–Back effect (i.e. an uncoupling of N and S) was noticeable. The simple Zeeman theory gives the shift in energy of an (NJM) level in a field H as

$$\Delta E = +g\beta HM$$

where

$$g = [J(J+1) + S(S+1) - N(N+1)]/[J(J+1)]. \tag{6.28}$$

Hill and Gordy[363] continued the work of Beringer and Castle but used such weak fields (≈ 100 G) that the simple theory held rigorously. Of course with fields of this order the splittings of a given (NJ) level are too small to give absorption in the microwave region, but these splittings can readily be inferred from the frequency displacements of the split components of the $(N = 1, J = 0) \rightarrow (N = 1, J = 1)$ and $(N = 1, J = 2) \rightarrow (N = 1, J = 1)$ lines. These are shown schematically in Fig. 6.13. The Zeeman splitting of the $27 \cdot 82 \text{ cm}^{-1}$ line is particularly interesting because Evenson, Broida, Wells, Mahler and Mizushima[364] have shown that the $M = -4 \rightarrow M = -4$ component of this line comes into coincidence with the HCN laser frequency at an applied field of $16 \cdot 418$ kG. The g values for $N = 3$ are given quite well by equation (6.28), but by introducing the effects of anomalous electron moment ($1 \cdot 0012$ instead of $1 \cdot 000$), and centrifugal interaction which mixes levels of the same J, extremely accurate values can be calculated. These are $+0 \cdot 1669$ ($N = 3$, $J = 3$), $+0 \cdot 4952$ ($N = 3$, $J = 4$), $-0 \cdot 6667$ ($N = 3$, $J = 2$). The uncoupling effect is extremely small for $M = \pm J$ and this is especially true for the states

$J = N \pm 1$ where N and S are parallel. The Zeeman effect of the state ($N = 3$, $J = 4$, $M = -4$) is therefore linear and, from equation (6.28) and the g value given above, it follows that at an applied field of 16·418 kG it will have shifted down in energy by an amount 1·524 cm^{-1}. The behaviour of the upper state ($N = 5$, $J = 5$, $M = -4$) is more complex. At low fields this level shifts down in energy, but at a much slower rate than the (3, 4, -4) level because the g value is only 0·066 74. At fields of the order of 2 kG, the shift passes through zero to positive values (see Fig. 6·13) and at 16·418 kG the displacement is $+0·368$ cm^{-1}. The transition wavenumber for

$$(N = 3, J = 4, M = -4) \rightarrow (N = 5, J = 5, M = -4)$$

is therefore 29·712 cm^{-1}, coincident with the HCN laser.

The observation of the resonance experimentally is hampered by the very low intensity of pure magnetic dipole transitions. The very long base White cells used for the earlier laboratory zero-field studies are out of the question since the whole sample must be mounted in a reasonably homogeneous magnetic field. Fortunately there is ample power available from the HCN laser (*unlike the black-body sources*) and the use of a high Q, hole-coupled, Fabry–Perot interferometer as a transmission cavity is feasible. Evenson and his colleagues[364] used a cavity 10 cm long with circular mirrors, one plane and the other spherical, each 1·7 cm in diameter. The coupling holes were 0·75 mm in diameter, leading to an estimated Q of 5×10^4. The gas pressures used were between 2 and 19 torr. The magnetic field was modulated to a depth of 10 G at a frequency of 13½ Hz and the signal from the Golay cell was amplified and phase detected at this frequency. Very small changes in the transmission could be detected in this way. The experimental record of the resonance was presented as a first derivative plot with a signal-to-noise ratio of greater than 10 to 1 when a 3 s integrating time was employed. The experimental arrangements were later improved by Wells and Evenson[365] who used an intracavity absorption cell with a consequent considerable increase in sensitivity. With a variant of this system they were able to detect[366] the $^2\Pi_{3/2}, J = \frac{3}{2} \rightarrow {}^2\Pi_{1/2}, J = \frac{1}{2}$ line of OH using the 79 μm line of the water-vapour laser as the probe. $^2\Pi$ states with $S = \frac{1}{2}$ split up into two series, $^2\Pi_{3/2}$ and $^2\Pi_{1/2}$, and each rotational level in either stack is a close doublet, whose two members have opposite parity (see Appendix 5). Evenson and Wells have suggested that in certain regions of the Galaxy, a relative Doppler shift could bring the radiation from H_2O emitters into coincidence with the $^2\Pi_{3/2}, J = \frac{3}{2}$ ($-$) to $^2\Pi_{1/2}, J = \frac{1}{2}$ ($-$) transition of OH. This is a magnetic dipole transition (no change of parity) but could be followed by the spontaneous electric dipole transition $^2\Pi_{1/2}, J = \frac{1}{2}$ ($-$) to $^2\Pi_{3/2}, J = \frac{3}{2}$ ($+$) and thus lead to a population inversion of the $^2\Pi_{3/2}, J = \frac{3}{2}$ lower state. The consequent stimulated emission could explain the Galactic maser action near 18 cm.

Hyperfine splitting of each level by the half-integral spin moment of the proton will lead to the observed line being a doublet, i.e.

$$^2\Pi_{3/2}, J = \tfrac{3}{2}\,(+) \begin{Bmatrix} F' = 2 \to F'' = 2 \\ F' = 1 \to F'' = 1 \end{Bmatrix} {}^2\Pi_{3/2}, J = \tfrac{3}{2}\,(-).$$

The use of Zeeman effect experiments at submillimetre frequencies to probe the electronic structure of free radicals promises to be a powerful technique. Not only is there the frequency-cubed advantage over microwave observations but additionally one may study the Zeeman splittings of pure rotational lines which may well be electric dipole allowed. Already Evenson and his colleagues have reported[367] experiments on the stable NO_2 and NO radicals and have detected[368] the $(J = \tfrac{5}{2}, N = 2) \to (J = \tfrac{7}{2}, N = 3)$ transition of the astronomically interesting CH radical, which lies close to the $118 \cdot 6 \ \mu m$ line of H_2O. Other examples such as NH_2 will doubtless be studied in the near future.

6.7. Power Saturation and Amplification at Submillimetre Wavelengths

The derivation of the line-shape functions in Chapter 5, and especially in Appendix 3, involves the tacit assumption that the population difference between two levels is independent of the intensity of the radiation field coupling them. Clearly this can only be absolutely true for negligibly small intensity, since the equilibrium state will arise as a balance between the pumping action of the field and the relaxing action of collisions and spontaneous emission. Nevertheless, under normal circumstances, discrepancies (which would take the form of a violation of Lambert's law) are seldom encountered in the near infrared or visible regions except when the enormous power level from a pulsed laser is involved. In the microwave region, on the other hand, where there are resonant cavities and very powerful sources available and where spontaneous emission is negligible, departures from simple behaviour are commonplace, especially at low pressure where collisions become less frequent.

Karplus and Schwinger[369] have given an elegant treatment of this phenomenon. What they do is to transcribe the classical derivation of the line-shape formula due to Van Vleck and Weisskopf[370] (see Appendix 3) into a fully quantum mechanical formulism. In order to achieve the most compact treatment they use the density matrix. This is defined in terms of the matrix Hamiltonian $H(t)$ by the relation

$$\rho(t) = C \exp\left(-H(t)/kT\right) \tag{6.29}$$

where C is a normalizing constant equal to the reciprocal of the spur (i.e. the sum of the diagonal elements) of $\rho(t)$. Density matrix formulism is convenient since the Boltzmann weighting and normalizing of levels is brought about automatically. The Hamiltonian can be considered as that due to the unperturbed molecule H_0, whose eigenvalues are the rotor levels, together with a perturbation due to the field. The time-dependent Hamiltonian may therefore be written

$$H(t) = H_0 + V \cos \omega t. \tag{6.30}$$

Karplus and Schwinger[369] carry the treatment on from this relationship and solve the equations of motion under the assumption of random strong collisions. With the further assumption that $h\nu \ll kT$, it may be shown that the line-shape equation becomes

$$\alpha = \frac{4\pi^2 hN\bar{\nu}_0 c\mu^2}{3(kT)^2} \exp\left[-hcBJ(J+1)/kT\right]$$

$$\times \left[\frac{\bar{\nu}^2 \Delta \bar{\nu}}{(\Delta\bar{\nu})^2 + (\bar{\nu}-\bar{\nu}_0)^2 + 4\pi^2 |\mu_{ij}|^2 I_0/(3h^2c^3)}\right]. \tag{6.31}$$

This is the analogue of equation (5.30) and reduces to that form when I_0 is very small. The second or "negative frequency" term involving $(\bar{\nu}+\bar{\nu}_0)$ has been omitted since it is virtually constant (and small) over the resonance region. Equation (6.31) has been independently demonstrated (in essence) by Snyder and Richards[369] and, interestingly, it has also been derived by Townes[15] through equilibrium arguments. On inspection of equation (6.31), it will be seen that when $4\pi^2 |\mu_{ij}|^2 I_0/(3h^2c^3)$ becomes comparable to $(\Delta\bar{\nu})^2$, the absorption coefficient is everywhere reduced (especially so near the peak) and additionally the half-width of the resonance increases. The best-known example comes from Townes' studies of the inversion spectrum of ammonia. With a gas pressure of 4×10^{-2} torr, $(\Delta\bar{\nu})$ is $3 \cdot 3 \times 10^{-5}$ cm^{-1} and when microwave radiation in the $1 \cdot 25$ cm region with an intensity of $3 \cdot 9$ mW cm^{-2} is applied, the additional term in the denominator has the value $0 \cdot 66 \times 10^{-9}$ and the condition mentioned above is satisfied. The effect in practice is that the peak height is only half its expected value and the half-width of the line is twice as great. At very high intensities, the absorption coefficient at peak asymptotically approaches zero which means that the power absorbed from the radiation asymptotically approaches a constant value. In this asymptotic region, the rate of absorption of energy (now independent of the incident power) is just equal to the rate of transformation of radiant energy into kinetic energy by collision. The half-width parameter $\Delta\bar{\nu}$ is linearly proportional to the pressure and it follows therefore that the radiant intensity at which saturation is noticed will vary directly as the square of the pressure. If $\Delta\bar{\nu}$ is extremely small, very weak radiation fields will be able to saturate the transition and reduce α_{max} to zero. This, together with the existence of a natural line-width and residual Doppler broadening, disposes of the paradox that α_{max} should be constant and independent of gas pressure even for vanishingly small pressures. It is interesting to note that it is impossible to bring about a population inversion merely by applying very high CW intensity to a two-level system. The system will merely absorb the limiting power and the remainder will be transmitted without attenuation. The phenomenon can, however, be turned to advantage in laser technology to aid in the construction of passive Q switches. These devices are similar in essential action to the high-speed rotating mirrors which are also used to ensure that the Q (quality or amplification factor) of the Fabry–Perot resonator is low most of the time and only reaches a high value for very short times. The laser will only radiate when the Q is high and the net effect is to concentrate the power which might have been radiated in a pulse of, say, 1 μs length into a pulse only 1 ns in length. The peak power can rise by a large factor. The operation of the passive Q switch is to depress the Q of the cavity by absorption. In the early stages of the emission pulse, the absorption coefficient is high but it steadily falls due to saturation and the Q rises. Eventually, if all the experimental conditions are properly adjusted, the Q will reach a high value for a very short time at the end of the normal emission pulse and the observed effect will be a "giant" or Q-spoiled pulse of very short duration and very high peak power. Another interesting facet of saturation is that, unlike the overall intensity, the effect depends only on the matrix element $(\mu_{ij})^2$ and not on the number of molecules in the ground state. This is particularly important at submillimetre wavelengths where the intrinsic intensity may be low due to the small population of high J states.

Karplus and Schwinger[369] are careful to point out that the broadening of the line does not arise from any fundamental modification of the line-shape, but rather is a consequence of a frequency-dependent population difference. If $\overline{\Delta N_I}$ is the mean population difference with the field on and ΔN the equilibrium thermal population difference then it follows that

$$\overline{\Delta N_I} = \frac{\Delta N}{1 + 4\pi \mid \mu_{ij} \mid^2 I_0 / \{3c^3 h^2 [(\bar{\nu} - \bar{\nu}_0)^2 + (\Delta \bar{\nu})^2]\}}. \tag{6.32}$$

The frequency dependence of the population difference leads to some very interesting effects. Senitzky and his colleagues[371] have considered the application of a very strong saturating field accompanied by weak amplitude-modulated side-bands. In order to derive the time dependence of the polarization and thus to obtain $\hat{\epsilon}$, they solve equation (31) of Appendix 3 under the condition that ΔN is no longer a constant but is determined by

$$d\Delta N/dt + \tau^{-1}(\Delta N - \Delta N_0) = -(2/hc\bar{\nu}_0)\,[P(t)/\tau + dP(t)/dt]\,E(t). \tag{6.33}$$

If the applied field has the form

$$E(t) = E_0 \cos \omega_0 t + E_S \cos [(\omega_0 + \delta)\,t + \phi_1], \tag{6.34}$$

i.e. single side-band operation, then the coupled differential equations can be approximately solved, provided $E_S \ll E_0$ and $\delta\tau \ll 1$, to give

$$P(t) = \{\epsilon''_{\omega_0}/[2\pi(1+\gamma^2)]\} \{E_0 \sin \omega_0 t + (1+\gamma^2)^{-1} E_S$$
$$\times \sin[(\omega_0+\delta) t + \phi_1] - \gamma^2(1+\gamma^2)^{-1} E_S \sin [(\omega_0-\delta) t - \phi_1]\} \quad (6.35)$$

where $P(t)$ is the induced dipole moment per unit volume, ϵ''_{ω_0} is the value of ϵ'' at $\omega = \omega_0$ and

$$\gamma^2 = 4\pi^2 |\mu_{ij}|^2 E_0^2\tau^2 h^{-2} = 4\pi |\mu_{ij}|^2 I_0/[3h^2c^3(\Delta\bar{\nu})^2] = I_0 \alpha_{\max} \tau/(h\nu_0 N)$$

is a saturation parameter. It is interesting to observe that as γ^2 becomes significant, the "image" side-band at frequency $(\omega_0-\delta)$ appears in the radiation transmitted through the gas. If there are two side-bands to start with then the saturation leads to each of them being partly amplified as well as attenuated. The absorption coefficient in any system can always be derived by noting that the power absorbed per unit volume is given by

$$I_0 - I = I_0[1 - \exp(-\alpha)] \approx I_0\alpha \quad (6.36)$$

if α is small. Now the power absorbed per unit volume must also equal the real part of the product of the electric field strength and the time derivative of the polarization or else, using a real formulism, the time average of the product of the field strength and the time derivative of the polarization. Therefore

$$I_0\alpha = \mathrm{Re}\,[\hat{E}\hat{P}^*] = \overline{E(t)\,\dot{P}(t)}. \quad (6.37)$$

Applying this relationship to equation (6.35), we have

$$\alpha_0 = \epsilon''_{\omega_0} \omega_0/[c(1+\gamma^2)] \quad (6.38)$$

which reduces as it should to equation (20) of Appendix 3 when γ^2 = zero. The absorption coefficient of either side-band is made up of two parts, one positive and the other negative, so we have

$$\alpha_s = \epsilon''_s(1-\gamma^2)\,(\omega_0 \pm \delta)/[c(1+\gamma)^2]. \quad (6.39)$$

When $\gamma^2 > 1$, α_s becomes negative which implies that the medium amplifies rather than attenuates the side-bands. If γ^2 is very large compared to unity ($\gamma^2 = 3$ corresponds to the condition mentioned earlier) then the sum of the power gain of the two side-bands becomes equal to the power loss of the saturating carrier. This is because by assumption $\omega_0+\delta \approx \omega_0$ and therefore $\epsilon''_0 \approx \epsilon''_s$. Senitzky and his colleagues have also investigated what happens when $\delta\tau$ is no longer very much smaller than unity.[371] Their essential conclusion is that useful amplification is possible only over a frequency interval which is equal to the power-broadened line-width. However, since this may be as much as 5 MHz, the phenomenon looks a promising source of a work-able amplifier for the submillimetre region.

The first attempts to realize this possibility came from Senitzky and his collaborators[371] who worked on the $(J = 0, M_J = 0) \rightarrow (J = 1, M_J = 0)$ line of $H^{12}C^{15}N$ which occurs at $86 \cdot 055$ GHz. A stabilized klystron provided this frequency and the radiation was then amplitude modulated at 70 MHz before being passed through a waveguide containing the isotopic HCN. The choice of this particular isotopic variety was made to avoid complications due to line broadening by the large ^{14}N nuclear quadrupole. It was found that with a gas pressure of 2×10^{-2} torr and a 20 ft long $\frac{3}{4}$ in. i.d. circular waveguide, the side-band attenuation for low input power was 26 dB, but that when the saturating power rose to $4 \cdot 8$ mW ($\gamma^2 = 10$) the side-bands were amplified with a gain of $1 \cdot 5$ dB. Later experiments[372] showed that $H^{12}C^{14}N$ would work just as well. The $J = 0 \rightarrow J = 1$ line of this species occurs at $88 \cdot 632$ GHz ($3 \cdot 38$ mm) and with the gas enclosed in a resonant cavity, side-band amplifications up to 20 dB with a bandwidth of 2 MHz were realized. It will be seen from inspection of equation (6.39) that the larger is the natural absorption coefficient, the larger the side-band amplification becomes under saturation conditions. It is natural therefore to work at as high a frequency as possible since the intensity of the pure rotation lines increases as the cube of the frequency for $h\nu \ll kT$. The saturating power, however, only depends on $| \mu_{tj} |^2$ which is a slowly varying function of frequency. For this reason Liebe[373] has investigated the $J = 2 \rightarrow J = 3$ line of $H^{12}C^{15}N$ which occurs at $258 \cdot 157$ GHz. It was found that, with the gas enclosed in a cylindrical cavity (3 mm diameter, 7 mm length), at a pressure up to 1 torr, saturation was achieved with 100 μW of power and that side-band amplifications of up to 20 dB with a bandwidth of $0 \cdot 5$ MHz were possible. Attempts to work at still higher frequencies have been frustrated by the lack of intense sources: the lasers are available but at the moment they can only be tuned over a very narrow range. So we return again to the topic of near coincidence. The molecule 1,1-difluoroethylene, as remarked earlier, has an absorption line very close to the HCN laser line at 890 GHz. Bradley and Knight[298] have measured the absolute frequency of this absorp-tion line and have found it to lie $0 \cdot 6$ MHz below the laser frequency, i.e. at $890 \cdot 7596$ GHz $\pm 0 \cdot 2$ MHz. If a gas cell containing $CF_2 = CH_2$ is included within the resonant cavity then the cavity fringes (cf. Fig. 6.3) show an interesting profile.[374] This is illustrated in Fig. 6.14 for the case of low excitation.

The sudden dip in output power occurs when the laser frequency has shifted into coincidence with the absorption line of the gas. The Q of the cavity drops and the power output falls. At very high levels of excitation—as might exist in a large laser with a hemispherical cavity—a dip is no longer

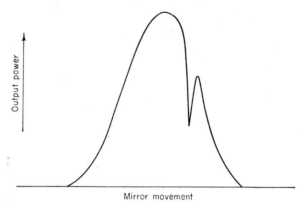

Fig. 6. 14. Cavity-fringe profile for HCN laser containing 0·05 torr $CF_2 = CH_2$ in a 50 cm long intracavity absorption cell.

observed.[375] In its place, passive Q-switching action occurs. This is illustrated in Fig. 6·15 where the asymmetry between the mirror travelling one way as compared with the other is clearly demonstrated. When the mirror is travelling in, towards the resonant position, no emission is noted until well after the position where emission begins with no $CH_2 = CF_2$ in the cavity (broken line in the Figure). Suddenly emission begins and it rapidly rises to a higher value than would be expected (P). Conversely, when the mirror is moving out, the laser "goes out" before it should, but at a much greater mirror separation from resonance than was the case for switching on with the mirror moving in.

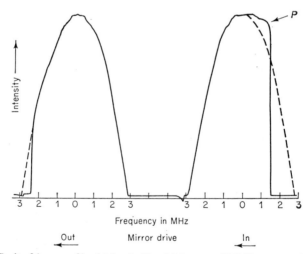

Fig. 6.15. Cavity-fringe profile obtained with a high-power HCN laser containing 0·05 torr $CF_2 = CH_2$ in 1 m long absorption cell. The moving mirror of the cavity is oscillated over a single fringe and the position has been calibrated in terms of the equivalent frequency shift.

The increase in power due to Q-switching action is very small but it does confirm the similar results obtained by Jones, Bradley, Chamberlain, Gebbie, Stone and Sixsmith[376] who worked with a rotating mirror. The reason for this small effect is still obscure but must be connected with some very efficient relaxation mechanism operative in the plasma. When radiation from an HCN laser is passed through difluoroethylene in a gas cell external to the cavity, the usual power-saturation effects are manifest.[375] Thus with $0 \cdot 04$ torr gas pressure at 296 K the absorption coefficient is $7 \cdot 5 = 10^{-4}$ neper cm^{-1} at peak for an input power of 100 μW cm^{-2}. When the power is increased to 10 mW cm^{-2} the peak absorption coefficient drops to 4×10^{-4} neper cm^{-1} and the half-width increases from 2 MHz to $2 \cdot 8$ MHz. With this demonstration of saturation effects using the radiation from a submillimetre laser, the immediate prospects for locking the laser frequency to the peak of a molecular absorption line are very good and the long-term prospects for the construction of submillimetre amplifiers look promising.

6.8. The Generation of Submillimetre Waves as Difference Frequency Radiation in Non-linear Media

In a formal sense, the topic of non-linear optics has a very long history, dating from the discovery of optical activity in 1811. This observation was followed by the discovery of the Faraday effect in 1845, the Kerr effect in 1875, the linear electro-optic effect in 1893 and the Cotton–Mouton effect in 1907. These classical examples arise either from the application of intense external (i.e. man-made) electrical or magnetic fields, or else from the effects of the high internal fields which are naturally present in some molecules due to an asymmetric disposition of the constituent atoms. Very high fields are necessary because of the small size of the non-linear coefficients in the expression for the polarization. If we write this

$$P = \chi E(1 + a_1 E + a_2 E^2 + \ldots), \qquad (6.40)$$

a_1, a_2 etc. are always very much less than unity. If two fields of amplitudes E_{ν_1} and E_{ν_2} are applied to a non-linear medium at frequencies ν_1 and ν_2, the intensities of the oscillating polarizations at frequencies $2\nu_1$, $\nu_1 \pm \nu_2$ and $2\nu_2$ will be proportional to

$$a_1\{E_{\nu_1}\}^2, \quad a_1\{E_{\nu_1}E_{\nu_2}\} \quad \text{and} \quad a_1(E_{\nu_2})^2.$$

With normal, non-coherent sources, high-power densities cannot be achieved and because of this E_ν is unlikely to exceed 10^{-3} V cm^{-1}. If an effect is to be observed when E_{ν_1} is an optical field, it follows that E_{ν_2} must be very large indeed. This implies either a "built in" atomic field which can range up to 10^{10} V cm^{-1}, or else an external man-made field which can readily be

10^5 V cm^{-1}. Similar remarks apply to magnetic effects. At the moment, intense external fields can only be generated at relatively low frequencies ($\nu_2 < 10^9$ Hz) and for this reason non-linear effects involving two optical frequencies had not been observed as late as 1960.

Then came the development of the optical maser or laser—a device which in its Q-spoiled form was capable of peak powers of the order of megawatts and which gave radiation so coherent that it could be focussed down into an area of the order of a few square wavelengths. The optical electric fields generated in this way could approach 10^8 V cm^{-1} and, not surprisingly, an array of non-linear phenomena was soon being reported from laboratories all over the world.[377] Some of the most interesting results have come from work with the ruby laser, a device whose mode of operation was described in Section 5.11. The ruby laser can be Q-switched to give "giant" pulses either by the use of a rotating mirror or else by the use of a passive absorber. If the radiation from two "giant pulse" lasers, one operating on R_1 and the other on R_2 (or else what has recently proved possible, the radiation from a single giant pulse laser operating on both simultaneously), is focussed in a non-linear crystal such as ammonium dihydrogen phosphate (ADP), then ultra-violet radiation at 3472 Å ($2R_1$), 3469 Å ($R_1 + R_2$) and 3465 Å ($2R_2$) is observed from the crystal. The experiment is not completely straightforward, since, for significant transfer of power into the harmonics and the sum frequency, the wavetrains generated must be propagating in the crystal at velocities appropriate to their frequencies. For this to be the case, it follows that when two frequencies, ν_1 and ν_2, are added to give ν_3, then

$$n_3 \bar{\nu}_3 = n_1 \bar{\nu}_1 + n_2 \bar{\nu}_2. \tag{6.41}$$

If there is no dispersion, the equation is automatically satisfied: if there is, then, by choosing suitably birefringent crystals at an appropriate angle to the laser beam, it can be arranged, via the angular dependence of the ordinary (n_0) and extraordinary (n_e) indices, that the equation be satisfied and phase or index matching be achieved. It is also necessary of course that the crystal be transparent at the three frequencies and that the non-linear coefficients be of reasonable size. Despite these restrictions, there is available an impressive range of suitable non-linear crystals including quartz, potassium hydrogen phosphate and the remarkable lithium metaniobate, $LiNbO_3$. Using these crystals, even third harmonics have been observed and the modulation of a laser beam at microwave frequencies has become commonplace; but in 1963, when Franken and Ward[378] wrote their review of non-linear optics, difference frequencies had not been observed.

The first successful observation of difference frequency radiation came in 1965 from Zernike and Berman.[379] They used a high-power neodymium in glass laser emitting a range of wavelengths between 1·059 and 1·073 μm.

The radiation was phase-matched in quartz and far infrared emission near 100 cm^{-1} was observed. The reason for earlier failures was now clear, the best non-linear crystals absorb very strongly due to reststrahlen effects in the far infrared. To avoid this difficulty Yajima and Inoue[380] went over to semi-conductor non-linear crystals and, using zinc telluride, they were able to observe emission at 29 cm^{-1} when the R_1 and R_2 lines of a single giant pulse laser were focussed on the crystal. Zinc telluride crystallizes in the cubic system, so the phase-matching equation for difference generation,

$$n_3 \bar{\nu}_3 = n_1 \bar{\nu}_1 - n_2 \bar{\nu}_2, \tag{6.42}$$

cannot be satisfied in the conventional manner. However, if a coherence length l is defined as $l^{-1} = 2(n_1 \bar{\nu}_1 - n_2 \bar{\nu}_2 - n_3 \bar{\nu}_3)$, it is found that l is fortunately quite large (0·6 mm). The non-linear coefficients for this material are much bigger ($\times 500$) than they are for quartz, so the combined effects permit efficient operation. The peak powers observed were 10^{-3} W which was very much less—presumably due to absorption—than the experimentalists were hoping for. The frequency of each of the lines R_1 and R_2 can be shifted by altering the temperature of the ruby crystal. The R_1 line occurs at 14 422 cm^{-1} (6934 Å) at $-180°$ C, whereas it shifts[381] to 14 376 cm^{-1} (6956 Å) at $+200°$ C. It follows therefore that by beating the radiation from two separate lasers which are at different temperatures, it is possible in principle to generate submillimetre radiation in the form of short pulses virtually from 0 to 100 cm^{-1}. Very recently this has been achieved in practice by Faries and his colleagues[382] who observed emission varying from 1·2 to 8·1 cm^{-1} at power levels of the order of milliwatts from the beating of two temperature-tuned lasers within a lithium niobate crystal and in quartz. The refractive indices of lithium niobate are $n_0 = 2·273$ and $n_e = 2·189$ at the laser wavelength and $n_0 = 6·55$ in the very far infrared near 8·1 cm^{-1}. The phase-matching angle is 9·5° from the optic axis but, due to the smaller $\bar{k}$ vector for far infra-red photons, there is very much less tolerance on the phase matching than there is for sum-frequency generation. In fact the angle must be right to better than a quarter of a degree for any radiation to be observed; this, together with absorption and crystal inhomogeneities, may explain previous failures. Still more recently, radiation in the band 21–37 cm^{-1} from a cold R_1 laser and a warm R_2 laser has been observed[383] and with facilities to go down smoothly to liquid nitrogen temperatures full coverage of the 1–50 cm^{-1} region should be possible.

Another possibility which may produce a workable and tunable source of submillimetre power lies in the Raman effect of crystals. The Raman effect is the inelastic scattering of photons by a quantized system. If the incident photons have frequency ν_0 and the system can undergo a transition of frequency ν_i, then the scattered radiation will contain frequencies $\nu_0 - \nu_i$

(Stokes scattering) and $\nu_0 + \nu_i$ (anti-Stokes scattering). Under normal circumstances, the Raman intensity is extremely feeble, being of the order of 10^{-6} of the incident power, and additionally the anti-Stokes radiation is weaker than the corresponding Stokes radiation by the Boltzmann factor, $\exp(-h\nu_i/kT)$. The Raman spectrum is similar in a way to the infrared spectrum in that both contain energy-level information, but the selection rules for Raman scattering are different from those for infrared absorption. Basically a mode of vibration is infrared active if it has the symmetry of a translation in the x, y, or z directions, whereas a mode is Raman active if it has the symmetry of x^2, y^2, z^2, xy, yz or zx. It is for this reason that, although physicists after 1930 had become disenchanted with so weak an effect, chemists continued to struggle to observe Raman spectra, for this was the only way of arriving at the complete vibrational spectra of many molecules (see Section 5.9). The development of the laser changed the situation to a great extent, for the much higher power levels meant that reasonable quality spectra could be obtained more readily and in a shorter time. The interest of physicists in the Raman effect was revived by this, especially since Raman studies were a necessary adjunct to infrared for exploring the dispersion curves of crystals, but the observation which changed the situation completely was the discovery of stimulated Raman scattering by Woodbury and his colleagues.[384] These workers noticed that when a giant pulse from a ruby laser was focussed in a liquid such as benzene, Raman emission in the form of a diffuse ring around the primary beam occurred and the total Raman power could be 10 per cent of the incident laser power. This represented an immense increase in Raman intensity. The Raman emission occurred, of course, at a frequency shift appropriate to a mode of vibration of the molecules in the liquid and, since this could be varied merely by changing the liquid, the stimulated Raman effect provided a convenient mechanism for altering the frequency of laser emissions.

The origin of the Raman effect can be seen from equation (6.40) for if the molecules are vibrating at a frequency ν_i we would expect χ^m (the molecular polarizability) to be modulated at this frequency in the following manner:

$$\chi^m(t) = \chi_0^m + (\partial \chi^m / \partial Q) Q \qquad (6.43)$$

where $Q = Q_0 \cos 2\pi\nu_i t$ is the appropriate normal coordinate of vibration. Due to the term χ_0^m, the scattered radiation from each molecule will contain a component at the same frequency and coherent with the incoming radiation. Because of the coherence, the scattered intensity will be expected to cancel in all directions except the forward direction, the situation being physically analogous to Huyghen's construction—but due to random fluctuations of density and temperature the cancellation is not perfect and some sideways scatter does occur. This is known as Rayleigh scattering and, being proportional (as also is Raman scattering) to the fourth power of the frequency, it explains such well-known phenomena as the blue colour of the sky. The second term in equation (6.43) will lead to components at frequencies $\nu_R = \nu_0 \pm \nu_i$—the Raman effect—but these components will have random phases since there is no phase correlation between the vibrations of molecules. The actual intensity of scattering can only be found by transcribing equation (6.43) into a quantum mechanical formulism[385] and the directional variation of intensity can only be calculated when the polarization of the laser radiation is known since χ is a second-rank tensor. Nevertheless, for most intents we can imagine that the normal (sometimes inaptly titled spontaneous) Raman effect involves the essentially isotropic emission of very feeble radiation. There have been several expositions of the theoretical background to stimulated Raman emission, ranging from the phenomenological approach of Hellwarth[386] to the sophisticated quantum mechanical treatment of Buckingham[387] which shows how the reaction

Molecule (ground state)$+ 2\,h\nu_0 \rightarrow$

Molecule (ground state)$+ h(\nu_0 - \nu_i) + h(\nu_0 + \nu_i)$,

involving the destruction of two laser photons with the simultaneous creation of a Stokes and an anti-Stokes photon, can occur. However, the simple almost classical theory of Townes[388] is able to give a good physical insight into the origin of the phenomenon. For simplicity, consider a homonuclear diatomic molecule X_2. We wish to consider the forced vibration of this molecule in an electromagnetic field whose frequency is much less than any electronic absorption frequency and much greater than the vibrational frequency. In the ordinary sense there can be no forced vibration leading to an absorption and a dispersion at ν_i since the centrosymmetry forbids the vibration to be infrared active. However, we note that the energy of a polarizable molecule in a field is given by

$$E = \tfrac{1}{2}\mu E = \tfrac{1}{2}\chi^m E^2, \tag{6.44}$$

so that if χ^m is a function of nuclear coordinates (i.e. vibrational motion) it follows that

$$F = \partial E/\partial r = \tfrac{1}{2}(\partial \chi^m/\partial r)\, E^2. \tag{6.45}$$

Under normal circumstances the fact that there are two optical fields present, one due to the laser and the other to the Stokes–Raman radiation, can be neglected because the latter is very feeble and there is no phase coherence. However, as the intensity of the laser radiation rises, the effect of that part of the Stokes radiation which is sensibly coherent with the laser becomes more and more significant. Eventually we have to consider $(E_{\text{laser}} + E_{\text{Raman}})^2$ and this contains a component at a frequency $|\,\nu_0 - \nu_R\,|$, i.e. ν_i. At this frequency the molecule is resonant and responds with maximum effect to the driving force. The net result is that the molecules are forced into vibration, the motion modulates the laser beam and this transfers still more intensity to the Raman field which, interacting back with the laser beam, forces the molecules to vibrate still more fiercely. At a sufficiently high initial laser intensity, the whole effect becomes a run-away chain reaction leading to the very high conversion ratios mentioned earlier. The full mathematical treatment indicates, not surprisingly, that the threshold for stimulated Raman action is lower, the more intense and the narrower is the ordinary Raman band, for both these make the response to a driving field at frequency ν_i larger. In practice, this means that the totally symmetric Raman modes are the easiest to obtain in stimulated emission.

If we have a molecule or crystal which has symmetry low enough for the totally symmetric modes to be also infrared active, the intriguing possibility arises that the oscillating molecules may emit infrared radiation at the vibrational frequency. This radiation, which arises as a difference mode between the laser and the Raman radiation, is sometimes called the "idler" radiation by analogy with three-level parametric amplifiers. The requirement, therefore, for difference frequency generation by way of the stimulated Raman effect, calls for crystals having transverse optical modes which are, simultaneously, strongly active in both Raman scattering and infrared absorption and which, further, have large non-linear coefficients at optical frequencies. In order to discuss the interaction of such a crystal with electromagnetic fields, it is necessary to introduce the concept of a polariton. A polariton is a quantized entity which can propagate in an ionic crystal and which can be regarded as a mixture of a photon and an optical phonon; thus its momentum is partly electromagnetic and partly mechanical. The coupling of the electromagnetic oscillations with the lattice vibrations arises from the strong dispersion near the transverse optic frequency. If the general result

$$v_\phi = \epsilon^{-1/2} c = 2\pi \bar{\nu} c / \bar{k} \tag{6.46}$$

for the propagation of an electromagnetic wave, is combined with the reststrahlen dispersion relation (equation 5.52), one obtains

$$\bar{k} = 2\pi \bar{\nu} \left[\epsilon_\infty + (\epsilon_0 - \epsilon_\infty) \, \bar{\nu}_{TO}^2 (\bar{\nu}_{TO}^2 - \nu^2)^{-1} \right]^{1/2} \tag{6.47}$$

as the dispersion relation for polaritons. This result is not different in physical essence from the previous results derived in Chapter 5. In particular, it will be observed that there are two branches and that there is a gap between $\bar{\nu} = \bar{\nu}_{TO}$ and $\bar{\nu} = \bar{\nu}_{LO}$ just as was noted before; but the equation written in the form of (6.47) is very helpful for discussing Raman scattering from non-linear ionic crystals. In the lower branch of the dispersion diagram, the particle is photon-like for $\bar{k} \ll \bar{\nu}_{TO}$ and propagates with the phase velocity $\epsilon_0^{-1/2} c$, whilst for $\bar{k}$ values much greater than $\bar{v}_{TO}$, the particle is phonon-like and approaches the frequency of the transverse optic mode at the zone-edge. This is illustrated in Fig. 6.16. The scattering of photons, in the Raman effect, has to be such that both energy and momentum are conserved; but, since no photon is absorbed, it is possible in principle to explore far more of the dispersion diagram than is the case with infrared absorption spectroscopy. If an incident photon of frequency v_0 is scattered at an angle θ (from the

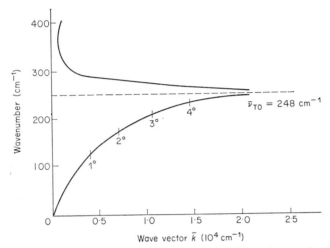

FIG. 6.16. Dispersion diagram for the 248 A_1 polariton in lithium niobate after Gelbwachs *et al.* [389] The curve does not agree with the prediction of equation (6.47), especially in the upper branch. This is due to the finite width of the transverse optic resonance.

direction of the incident beam) and with a frequency shift (Stokes) of v_p, then momentum conservation demands that the wave vector of the phonon $\bar{k}_p$ should complete the triangle between the wave vector of the incident photon $\bar{k}_L$ and the wave vector of the scattered photon $\bar{k}_s$. Applying the cosine rule to this triangle, it follows that

$$(\bar{k}_p)^2 = (\bar{k}_s)^2 + (\bar{k}_L)^2 - 2\bar{k}_L\bar{k}_s \cos\theta. \tag{6.48}$$

The wave vectors $\bar{k}_s$ and $\bar{k}_L$ are both greater than 10^4 cm^{-1}, so the value of $\bar{k}_p$ will correspond to the asymptotic region of the lower branch of Fig. 6.16 unless θ is very small. If the discussion is restricted to the case of near forward scattering (θ very small) and if there is only weak dispersion near the laser frequency, equation (6.48) may be approximated by

$$(\bar{k}_p)^2 = 4\pi^2 n^2 \bar{v}_p^2 + \bar{k}_L\bar{k}_s\theta^2. \tag{6.49}$$

This represents a family of hyperbolae in the dispersion diagram and the intersections of these hyperbolae with the polariton dispersion curve give the frequencies of the Raman displacements for the appropriate angles.

Puthoff, Pantell, Huth and Chacon[390] found that the frequency shift of the spontaneous Raman scattering from $LiNbO_3$ was strongly angle dependent for θ less than 5°. They constructed dispersion diagrams for the 628 cm^{-1} A_1 polariton and confirmed the basic theory. Gelbwachs, Pantell, Puthoff and Yarborough[389] obtained similar results from the observation of stimulated Raman scattering of the A_1 248 cm^{-1} polariton. The frequency shift was again strongly angle dependent for angles of scatter less than 5°. Some of their experimental values are included in Fig. 6.16. They mounted a crystal of lithium niobate inside a Fabry–Perot resonator and introduced a beam from a Q-switched ruby laser into the crystal at a suitable angle of incidence to produce, inside the crystal, the desired angle θ between the direction of the laser beam and the resonator axis. As θ was varied from 5° to 0·5° the Raman displacement went from 248 to 50 cm^{-1}. The scattering for all angles greater than 5° is just the straightforward Raman effect of the 248 cm^{-1} TO mode: the scattering very close to the forward direction is, however, formally equivalent to the scattering of a photon by a photon. This process can occur in lithium niobate because of the large non-linear susceptibility and is best thought of as a parametric process dominated by the nearby vibrational resonance. Yarborough and his colleagues[391] have observed similar effects with a $LiNbO_3$ crystal having two plane parallel polished faces cut in it to serve as the Fabry–Perot reflectors. Through an additional face cut at 60° on one corner of the crystal they were able to detect the far infrared difference or idler radiation. No quantitative power measurements were made but an estimate gave the peak power of the pulses as 5 W. Subsequently, Yarborough and Amman[392] demonstrated simultaneous optical parametric oscillation, second harmonic generation and difference-frequency generation in lithium niobate and Johnson et al.[393] showed that the difference-frequency peak power was of the order 3 W at 200 μm and had a line-width of 0·5 cm^{-1}. It has thus been demonstrated that high-power pulsed coherent radiation can be produced in the far infrared and that the output frequency can be tuned by merely rotating a crystal. It goes without saying that such a device would be most valuable and now that some of the difficulties, such as damage to the optical components by the intense Q-spoiled pulses, have been overcome it may well become the chosen spectroscopic system for the more difficult type of submillimetre experiment.

Very intense optical lasers are necessary for experiments involving difference-frequency generation for the reasons given earlier. The CO_2 laser operating in two bands near 10 μm is one of the most intense lasers known, giving CW power of the order of kilowatts. It may also be Q-switched, either by means of a rotating mirror or else by the use of saturable absorbers (see

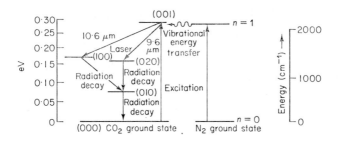

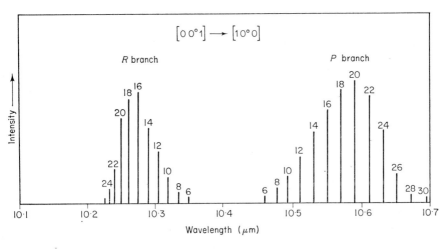

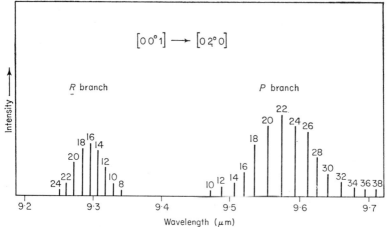

FIG. 6.17. Energy levels and observed emission spectrum of the CO_2 laser. The state labels (10°0) and (02°0) have only schematic meaning because of the strong Fermi resonance.

Section 6.11). Not surprisingly, therefore, a great deal of attention has been devoted to using the CO_2 laser to produce difference frequencies. The spectrum obtainable from this laser is shown schematically in Fig. 6.17. Because the oxygen nuclei in the common ($^{12}C^{16}O_2$) form of carbon dioxide have zero spin, only those rotational levels of $\Sigma_g(A_{1g})$ states which have even values of J can exist. Conversely, for antisymmetric [ungerade] states, only those rotational levels which have odd values of J can exist. In a $\Sigma_u \rightarrow \Sigma_g$ band such as the 10 μm system of CO_2, there will therefore be no Q branch, but an R branch ($\Delta J = +1$) and a P branch ($\Delta J = -1$) will occur and the line spacing in these will be roughly $1 \cdot 6$ cm^{-1}, i.e. $\approx 4B$. The distribution of intensity amongst the various lines of the bands follows roughly that observed in absorption. The strongest line is the $P(20)$ line of the $(001) \rightarrow (100)$ band at $10 \cdot 6$ μm. The two vibration bands and the P and R branches of individual bands are in competition with each other and the operation of the laser to give a specific line requires the use of a frequency-selective cavity (see Section 6.5).

Bridges and Chang[292] obtained beat frequencies between adjacent lines of the CO_2 laser by using the radiation from two CW feedback stabilized lasers mixed in a bulk GaAs crystal. Their work was an extension of that of Chang, Van Tran and Patel[394] who were able to satisfy the index-matching requirement by using the GaAs crystal to fill a waveguide. The phase velocity at the difference frequency will be determined by the refractive index of the filler and by the physical dimensions of the waveguide (see Section 4.4) and, by an appropriate choice of waveguide size a long coherence length can be ensured. The beat frequencies obtained ranged from $83 \cdot 663$ 36 GHz $[R(14) - R(10)]$ in the $[00^\circ 1] \rightarrow [10^\circ 0]$ band to $51 \cdot 352$ 69 GHz $[P(12) - P(14)]$ in the same band. The observed frequencies from beating lines in the $[00^\circ 1] \rightarrow [02^\circ 0]$ band covered roughly the same range. The $[P(18) - P(20)]$ beat frequency has the value $53 \cdot 548$ 16 GHz which agrees very well with that obtained from subtraction of their absolute frequencies (see Table 6.2). The availability of essentially microwave methods for studying an infrared band system has, not unexpectedly, led to an enormous increase in accuracy in the determination of some of the molecular parameters. As an example, Bridges and Chang[292] give the B value for the $[00^\circ 1]$ vibrational state as $0 \cdot 387$ 140 44$\pm$ $0 \cdot 000$ 000 37 cm^{-1}, which is to be compared with the best previous value $0 \cdot 387$ 132$\pm 0 \cdot 000$ 040 cm^{-1}. The uncertainty is thus reduced by two orders of magnitude.

Van Tran and Patel[395] have produced far infrared radiation in the 100 cm^{-1} region by beating the radiation from a CO_2 laser operating in the $10 \cdot 6$ μm band with that of another operating in the $9 \cdot 6$ μm band. The mixing crystal that they used was n-type indium antimonide and to secure the necessary phase matching they took advantage of magnetoplasma effects in the semiconductor. The reststrahlen region for indium antimonide (as remarked earlier) occurs in the 190 cm^{-1} region ($\bar{\nu}_{TO} = 183$ cm^{-1}, $\bar{\nu}_{LO} = 197$ cm^{-1}), and because of this the refractive index is high in the 100 cm^{-1} region. However, the dispersion due to the plasma absorption can reduce the index (see equation 5.121) and there will also be an effect, if the sample is in a magnetic field, due to the dispersion associated with the cyclotron resonance absorption. Van Tran and Patel, quoting Palik and Wright, give a relation for the complex dielectric constant of an impure semiconductor in a magnetic field. From this ϵ' can be derived by rationalization, the result being

$$\epsilon(\nu)/\epsilon_\infty$$

$$= 1 + \frac{(\epsilon_0 - \epsilon_\infty)\,\nu_{TO}^2}{\epsilon_\infty(\nu_{TO}^2 - \nu^2)} - \frac{\nu_p^2}{(\nu^2 + \nu_e^2)}$$

$$\times \left\{ \frac{\nu_p^2(\nu_p^2 - 2\nu^2) + \nu^2(\nu^2 + \nu_e^2) + \nu_c^2(\nu_p^2 - \nu^2)}{\nu_p^2(\ \nu_p^2 - 2\nu^2) + \nu^2\ (\nu^2 + \nu_e^2) + \nu^2\nu_c^2\ [2\nu_p^2 + \nu_c^2 - 2\ (\nu^2 - \nu_e^2)][\nu^2 + \nu_e^2]^{-1}} \right\}$$

$$(6.50)$$

where ν_p is the plasma frequency, here defined to be

$$\nu_p^2 = N_e\, e^2/(\pi m^*\, \epsilon_\infty), \tag{6.51}$$

ν_c is the cyclotron resonance frequency and ν_e the electron–ion collision frequency $= (2\pi\tau)^{-1}$. Equation (6.50) is rather complicated, but a good insight into its physical significance can be obtained by the approximation that ν_e is very small. With this assumption the equation reduces to

$$\epsilon(\nu) = \epsilon_\infty \left\{ 1 + \frac{(\epsilon_0 - \epsilon_\infty)\,\nu_{TO}^2}{\epsilon_\infty(\nu_{TO}^2 - \nu^2)} - \frac{\nu_p^2(\nu_p^2 - \nu^2)}{\nu^2(\nu_p^2 - \nu^2 + \nu_c^2)} \right\}$$

which can be written

$$\epsilon(\nu) = \epsilon_\infty \left\{ 1 + \frac{(\epsilon_0 - \epsilon_\infty)\,\nu_{TO}^2}{\epsilon_\infty(\nu_{TO}^2 - \nu^2)} - \frac{\nu_p^2}{\nu^2} \left[1 - \frac{\nu_c^2}{\nu^2 - \nu_p^2} \right]^{-1} \right\}. \tag{6.52}$$

Clearly if ν is greater than ν_p, there will always exist values of ν_p and ν_c which are such that the third or Drude term exactly cancels the second and the refractive index at the far infrared difference frequency equals that at the CO_2 laser frequency. For the particular sample studied by Van Tran and Patel, ϵ_∞ was 15·68, ϵ_0 was 18·17, N_e was $1·6 \times 10^{15}$ cm^{-3}, ν_p was 0·75 THz ($m^* = 0·0136\, m_e$) and ν_e was 0·15 THz. The difference wavenumber obtained by beating $P(20)$ of the $(001) \rightarrow (100)$ band with $P(12)$ of the $(001) \rightarrow (020)$ band was 101 cm^{-1} and so the two terms will cancel for $\nu_c = 2·2$ THz. This requires a magnetic field of 11 kG and the plot of output power at 101 cm^{-1} versus field strength showed a sharp resonance at this value of the field. The peak output power levels obtained were of the order of some microwatts, so this device may be very useful as a source of discretely tunable far infrared radiation.

A most exciting outcome of studies of the pumping of indium antimonide by CO_2 radiation in the presence of a magnetic field is the discovery by Patel and his colleagues of the "spin-flip" Raman laser. Transitions between the split components of a Kramers doublet are allowed by virtue of a magnetic dipole coupling as was shown in Section 5.11, leading to absorption of the frequency given by equation (5.99). This transition is also Raman active and if a photon of frequency v_0 is incident on a material containing unpaired electrons, it may be scattered at a frequency given by

$$v_s = v_0 \pm g\beta H. \tag{6.53}$$

Spontaneous Raman scattering from the conduction electrons in semiconductors had been reported earlier by Patel and his group[396] but late in 1969, using a repetitively Q-switched frequency selective laser delivering the $P(20)$ line at $10 \cdot 5915$ μm, they observed stimulated Raman scattering.[397] Magnetic fields of up to 100 kG provided by a superconducting magnet were used and it was found possible to tune the Stokes–Raman line from $11 \cdot 7$ to $13 \cdot 0$ μm. The gain in the Raman line is a sensitive function of H for low H and, because of this, it was not possible to observe stimulated emission closer in to the exciting line than $11 \cdot 7$ μm. At fields above 100 kG, free carrier absorption— which also increases with field strength (see Section 6.12) suppresses the stimulated action. The large frequency shifts (≈ 168 cm^{-1} for $H = 100$ kG) are a consequence of the high g values for the conduction electrons in n-InSb which range from 48 at $H = 0$ to 35 for $H = 100$ kG. Patel and Shaw observed Raman pulses of peak power 1 W and the radiation had a line-width of less than $0 \cdot 05$ cm^{-1}. Patel, Shaw and Kerl have used the Stokes spin-flip radiation to study part of the v_2 band of ammonia and were able to resolve some groups of lines which had resisted conventional[399] techniques, even though these had a claimed resolving power of $0 \cdot 1$ cm^{-1}.

Anti-Stokes scattering was observed later by Shaw and Patel[400] but was found to be much weaker than the Stokes scattering and was only observable for fields between 30 and 65 kG. The radiation could therefore be tuned from ≈ 10 to $\approx 9 \cdot 4$ μm with the $P(20)$ line as the pump. The much reduced intensity of the Anti-Stokes compared with the Stokes radiation is a consequence of the requirement for momentum conservation in the scattering process. If an excitation process, in a crystal, of frequency v and wave vector $\bar{k}$ is to be involved in Raman scattering, then for Stokes radiation $\bar{k}_s$ must equal $\bar{k}_0 - \bar{k}$ whilst for anti-Stokes radiation $\bar{k}_{as}$ must equal $\bar{k}_0 + \bar{k}$. These equations can only be solved in general knowing the dispersion relation for the excitation process, but for $\bar{k}_0$, $\bar{k}_s$ and $\bar{k}_{as}$ all parallel to each other along the

x axis and H along the z axis they can be combined to give

$$2\bar{k}_0 = \bar{k}_s + \bar{k}_{as}. \tag{6.54}$$

Now, provided there is little dispersion at ν_0, this equation is automatically satisfied and strong anti-Stokes emission will be observed but confined to a narrow range of directions close to the forward direction. The initial experiments adopted the traditional Raman geometry ($\bar{k}_s \perp \bar{k}_0$) and for this reason no anti-Stokes emission was observed. The combined Stokes and anti-Stokes emission gives an infrared source tunable from $9 \cdot 4$ to $12 \cdot 2$ μm with a small gap near the pump wavelength.

It is a familiar observation in molecular Raman spectroscopy that the intensity of a given Raman line may dramatically increase as the exciting line frequency approaches a strong absorption band of the scatterer. This is usually called the "Resonance Raman" effect and arises from terms such as $(\nu_{ex} - \nu_0)^{-1}$ in the expression for the Raman scattering cross section where ν_{ex} is the frequency of the absorption band. A similar effect is noted for semiconductors when the incident laser photon is close in energy to the band gap. Brueck and Mooradian[401] observed stimulated "spin-flip" emission from InSb when it was irradiated with CO laser radiation near $5 \cdot 3648$ μm. This is very close to the band gap which for zero field is $0 \cdot 18$ eV or 1548 cm^{-1} (see Fig. 4.28). Patel has reported a similar observation,[402] but has in addition observed Stokes–Raman lines with twice the frequency separation. The latter which he calls the "second Stokes spin-flip scattering" arises as the result of the Raman effect due to the initial first Stokes line. In other words, it is a Raman line excited by another Raman line. The band gap is a function of magnetic field both because the Fermi energy is a function of field and because of the break-up of the bands into discrete Landau levels and their consequent further splitting due to the effects of electron spin. The Raman scattering cross-section is thus sensitively dependent on field strength but for fields between 20 and 60 kG, the enhancement is sufficient for threshold to be achieved with CW power levels as low as 200 mW. The second Stokes scattering was only observed for fields between 25 and 46 kG and the lines were tenfold weaker compared with the first Stokes line. Nevertheless, the combined effect provides a source tunable between $5 \cdot 5$ and $5 \cdot 9$ μm. Unfortunately it may not prove easy to observe anti-Stokes scattering because of the heavy absorption in the crystal.

So far it has not proved possible to extract the "idler" far infrared radiation from these devices, but they represent examples of direct frequency spectroscopy of the microwave type at optical frequencies. It is not perhaps too fanciful to imagine that they will ultimately replace delay-type spectrometers for high-resolution infrared spectroscopy. This, coupled with the methods described earlier for overcoming Doppler-width problems, may imply that we are on the verge of enormous advances in high resolution infrared work.

The rapid development of dye-lasers[403] has opened up some additional prospects for the generation of infrared difference frequencies. An early form of dye-laser[404] was accidentally discovered (*and incorrectly identified*) at NPL in 1964 when alcoholic solutions of the cyanine dye, diethyl thia-tricarbocyanine iodide (DTTCI), were exposed to the focussed radiation from a gallium arsenide junction laser. This laser gives out intense pulses of radiation at a wavelength $0 \cdot 84$ μm and frequency-shifted radiation from the pumped dye solution was observed in a broad band from $0 \cdot 84$ to $0 \cdot 88$ μm with weaker emission at longer wavelengths. Since then many dye-stuffs have been made to lase ;[405] a popular choice is rhodamine 6G, pumped by means of a flushtube. A remarkable property of dye-lasers is the wide frequency range over which they give observable power. The rhodamine laser[406] gives output at wavelengths between $0 \cdot 57$ and $0 \cdot 62$ μm which is a frequency range of 1400 cm^{-1}. If a frequency-selective element such as a grating or a multiple prism assembly is included in the cavity, moderately monochromatic radiation may be obtained anywhere within the operating range of the laser.[403] The problem of producing highly monochromatic radiation from dye-lasers is one that is receiving considerable attention at the moment.[407]

Dewey and Hocker[408] have generated difference frequencies in the 3–4 μm region by beating the output of a Q-switched ruby laser with that of a tunable (DTTCI) dye-laser in a phase-matched LiNbO$_3$ crystal. The dye-laser was pumped by part of the output of the ruby laser and there was no problem therefore in synchronizing the two sets of pulses. The dye-laser had a diffraction grating as the rear cavity reflector and the output had a bandwidth of the order ~ 6 cm^{-1}. The difference-frequency bandwidth was estimated to be less than 10 cm^{-1}. The conversion efficiency was remarkably high (> 1 per cent) so that the difference-frequency pulses had peak powers of the order 6 kW for a total available ruby power of 4 MW. Dewey and Hocker[408] used their tunable source to scan the $3 \cdot 5$ μm absorption band of polyethylene (see Fig. 4.28). They were able to resolve a feature at $3 \cdot 69$ μm which only appeared as a shoulder in a spectrum observed with a conventional spectrometer. In the future, line-widths of the order ~ 1 cm^{-1} may be feasible and again there will be a direct spectroscopy method which can compete with delay-type techniques. With the availability of several dye-lasers and several possible mixing crystals it may be possible to cover a wide range of the infra-red. The minerals proustite and pyrargyrite (Ag$_3$AsS$_3$ and Ag$_3$SbS$_3$ respectively) may prove very valuable here, since they have very high non-linear coefficients and are transparent to quite long wavelengths (≈ 13 μm).

Many of the practical systems discussed in this book can be regarded as special cases of the parametric oscillator. In such a device there are three frequencies present, ν_p, ν_s and ν_i (where p means pump, s means signal and i means idler), and the three frequencies are connected by the energy conservation requirement, namely

$$\nu_p + \nu_s + \nu_i = 0. \tag{6.55}$$

In this equation, a positive sign for a frequency implies absorption of the corresponding photon and a negative sign implies emission. It will be realized therefore that this equation covers frequency multiplication, laser oscillation and Raman scattering amongst others. However, to give the term some precise meaning it is usual to call a device a parametric oscillator only if there is a phase coherence requirement on the three waves. The simplest parametric oscillator consists of a non-linear crystal such as ADP or $LiNbO_3$ mounted in a Fabry–Perot resonator. If the angle between the optic axis of the crystal and the axis of the resonator is such that phase-matched interaction can occur at frequencies ν_p, ν_s and ν_i, then, if the crystal is pumped with intense radiation at frequency ν_p, emission will be observed at frequencies given by

$$\nu_p = \nu_s + \nu_i. \tag{6.56}$$

An immense amount of work has been done in this field, but as a recent example we will mention the experiments of Yarborough and Massey.[409] These workers took the radiation at $1 \cdot 064\ \mu$m from a Nd : YAG laser, frequency-doubled this in a phase-matched 5 cm long potassium dideutero phosphate (KD*P) crystal and then further frequency-doubled the resulting radiation in a 5 cm long ADP crystal. The result was pulsed emission with peak power of the order 200 kW at a wavelength of $0 \cdot 2662\ \mu$m. When this radiation was passed into a further ADP crystal, visible radiation was observed without the need for the crystal to be in a resonator. By altering the temperature of the crystal or its angle to the beam it was possible to tune the output over the entire visible region. The angle tuning was particularly dramatic since the signal and idler radiation emerged as separate beams on each side of the pump beam.

The generation of far infrared radiation by parametric processes is handicapped by the requirement that the non-linear crystal be transparent at all three frequencies. However, Hordvik, Schlossberg and Stickley[410] have demonstrated parametric oscillation in proustite pumped by a ruby laser. By varying the angle of the crystal axis to the beam, they were able to tune the signal wavelength from $0 \cdot 7\ \mu$m to $1 \cdot 1\ \mu$m and, although they did not attempt to observe the idler radiation, it lay presumably between $14 \cdot 6$ and $1 \cdot 93\ \mu$m. This is a promising advance, but even if direct parametric generation of far infrared radiation fails there is always available the method of beat frequency generation, between the radiation of an optical parametric oscillator and that of a fixed frequency laser, to provide a tunable source of far infrared radiation.

6.9. Miscellaneous Submillimetre Lasers

6.9.1. *Noble Gas Lasers*

In addition to the powerful HCN and H_2O lasers there are some others which give emission in the submillimetre region, occasionally with sufficient power to be technologically interesting. The higher analogues of the transitions which lead to visible and near infrared laser action in the noble gases should lead to emission in the mid- and far infrared if the necessary population inversions can be built up. This is indeed the case and several lines have been obtained from neon, for example, which extend in wavelength to beyond 100 μm. The discussion of such transitions in neon is complicated by the intermediate coupling scheme which prevails in the excited states. The ground state of neon has the configuration $(1s)^2(2s)^2(2p)^6$ and the excited states of interest, as far as lasers are concerned, are derived from this by promotion of one $2p$ electron to any of the orbitals $3s$, $4s$, $3p$, $4p$, $3d$, $4d$ ... etc. If the electron is promoted to an s orbital, the configuration $(1s)^2(2s)^2(2p)^5(ms)^1$ will lead to four multiplet components which, within the Russell–Saunders notation, would be written $^1P_1$ (i.e. $L = 1$, $S = 0$), $^3P_2$ ($L = 1$, $S = 1$, $J = 2$), $^3P_1$ ($L = 1$, $S = 1$, $J = 1$) and $^3P_0$ ($L = 1$, $S = 1$, $J = 0$). In fact the Russell–Saunders scheme holds only very approximately and the four multiplet components are best regarded as a stack of four rather closely spaced levels. The old Paschen notation is still in frequent use in the literature and the four states of, say, $(1s)^2(2s)^2(2p)^5(3s)^1$ would be numbered in order of decreasing energy $1s_2$, $1s_3$, $1s_4$ and $1s_5$. Recently the Racah notation has found increasing favour and these four states would be labelled $3s^1[\frac{1}{2}]^0_1$, $3s^1[\frac{1}{2}]^0_0$, $3s[\frac{3}{2}]^0_1$ and $3s[\frac{3}{2}]^0_2$. This notation is much to be preferred since it indicates the true principal quantum number of the optical electron, the J value (right subscript), the parity (right superscript) and the $l_i s_i$ resultants for the limiting case of jj coupling. If an electron is promoted to a p orbital ten multiplet components result. The configuration $(1s)^2(2s)^2(2p)^5(3p)^1$ gives a stack which is numbered in the Paschen system as $2p_1$ ... $2p_{10}$ and, in the Racah notation, $3p'[\frac{1}{2}]_0$, $3p'[\frac{1}{2}]_1$, $3p[\frac{1}{2}]_0$, $3p'[\frac{3}{2}]_2$, $3p'[\frac{3}{2}]_1$, $3p[\frac{3}{2}]_2$, $3p[\frac{3}{2}]_1$, $3p[\frac{5}{2}]_2$, $3p[\frac{5}{2}]_3$ and $3p[\frac{1}{2}]_1$. The only selection rule which holds rigidly (apart, of course, from parity reversal which would, for example, prohibit transitions within a stack) is the rule for electric dipole radiation,

$$\Delta J = 0 \pm 1, \tag{6.56}$$

for J as always is a good quantum number. It will be seen from this that for the transition $3s_2 \rightarrow 2p$, nine out of the ten possible components are allowed and not only do these occur in the spectrum of neon but all the transitions $3s_2 \rightarrow 2p_1$ ... $2p_8$ have been obtained in oscillation from helium–neon lasers. Nothing could more emphasize the breakdown of the Russell–Saunders scheme, for in that limit some of these transitions are $p \to p$ class and some are singlet to triplet transitions—both rigidly forbidden. Nevertheless, there are still some intimations of the limiting selection rules for only one of these eight lines is radiated with great power and that is the $3s_2 \to 2p_4$ line at 6328 Å which, in the Russell–Saunders scheme, would correspond to the strongly allowed $^1P_1 \to {}^1D_2$ transition. The multiplet splitting gets rapidly smaller with increasing principal quantum number, corresponding to less and less penetration of the $(1s)^2(2s)^2(2p)^5$ core by the optical electron and hence to increasingly hydrogen-like character. As an illustration, the $2p_i$ levels span an interval of over 3000 cm^{-1} whereas the $6p_i$ levels are contained within a range of 150 cm^{-1}.

The narrow multiplet intervals, combined with the equalization of energy of levels with the same principal quantum number, implies that transitions from high p to high d states will lead to closely spaced lines in the far infrared. The extensive investigations of Patel and his colleagues[411] have confirmed this. They used excitation by electron impact as well as inelastic collision with helium to produce (in Racah notation) the series $4p - 3d$ ($3 \cdot 77$–$10 \cdot 98$ μm), $5p - 4d$ ($12 \cdot 82$–$22 \cdot 8$ μm), $6p - 5d$ ($20 \cdot 48$–$41 \cdot 74$ μm), $7p - 6d$ ($35 \cdot 602$–$68 \cdot 329$ μm) and $8p - 7d$ ($72 \cdot 15$–$89 \cdot 86$ μm). Some lines of the $9p$ to $8d$ and the $10p$ to $9d$ series were observed and, additionally, a few lines, including one at 133 μm which could not be identified with certainty. None of these lines in the far infrared is really intense (power levels of the order of 7×10^{-9} W prevailing) but the generation is easy and the host of lines available may prove valuable as sub-standards of frequency as well as for spot spectroscopic observations. In the latter connection, the lines at $106 \cdot 02$ μm, $10p[\frac{1}{2}]_0 \to 9d[\frac{3}{2}]_1^0$, and $124 \cdot 4$ μm, $9p[\frac{3}{2}]_2 \to 8d[\frac{5}{2}]_3^0$, should prove especially useful.

Laser action at $95 \cdot 8$ μm has been obtained from pure helium using pulsed excitation by Mathias, Crocker and Wills[412] and this line, together with another at $216 \cdot 3$ μm, has been obtained in CW action by Levine and Javan.[413] The Russell–Saunders scheme applies well to helium and these lines arise from the transitions

$$3^1P \to 3^1D \quad \text{and} \quad 4^1P \to 4^1D.$$

This system is important practically because of the high power levels ($\approx 1 \cdot 5$ mW) available and also theoretically because both the mechanism and the frequency intervals are amenable to theoretical analysis. A practical point of importance is that emission is only obtained from a very clean discharge—the authors remark that even small traces of impurities were sufficient to inhibit oscillation. An at first sight extraordinary feature of this system is that it appears to violate the principle laid down earlier in the chapter that the upper state should not be connected to the ground state by an allowed transition. All ^1P states of helium are connected to the ground

N

state ^1S by very strongly allowed transitions. This is the answer to the paradox; the transitions are so strongly allowed that the radiation (which will be very short wavelength ultraviolet) is trapped in the plasma and cannot escape. For this reason there is only a slow spontaneous decay of the population in the ^1P states and this can easily be overcome by the electron impact populating processes. The lower ^1D states are not connected optically to the ground state and are therefore not directly populated by electron impact, since this follows the same (electric dipole) selection rules, but they can decay to the ground state via the cascade $^1D \rightarrow {}^1P \rightarrow {}^1S$. It follows that electron impact will naturally bring about a population inversion between ^1P and ^1D states resulting in the observed laser action. A corollary of these phenomena is that helium can pump neon by inelastic collisions involving non-metastable levels. As an example of this, collisions between 2^1P, helium atoms (present in reasonable concentration due to radiation trapping) and neon ground-state atoms can transfer the latter into the $7p$ (Racah) levels since the energies, 171, 129 and 171 000–171 150 cm^{-1} respectively, closely match.

6.9.2. *Other Vibration–rotation Lasers*

Submillimetre emission has been obtained from several further molecular systems including H_2S, OCS and SO_2, but the latter system is the most important and may soon assume equal rank with the H_2O and HCN lasers. Intense radiation at 141 and 193 μm was first reported from SO_2–He mixtures by Dyubko and his colleagues[414] in Russia and this was soon confirmed in separate publications from Hard[415] and from Hassler and Coleman.[416] The experimental arrangements used were the familiar semi- or fully confocal cavities with hole coupling: the tube was typically 2 m long and 7·6 cm in diameter. In CW operation (0·4 A) the two strong lines at $\lambda_{air} = 140 \cdot 85$ and $192 \cdot 67$ μm ($70 \cdot 98$ and $51 \cdot 89$ cm^{-1} respectively) were obtained, whilst in pulsed operation two additional lines at $66 \cdot 14$ and $46 \cdot 44$ cm^{-1} appeared. The power output from a pulsed SO_2–He laser at $140 \cdot 85$ μm is stated to be approximately the same as that at $118 \cdot 6$ μm from a pulsed H_2O laser. This makes the SO_2–He laser a most promising device. The mechanism of operation is, however, as yet unknown. Emission from H_2S at wavelengths between $33 \cdot 47$ and $225 \cdot 3$ μm has also been reported.[416] The difficulty with this material as compared with H_2O is that the decomposition in the discharge leads to solid sulphur and it is therefore not possible to establish an equilibrium of the kind $H + OH \rightleftharpoons H_2O$ which is probably present in the H_2O laser. Because of this, laser emission is only observed at very low repetition frequencies (≈ 2 Hz) and with very high pumping rates. For these reasons the H_2S laser is unlikely to be of great technological interest in the immediate future. Similar remarks apply to OCS which gives[416] lines at 123 and 132 μm.

6.10. Far Infrared Chemical Lasers

The helium or helium–neon lasers are perfect examples of what may be called physical lasers. The population inversion is brought about by collisional processes and/or the operation of various selection rules. A chemical laser, on the other hand, owes its operation to population inversions brought about by chemical reactions. In any exothermic reaction of the type

$$A+B = C+D, \tag{6.57}$$

the amount of energy produced is perfectly definite and the reaction mechanisms tend to channel this in specific ways. What this means in practice is that the products C and D tend to leave the reaction zone with a narrowly defined range of internal excitation energy. The excited states of molecules tend to be widely separated and therefore it is not uncommon for large numbers of molecules to be formed in a given state with the neighbouring states remaining relatively unpopulated. Under normal circumstances collisional processes, which are very efficient at converting translational into rotational energy and vice versa, rapidly bring about an equilibration of population and the ultra-violet or infrared emission spectra of continuous reactions show only indirect evidence of the initial population inversions. The evidence gets more obvious as the pressure falls and the time between collisions lengthens—as an example Polyani has reported[417] non-Boltzmann distributions for $J > 17$ in the HCl formed by the reaction

$$Cl_2 + H \rightarrow HCl + Cl \tag{6.58}$$

at pressures of the order of 1–2 torr. At still lower pressures (0·01 torr) the anomalies set in for J values as low as 9. Another well characterized system is the production of OH radicals by an electric discharge through water vapour. Here again very non-thermal population distributions prevail.[320] The observed emission spectrum in the $^2\Sigma^+ \rightarrow {}^2\Pi$ system shows a distribution of intensity amongst the rotational fine structure which shows peaks at $N' = 5$ and $N' = 17$ and which features a sudden drop off in intensity for $N' > 22$. This latter feature is thought to arise because, if it is imagined that the excitation energy ruptures an O–H bond, the hydrogen atom will leave at an angle to the remaining OH bond and thus set the radical rotating quickly. The break off at $N' = 22$ corresponds to the maximum possible transfer of angular momentum in this fashion concordant with conservation of overall energy. The energies involved in bond rupture cover a wide range but a typical value would be 45 kcal mol^{-1}. This corresponds to a frequency of 15 742 cm^{-1}, so it will be seen that population inversions brought about by chemical means will be mostly confined to vibrational levels with only the occasional electronic case. Despite this caveat which is generally true, the very first chemical laser[418] involved the electronic transition $^2P_{1/2} \rightarrow {}^2P_{3/2}$

at 7604 cm^{-1} in iodine atoms produced by the flash photolysis of CF$_3$I. Several other systems are now known operating on vibrational transitions in NO, CO, HF, HCl etc. The position has been summarized in an excellent review article by Pimentel.[419]

The first indubitably chemical laser operating in the mid- to far infrared region was reported by Deutsch[420] in 1967. The reaction used was

$$CF_4 + H_2 \rightarrow CF_3H + HF \tag{6.59}$$

taking place in an electric discharge between cold cathode and anode. Pulsed operation was employed and the active medium was confined in the usual resonator cavity. Total gas pressure was measured to be between 0·75 and 5·0 torr at the exit point of the flowing system. A large number of lines were observed stretching between 11 and 22 μm. Deutsch[420] has assigned all of these to pure rotational transitions in HF, either taking place in the ground state or in vibrationally excited states up to $n = 4$. Ground-state transitions have been observed with $J'' = 15$ and 17 to 27, the corresponding frequencies ranging from 624·16 to 980·60 cm^{-1}. The strongest lines occur for $J'' \approx 22$ and this pattern is repeated in the excited states—presumably the dynamics of the chemical reaction favour transfer of this quantity of angular momentum to the HF product molecules. Molecules such as HF which have only a single non-hydrogenic atom show very large centrifugal distortion effects and so the frequencies of the lines originating on high J levels cannot be fitted with the first-order centrifugal distortion theory (equation 5.6). Still higher terms are required and it is found that up to $J'' = 28$ the transitions are fitted (to within a few hundredths of a wavenumber) by the equation

$$\bar{\nu} = 41 \cdot 118(J''+1) - 8 \cdot 476 \times 10^{-3}(J''+1)^3$$
$$+ 9 \cdot 66 \times 10^{-7}(J''+1)^5 - 10^{-10}(J''+1)^7. \tag{6.60}$$

It is interesting to observe that the level $J = 23$ of the vibrational ground state of HF lies 10 729 cm^{-1} above the rotationless state and that this quantity represents 30·67 kcal mol^{-1}—a large fraction of the energy produced in the reaction, i.e. 32 kcal mol^{-1}.

Emission from HCl in the wavelength range 13–26 μm has been obtained[421] with the same apparatus and a variety of reactions such as

$$CH_3Cl + Cl_2 \rightarrow CH_2Cl_2 + HCl. \tag{6.61}$$

With natural abundances of isotopes nearly all the lines have been attributed to H^{35}Cl. Just one emission at 406·211 cm^{-1} is attributed to H^{37}Cl; this transition is assigned as $n = 1$, $J(21) \rightarrow J(20)$. This illustrates the highly non-linear behaviour of lasers where a slight difference in gain in two lines may lead to enormous differences in the ultimate powers radiated. Once again there is a peaking of the observed emission round high J numbers but the spread is larger, covering $J = 18$ almost completely to $J = 40$. The transitions in $H^{35}Cl$ are given by the relation

$$\bar{\nu} = 20 \cdot 8805(J''+1) - 2 \cdot 113 \times 10^{-3}(J''+1)^3$$
$$+ 1 \cdot 025 \times 10^{-7}(J''+1)^5 - 0 \cdot 75 \times 10^{-11}(J''+1)^7 \quad (6.62)$$

so that again it will be seen that the reaction leads to a channelling of a large fraction of the available energy (45 kcal mol^{-1}) into rotational motion of the HCl molecules.

Pulsed electrical discharges through BF_3, BCl_3 or BBr_3 confined in a confocal cavity leads to emission at a very large number of wavelengths between 11 and 41 μm.[422] This is not related to the pumped emission from BCl_3 (see Section 6.11) but arises from pure rotational transitions in HF, HCl or HBr. The hydrogen comes presumably from impurities on the walls or else from reaction of the gases with rubber pipes on their way to the laser. Deliberate addition of traces of water vapour to the discharge considerably enhances most of the lines. Helium too seems to increase the intensity of many of the lines. The strongest line with BF_3 corresponds to $n = 0, J = 22 \rightarrow J = 21$ of HF at $819 \cdot 062$ cm^{-1} and power levels available range from 10 to 100 mW. The emissions from BCl_3 are interesting in that copious emission is obtained from both $H^{35}Cl$ and $H^{37}Cl$. The strongest lines correspond to J values near 29 which means that there are several intense lines in the 18–20 μm region. With BBr_3 there is again emission from two isotopic molecules $H^{79}Br$ and $H^{81}Br$. The strongest lines occur in the 20 to 22 μm region but there is a useful line at $31 \cdot 849$ μm (314 cm^{-1}) attributed to the transition $J(20) \rightarrow J(19)$ in $n = 1$ of either $H^{79}Br$ or $H^{81}Br$.

It seems likely that many more chemical lasers will be discovered in the future and the fortunate occurrence of oscillation on pure rotational transitions should be most significant for providing further high-power sources in the submillimetre band.

6.11. Optically Pumped Lasers

The discovery of optically pumped submillimetre lasers followed on quite naturally from the use of various gases and vapours to passively Q-switch the CO_2 laser. There are quite a number of molecules which have intense vibrational–rotational absorption bands in the 10 μm region, and if a cell containing such molecules is included in the cavity of a CO_2 laser the possibility of Q-switching arises, provided one of the lines of the absorption band is in reasonable coincidence with a strong emission line of the laser. It is normally necessary to use a frequency-selective cavity, for otherwise the absorption by the gas will merely transfer the laser to CW operation on those lines which are not heavily absorbed. Wood and Schwarz[423] calculated that

γ^2 (see equation 6.35) for SF_6, whose ν_3 band overlaps the $10\cdot59\ \mu m$ band of CO_2, would be 32 for a gas pressure of 1 torr and a radiation intensity of 5 W focussed down into an area of $0\cdot03\ cm^2$. They therefore assembled a CO_2 laser with a prism to give frequency selectivity and found that whereas the laser, without the prism, would normally operate CW on the P branch lines of the $10\cdot59\ \mu m$ band, it would switch to CW operation on some R branch lines when SF_6 was included in the cavity. When both the gas and the prism set for the $10\cdot6\ \mu m$ region were included in the cavity, the laser went over to pulsed emission on the P-branch lines between $10\cdot4$ and $10\cdot7\ \mu m$ with the $P(20)$ line the most intense. The frequency of the pulses was between 10^3 and 10^4 Hz, the pulse length of the order of 1 μs and the peak power about 1 kW. They correctly identified the behaviour as arising from repetitive Q-switched operation of the laser. Since then several other gases have been shown[424] to induce similar behaviour including CH_3F and PF_5 which latter is remarkable in that it will Q-switch virtually all the lines of the P-branch.

The saturation of one or more vibration–rotation transitions by the intense pumping action of the laser will result in non-thermal population distributions in both the ground and the excited states. If the pumping intensity is high enough, population inversions between adjacent rotational states will be brought about and, provided the molecule has a dipole moment and the gas is enclosed in a Fabry–Perot resonator, stimulated emission will be observed. This type of laser may either be called a "stimulated fluorescence" device or else an optically pumped laser. Chang and his colleagues[425] have observed stimulated emission from three vapours, methanol, vinyl chloride and methyl fluoride, pumped by the CO_2 laser. An energy-level diagram showing the origin of the emission from CH_3F is shown in Fig. 6.18. Six lines in the $20\ cm^{-1}$ (600 GHz) region were observed using a Q-switched CO_2 laser as the pump. The strong $P(20)$ line of the CO_2 laser at $9\cdot55\ \mu m$ (see Fig. 6.17) has a close coincidence with the $Q(12)$ line of the ν_3 (CF stretch) band of CH_3F. The $K = 1$ and $K = 2$ components of the $Q(12)$ line lie within the tuning range of the $P(20)$ CO_2 line and for these two the coincidence can therefore be made exact. The pumping action of the laser overpopulates $J(12)$, $(K1)$ and $J(12)$, $K(2)$ of the upper state, leading to stimulated emission B, b and cascade emission C, c. It also depopulates $J(12)$, $K(1)$ and $J(12)$, $K(2)$ of the ground state, leading to stimulated emission A, a. The observed wavenumbers of the lines are $B = 20\cdot1584$, $b = 20\cdot1570$, $C = 18\cdot4804$, $c = 18\cdot4793$, $A = 22\cdot1286$ and $a = 22\cdot1776\ cm^{-1}$. The transitions B and b can also be obtained in continuous oscillation.

The experimental arrangements used by Chang et al.[425] featured an ~ 80 cm Fabry–Perot cavity which contained the gas. The cavity was plano-concave and CO_2 pump radiation was coupled in through a $1\cdot2$ mm hole in the centre of the plane mirror. The concave mirror had a radius of curvature 190 cm

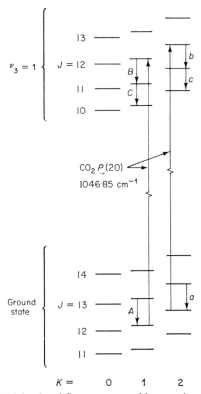

FIG. 6.18. Stimulated fluorescence and laser action in CH_3F.

and it was mounted on a motor-driven micrometer stage to facilitate cavity-length tuning. The CO_2 radiation after entering the cavity expanded into a diverging beam and became trapped for a large number of round trips. The submillimetre output was taken from the same coupling hole via a cylindrical horn to reduce the divergence. The beam then passed via a 45° mirror to the detector which was either a Rollin[267] InSb detector or else a point-contact diode. The absolute time frequencies of the methyl fluoride emission lines were measured in the usual way by mixing the submillimetre signal with harmonics of a microwave signal in the point-contact diode. The rotational parameters of the ground state of CH_3F are known from the work of Winton and Gordy[300] (see Section 6.4) and, by comparing the time frequencies of the emission lines with the calculated values, the two ground-state transitions can be identified. From the frequencies of the other four lines, more accurate rotation and distortion constants for the ν_3 state of CH_3F may be deduced. The polarization of the submillimetre laser output is perpendicular to that of the pumping radiation, which agrees with theory since the absorption is a

$\Delta J = 0$ transition and the emission is a $\Delta J = -1$ process. With the Q-switched pump, the bandwidth of the radiation varies from 60 MHz at a gas pressure of 50 mtorr, up to at least 160 MHz at higher pressure where it exceeds the free spectral range of the cavity. The active medium in this type of submillimetre laser is not ionized and it is possible therefore to calculate the gain as a function of the molecular parameters. For CH_3F this gives the gain in the small signal limit as 27 dB m^{-1} which is much larger than that of the HCN laser at 337 μm where the gain is only 2 dB m^{-1}. The superiority of optically pumped lasers over electrically excited lasers must in part be due to the absence of any disruptive discharge in the former.

Stimulated emission from ammonia has always been a central topic in the development of long-wave masers and lasers. The very first maser was constructed by Gordon, Zeiger and Townes[294] who used an electrostatic state selector to separate molecules in the two inversion states of the vibrational ground state of NH_3 (see Section 5.1). The inversion doublets are separated by $0 \cdot 7934$ cm^{-1} (24 GHz) and the ammonia maser can be used therefore as a continuous oscillator and amplifier for the 24 GHz region. Later on, ammonia was one of the series of gases studied in a pulsed electrical discharge by Mathias[426] and his colleagues. They observed seven lines in the region 312–465 cm^{-1}. Lide[427] has suggested that five of these seven lines can be assigned to vibration–rotation transitions between excited states of the ν_2 fundamental; in fact between 3^s and 2^a where the superscripts indicate symmetrical and antisymmetrical behaviour with respect to inversion. An energy-level diagram for the vibrational states of ammonia is shown in Fig. 6.19, which also shows Lide's assignment. The laser mechanism is not yet fully understood, though it is significant—as suggested by Lide—that the upper state (3^s) has an energy, relative to the vibrational ground state, of 2384 cm^{-1} and there is thus a close match with the first (see Fig. 6.17) vibrationally excited state of nitrogen. Nitrogen will presumably be present in the plasma due to decomposition of NH_3 molecules. The situation has been complicated by the work of Akitt and Wittig[428] who have observed twelve more lines which apparently do not belong to the $3^s \rightarrow 2^a$ system. The observed spectrum of ammonia now stretches therefore from 311 to 677 cm^{-1}. No complete assignment of the whole spectrum is yet available but when it has been worked out it will almost certainly be in terms of further transitions, within the ν_2 system, similar to those identified by Lide.

Stimulated fluorescence from ammonia has been observed by Chang, Bridges and Burkhardt[429] using an N_2O laser as the pump. The work followed on naturally from that of Shimizu[430] who showed that there were many close coincidences between lines of the ν_2 band of ammonia and lines of the CO_2 and N_2O lasers. Most of these could be brought into exact coincidence using the Stark effect (see Section 6.6.3). The nitrous oxide molecule N_2O

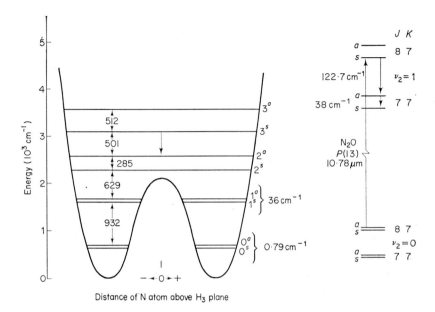

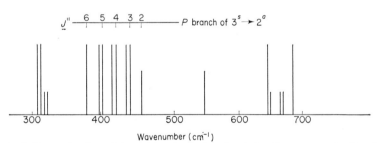

FIG. 6.19. Energy levels and the origin of stimulated emission from ammonia. The data is from references 15, 426, 427, 428 and 429.

is isoelectronic with the CO_2 molecule, and the N_2O laser gives a similar spectrum to that of the CO_2 laser. The $P(13)$ line of the N_2O laser at $10 \cdot 78$ μm lies in virtually perfect coincidence with the $a \to s$ component of the Q ($J = 8$, $K = 7$) line of the ν_2 fundamental of NH_3. This coincidence has been used to provide a passive Q-switch for the N_2O laser.[431] Pumping of NH_3 by the $P(13)$ line produces a population inversion between the $J = 8$ and $J = 7$ levels and stimulated emission is observed at $81 \cdot 48$ μm, corresponding to the transition

$$(J = 8, K = 7)^s \to (J = 7, K = 7)^a$$

within the $\nu_2 = 1$ state. This is followed by the cascade (inversion) transition

$$(J = 7, K = 7)^a \rightarrow (J = 7, K = 7)^s$$

at $263 \cdot 4$ μm (38 cm^{-1}). Absolute frequency measurements of these two lines using mixing techniques should provide very accurate data for refining the treatment of inversion in the ammonia molecule.

An experiment which may be another example of optical pumping has been described by Karlov and his colleagues.[432] They used boron trichloride admixed with the gas mixture of a CO_2 laser. The use of boron trichloride as a passive Q-switching agent for the CO_2 laser depends on the coincidence of lines in the ν_3 band of BCl_3 with lines of the laser. When the BCl_3 is added to the discharge at low concentrations, giant pulse operation of the CO_2 laser occurs, but at higher concentrations the CO_2 emission ceases and is replaced by weak continuous emission between 13 and 24 μm. The observed lines are vibration–rotation transitions in $^{10}BCl_3$ and $^{11}BCl_3$. Because the gas was actually present in the discharge it is not possible to say definitely whether optical pumping occurred or not.

6.12. Direct Generation of Submillimetre Waves by Electrical Stimulation of Semiconductors

It has been shown earlier in this book that progress in laser technology has produced several tunable devices generating submillimetre waves. This is a very encouraging situation since it has been the forced dependence on the feeble emission from black-body sources which has slowed down progress in submillimetre spectroscopy for so long. Nevertheless, the available devices are clumsy to use and are very expensive to make and to maintain. What is really required is a simple submillimetre "lamp" which can be connected to a conventional power pack and which will give out milliwatts of tunable submillimetre power. Electron-beam devices which give out power in the millimetre waveband have been described by Bott[433] and in the mid-infrared there are available junction diode lasers which can be tuned over tens of cm^{-1}. Unfortunately neither type can yet be constructed to operate in the submillimetre band.

Semiconductor lasers made from material whose constitution can be written $Pb_{1-x}Sn_xTe$ can be operated at wavelengths between $6 \cdot 5$ and 32 μm. An account of some spectroscopic measurements made using them has been given by Hinkley and Kelley[434] who give a good bibliography of the original literature. The emission wavelength is determined by the value of x and it may be slightly varied from this value either by heating or—what amounts to the same thing—by increasing the current. Operation beyond 32 μm is not possible because of the onset of reststrahlen absorption in the material.

Spontaneous recombination radiation near 282 μm in GaAs has been observed by Melngailis and his colleagues[435] but the power level (10^{-7} W) is too low for practical use. Nevertheless, this partial success may hint at a future successful development of the desired submillimetre "lamp". Should this come about, it will be possible to do submillimetre experiments with the scope of microwave techniques and the ease of infrared techniques. When this has been achieved the submillimetre barrier will truly have been surmounted.

Appendix 1

Treatment of Multiple-beam Interference by the Method of Complex Amplitudes

The treatment given earlier of multiple-beam interference in a transparent dielectric film was relatively simple and quite sufficient to derive the intensity distribution in the image planes. If, however, we take the problem a stage further and ask ourselves what the relationship is between the phase of the reflected (or transmitted) wavefront and the incident wavefront, the question is best answered by more sophisticated mathematical methods. These methods introduce the complex amplitude of an electromagnetic wave, so that

$$\hat{A}(t) = A_0 \exp\left[i(2\pi vt + \alpha)\right] \tag{A1.1}$$

where α is the phase angle. The intensity when two such waves interfere is given by

$$I \propto [\hat{A}(t) + \hat{B}(t)][\hat{A}^*(t) + \hat{B}^*(t)] \tag{A1.2}$$

where the star indicates the complex conjugate, namely

$$\hat{B}^*(t) = B_0 \exp\left[-i(2\pi vt + \beta)\right]. \tag{A1.3}$$

Thus we have

$$I \propto A_0^2 + B_0^2 + 2A_0 B_0 \cos(\alpha - \beta) \tag{A1.4}$$

which is the same result as that given by the elementary theory. It will be observed, of course, that for incoherent superposition, where α and β have random values, the time-averaged intensity corresponds to simple addition of the intensities contributed by each source.

We can now derive the phase of the reflected wavefront by introducing a complex amplitude reflection factor $\hat{r}$ which can be derived directly by rewriting equation (3.55) as follows:

$$\hat{r} = r[-1 + t^2 e^{i\delta} + t^2 r^2 e^{i2\delta} + \ldots]$$
$$= -r(1 - e^{i\delta})/(1 - r^2 e^{i\delta}). \tag{A1.5}$$

To obtain the amplitude and phase of the reflected wave it is only necessary to rewrite this complex number in polar form, i.e.

$$\hat{r} = -\left[\frac{2r^2(1 - \cos\delta)}{1 - 2r^2 \cos\delta + r^4}\right]^{1/2} \exp\left[i \arctan \frac{-\sin\delta(1 - r^2)}{(1 - \cos\delta)(1 + r^2)}\right]. \tag{A1.6}$$

This represents a wavefront of intensity

$$\frac{2r^2(1-\cos \delta)I_0}{1-2r^2 \cos \delta+r^4}$$

and of phase

$$\psi = \pi - \arctan \frac{\cos \frac{1}{2}\delta(1-r^2)}{\sin \frac{1}{2}\delta 1(+r^2)}. \qquad (A1.7)$$

The complex transmission coefficient can be shown, in a similar fashion, to be

$$\hat{t} = t^2/(1-r^2e^{i\delta}) \qquad (A1.8)$$

which in polar form is

$$\hat{t} = \left[\frac{(1-r^2)^2}{1-2r^2 \cos \delta+r^4}\right]^{1/2} \exp \left[i \arctan \frac{r^2 \sin \delta}{1-r^2 \cos \delta}\right] \qquad (A1.9)$$

where the phase origin is that of the emerging directly transmitted ray. If the phase is referred back to that of the incident ray then the expression becomes

$$\hat{t} = \left[\frac{(1-r^2)^2}{1-2r^2 \cos \delta+r^4}\right]^{1/2} \exp \left\{i\left[\frac{\delta}{2}+\arctan \frac{r^2 \sin \delta}{1-r^2 \cos \delta}\right]\right\}. \qquad (A1.10)$$

This represents a transmitted wave of intensity

$$\frac{(1-r^2)^2I_0}{1-2r^2 \cos \delta+r^4}$$

and of phase

$$\phi = \arctan \frac{\sin \frac{1}{2}\delta(1+r^2)}{\cos \frac{1}{2}\delta(1-r^2)}.$$

It is interesting to observe that, because the arguments of the arc tan function are negative reciprocals of each other,

$$\psi-\phi = \frac{1}{2}\pi(2l+1), \qquad l = 0, 1, 2 \text{ etc.} \qquad (A1.11)$$

The intensity distribution in the two image planes of a Michelson interferometer set to zero path difference follows immediately from this theory. The intensity reaching the detector (S') has been once reflected (in the multiple beam fashion described in the text) and once transmitted (in the same fashion). Therefore

$$I(S') = 2\hat{r}\hat{t}\hat{A}(t).2\hat{r}^*\hat{t}^*\hat{A}(t)^* = 4\,|\,r\,|^2\,|\,t\,|^2\,I_0$$
$$= \frac{8I_0r^2(1-r^2)^2(1-\cos \delta)}{(1+r^4-2r^2 \cos \delta)^2}. \qquad (A1.12)$$

The intensity reflected back to the source is

$$I(S'') = [\hat{r}^2 + \hat{t}^2][\hat{r}^{*2} + \hat{t}^{*2}] I_0$$
$$= [\,|\,r\,|^{\,4} + |\,t\,|^{\,4} + 2\,|\,r\,|^{\,2}\,|\,t\,|^{\,2} \cos 2(\psi - \theta)] I_0 \quad (A1.13)$$

which, by (A1.11), is

$$I(S'') = [\,|\,r\,|^{\,4} + |\,t\,|^{\,4} - 2\,|\,r\,|^{\,2}\,|\,t\,|^{\,2}] I_0$$
$$= I_0 \left[\frac{2r^2(1 - \cos\delta) - (1 - r^2)^2}{1 - 2r^2\cos\delta + r^4} \right]^2. \quad (A1.14)$$

Appendix 2

Normal Vibrations of Crystals and Long-chain Molecules

In Chapter 5 the vibrations of a simple diatomic infinite linear lattice were discussed. Although this example is rather artificial, nevertheless, from the analysis, such important concepts as the wave vector, the optical and acoustical branches of the dispersion diagram and the $\Delta \bar{k}$ = zero selection rule emerged. When one is dealing with the vibrations of small molecules, a rather different mathematical framework is employed and in this appendix an attempt will be made to show how these two approaches are related and how the concepts of either can be interpreted in terms of the concepts of the other.

In conventional molecular vibration theory,[220] the problem as presented is this: knowing all the atomic masses, the molecular geometry and all the interatomic forces, we must calculate the vibrational frequencies. In practice it tends to be the other way round, i.e. knowing the frequencies (from infrared and Raman data combined with heat-capacity studies) the interatomic forces must be computed; but despite this we will proceed as above. We first of all choose a suitable coordinate system to describe the departures of the atoms from their equilibrium position. Suitable choices might be the Cartesian coordinates of the atoms or else the internal coordinates, i.e. changes of bond length, interbond angle etc. If we denote the coordinates by the column vector $\mathbf{R}$, the kinetic and potential energies may be written

$$2T = \tilde{\mathbf{R}} \, G^{-1} \dot{\mathbf{R}} \text{ and } 2V = \tilde{\mathbf{R}} \, F \, \mathbf{R} \tag{A2.1}$$

where the tilde signifies transposition and G^{-1} and F are square matrices. Commonly, the coordinate system is such that the three rotations and the three translations of the molecule as a rigid body have been removed and both G^{-1} and F are square matrices of order $3N-6$, where N is the number of atoms in the molecule. If we denote the $3N-6$ latent roots of the matrix product GF by $\lambda_1 \ldots \lambda_{3N-6}$, then the vibration frequencies are given by

$$\lambda_i = 4\pi^2 \nu_i^2. \tag{A2.2}$$

To prove this it should be noted that there always exists a transformation of coordinates

$$Q = L^{-1}R \tag{A2.3}$$

in terms of which both the kinetic and the potential energies take on simple diagonal forms

$$2T = \tilde{Q}\dot{Q} \text{ and } 2V = \tilde{Q}\Lambda Q \tag{A2.4}$$

in which Λ is a diagonal matrix with the λ_i running down its principal diagonal and zero entries everywhere else. By substituting (A2.3) into (A2.1) and comparing corresponding terms with those in (A2.4) it follows that,

$$L\tilde{L} = G \text{ and } \tilde{L}FL = \Lambda \tag{A2.5}$$

and therefore

$$GF = L\Lambda L^{-1}. \tag{A2.6}$$

The matrix product GF is related to Λ by a simple similarity transform (a rotation of axes) and has therefore the same roots. The coordinates Q are called the normal coordinates and the transformation matrix L is obtained by assembling suitably normalized eigenvectors of GF. The normal coordinates are very important, apart from the strict vibrational problem, since any physical quantity depending on the vibrational motion such as infrared or Raman intensities, vibration amplitudes, damping of electron diffraction patterns etc. will be governed by the normal coordinates.

The problem as outlined above is to assemble the matrix G in any of the ways discussed in the standard textbooks,[220] to assemble F (whose elements are the force constants) in the same manner and to determine the roots of the $(3N-6) \times (3N-6)$ matrix product GF. If N is at all large, this problem can be formidable, requiring the services of a large high-speed computer. To overcome this difficulty, it is usual to invoke any symmetry which the molecule has by means of Group Theoretical methods. The normal coordinates form a representation of the molecular point group and in general this representation can be reduced, as

$$\Gamma_Q = n_1\Gamma_1 + n_2\Gamma_2 + n_3\Gamma_3 + \text{etc.}, \tag{A2.7}$$

where Γ_i is an irreducible representation of the molecular point group and $n_1 + n_2 + \ldots n_n = 3N - 6$. It follows from this that one can always find a new set of coordinates S, related to R by the orthonormal transformation

$$S = UR \tag{A2.8}$$

in terms of which the matrix product $\mathscr{G}\mathscr{F}$ defined by

$$\mathscr{G} = UG\tilde{U} \text{ and } \mathscr{F} = UF\tilde{U} \tag{A2.9}$$

breaks up into blocks of size $n_1 \times n_1$, $n_2 \times n_2$, etc. running down the principal diagonal. The coordinates **S** are called symmetry coordinates and the elements of the matrix U (which are always simple arithmetical functions) are found by standard Group Theoretical means. In fact, if an element of **R**, say R_i, is transformed into R_i^p by the pth symmetry element of the group one can derive a set of symmetry coordinates by the operation

$$S'(\Gamma_l) = \sum_{p=1}^{p=h} \chi_{\Gamma l}(p) R_i^p. \tag{A2.10}$$

where h is the order of the group and $\chi_{\Gamma l}(p)$ is the character of the lth irreducible representation for the pth symmetry element. We have put a prime on $S'(\Gamma_l)$ because sometimes it is advisable to take simple linear combinations of the $S'(\Gamma_l)$ to get a more immediately useful set of symmetry coordinates. There is always a degree of flexibility about this operation but, provided the coefficients have been derived using (A2.10) and are suitably normalized so that

$$U\tilde{U} = E, \tag{A2.11}$$

then the matrix U will properly factorize both G and F. Having sketched out briefly this theory we will now illustrate and apply it by considering some examples.

Vibrations of Ring Molecules

One of the assumptions made in discussing the vibrations of infinite assemblies is that, if all the entities are translated one repeat unit along, an indistinguishable configuration results. The only simple finite system which can reproduce this condition is an assembly of atoms constrained to move on a circle. Suppose that we have $2N$ atoms of one kind with mass M and $2N$ atoms of a different kind of mass m arranged alternately round a circle, and suppose that the force constant between adjacent pairs is f and that between non-adjacent pairs is zero. The appropriate coordinate system is the displacement of each atom from its equilibrium position along the circle, which we shall denote by x_i. With this choice the G matrix is particularly simple, being diagonal with entries $\mu_M = M^{-1}$ and $\mu_m = m^{-1}$ alternately along its principal diagonal. The reason for this is that the kinetic energy is always a simple quadratic function without cross-term when expressed via the Cartesian coordinates. If G^{-1} is diagonal, it follows that so is its inverse G. The F matrix has also a relatively simple form. If we start the coordinate numbering by choosing one atom of mass M to be x_0, then F has the form

	x_0	x_1	x_2	$\ldots\ldots$	x_{4N-1}
x_0	$2f$	$-f$	0	$\ldots\ldots$	$-f$
x_1	$-f$	$2f$	$-f$	$\ldots\ldots$	0
x_2	0	$-f$	$2f$	$-f \ldots$	
.	.	.	.		
.	.	.	.		
.	.	.	.		
x_{4N-1}	$-f$				

On expansion of $\tilde{\mathbf{R}}F\mathbf{R}$, this is seen to lead to the quadratic form

$$2V = f\,[(x_0 - x_1)^2 + (x_1 - x_2)^2 + \ldots (x_{4N-1} - x_0)^2] \qquad (A2.12)$$

appropriate to nearest-neighbour-only interaction. The symmetry operations which send the assembly into an identical configuration are the set of integral multiples of rotation through an angle π/N. The appropriate group is therefore C_{2N} whose character table may be written

C_{2N}	E	C_{2N}^1	C_{2N}^2	$\ldots$	C_{2N}^{2N-1}	$\epsilon = \exp(i\pi/N)$
$A = R_0$	1	1	1	$\ldots$	1	
$B = R_N$	1	-1	1	$\ldots$	-1	
R_1	1	ϵ	ϵ^2	$\ldots$	ϵ^{2N-1}	
R_{N+1}	1	ϵ^{N+1}	$\epsilon^{2(N+1)}$	$\ldots$	$\epsilon^{(N+1)(2N-1)}$	
.	.	.	.	$\ldots$	.	
.	.	.	.	$\ldots$	.	
.	.	.	.	$\ldots$	.	
.	.	.	.	$\ldots$	.	
R_{N-1}	1	$\epsilon^{(N-1)}$	$\epsilon^{2(N-1)}$	$\ldots$	$\epsilon^{(2N-1)(N-1)}$	
R_{2N-1}	1	$\epsilon^{(2N-1)}$	$\epsilon^{2(2N-1)}$	$\ldots$	$\epsilon^{(2N-1)^2}$	

The individual characters appearing in this table are complex and so, in applying the orthogonality relation between irreducible representations, the complex conjugate form must be used, i.e.

$$\sum_{p=1}^{p=h} \chi_{\Gamma_k}(p)\,\chi_{\Gamma_l}^{*}(p) = h\delta_{kl} \qquad (A2.13)$$

where δ_{kl} is the Kronecker delta function. The elements of U will also be complex, so we must replace equation (A2.9) with

$$\mathcal{G} = UG\tilde{U}^* \text{ and } \mathcal{F} = UF\tilde{U}^* \tag{A2.14}$$

where

$$U\tilde{U}^* = E. \tag{A2.15}$$

The columns of $\tilde{U}^*$ are obtained by taking complex conjugates of the corresponding rows of U. It will be noticed that the complex conjugate of any irreducible representation is another irreducible representation and therefore we expect that, apart from A and B, the calculated frequencies will occur in degenerate pairs. The distribution of the vibrational frequencies amongst the symmetry species is found by reducing the representation formed by the Cartesian coordinates. This has a particularly simple character since only for $E = C_{2N}^{2N}$ is any atom sent into itself; therefore $\chi_{\Gamma x}(p)$ equals $4N$ for E and equals zero for all other symmetry elements. Applying the usual relationship,

$$n(\Gamma_k) = h^{-1} \sum_{p=1}^{p=h} \chi_{\Gamma x}(p)\chi_{\Gamma k}(p), \tag{A2.16}$$

for determining the number of times a given irreducible representation occurs in a reducible representation, it is found that the $4N$ vibrations occur as pairs—two in each of the $2N$ irreducible representations.

The symmetry coordinates (two for each species) are found by taking the sum and the difference of the combinations found using equation (A2.10) with x_0 and x_1 respectively as generating elements. As an example the symmetry coordinates for the kth irreducible representation will be

$$S_{\pm}^k = 2^{-1}N^{-1/2}\begin{bmatrix} x_0 + \epsilon^k x_2 + \epsilon^{2k} x_4 + & \cdots & \epsilon^{(2N-1)k} x_{4N-2} \\ \pm(x_1 + \epsilon^k x_3 + \epsilon^{2k} x_5 + & \cdots & \epsilon^{(2N-1)k} x_{4N-1} \end{bmatrix}. \tag{A2.17}$$

Taking these coordinates and their kin, the U matrix can be constructed and used to factor G and F. The 2×2 blocks of $\mathcal{G}$ take on the form

$$\begin{bmatrix} \frac{1}{2}(\mu_M + \mu_m) & \frac{1}{2}(\mu_M - \mu_m) \\ \frac{1}{2}(\mu_M - \mu_m) & \frac{1}{2}(\mu_M + \mu_m) \end{bmatrix}.$$

The factoring of F involves somewhat more tedious algebra. It is convenient to consider the elements of UF which can be shown to be

$$[S_+^k, x_{2n}] = [f/(2\sqrt{N})][1 - \epsilon^{(2N-1)k}]\,\epsilon^{2nk},$$
$$[S_+^k, x_{2n+1}] = [f/(2\sqrt{N})][1 - \epsilon^k]\,\epsilon^{2nk},$$
$$[S_-^k, x_{2n}] = [f/(2\sqrt{N})][3 + \epsilon^{(2N-1)k}]\,\epsilon^{2nk}, \tag{A2.18}$$
$$[S_-^k, x_{2n+1}] = [f/(2\sqrt{N})][3 + \epsilon^k]\,\epsilon^{2nk}.$$

The elements of $\mathcal{F} = UF\tilde{U}^*$ can then be seen to be

$$[S_+^k \, S_+^l] = \frac{f}{4N} \left[\sum_0^{2N-1} [l - \epsilon^{(2N-1)k}] \, \epsilon^{2nk}(\epsilon^{2nl})^* \right.$$

$$\left. + \sum_0^{2N-1} [1 - \epsilon^k] \epsilon^{2nk}(\epsilon^{2nl})^* \right] \quad \text{(A2.19)}$$

which is zero, unless $k - l$ is zero when it has the value $1 - \cos(2\pi k/2N)$

$$[S_-^k \, S_-^l] = \frac{f}{4N} \left[\sum_0^{2N-1} (3 + \epsilon^{(2n-1)k}) \, \epsilon^{2nk}(\epsilon^{2nl})^* \right.$$

$$\left. + \sum_0^{2N-1} (3 + \epsilon^k) \epsilon^{2nk}(\epsilon^{2nl})^* \right] \quad \text{(A2.20)}$$

which again is zero unless $k - l$ is zero when it has the value $3 + \cos(2\pi k/2N)$

$$[S_+^k \, S_-^k] = [S_-^k \, S_+^k]^* = i \sin(\pi k/N). \quad \text{(A2.21)}$$

The matrix $\mathcal{F}$ is therefore Hermitian and consists of 2×2 blocks running down the principal diagonal. These blocks may be written

$$f \begin{bmatrix} 1 - \cos(\pi k/N) & i \sin(\pi k/N) \\ -i \sin(\pi k/N) & 3 + \cos(\pi k/N) \end{bmatrix}, \quad k = 0, 1, 2 \ldots 2N-1. \quad \text{(A2.22)}$$

The roots of the matrix product $\mathcal{GF}$ for any given value of k are given by

$$\lambda = f(\mu_M + \mu_m) \pm f[(\mu_M + \mu_m)^2 - 4\mu_M\mu_m \sin^2(\pi k/2N)]^{1/2}. \quad \text{(A2.23)}$$

It will be seen that this is identical with equation (5.44) since $\lambda = 4\pi^2\nu^2$. The pure number k is to be related to the wave vector $\bar{k}$ by the relation

$$k = 2Na\bar{k}/\pi. \quad \text{(A2.24)}$$

The vibrational frequencies of the molecule can therefore be plotted as discrete points along the two branches of Fig. 5.7. As N increases without limit, the points become more and more crowded along the branches until ultimately we come to the continuous curves shown in Fig. 5.7. When N is infinite, any section of the cyclic molecule will be linear and will have perfect translational symmetry. This is the system shown in Fig. 5.6 and reflected in the symmetry of equation (5.41). One immediate difference, however, will be noted in that the maximum value of k is $2N-1$; we have for the infinite case, therefore, that the argument of the $\sin^2$ function can range from zero up to π. The positive half of the dispersion diagram will therefore be as in Fig. 2.1. This is a consequence of the degeneracy mentioned earlier, for the representations R_k and R_{2N-k} are necessarily degenerate and must lead to two vibrations of identical frequency. The difference is more apparent than real, however, since we may redefine k so that it runs from negative numbers up to positive numbers and, as a result, $\pi k/2N$ runs from $-\pi/2$ up to $+\pi/2$. We thus reobtain the original dispersion diagram and, furthermore, see that the degeneracy merely involves identical waves moving either clockwise or anti-clockwise round the ring.

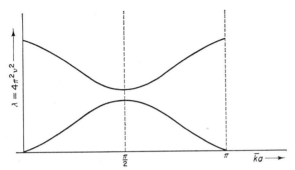

FIG. A2.1. Dispersion diagram for a linear diatomic chain.

We now come to consider the absorption of infrared radiation by this system. The Group Theoretical rule for infrared activity is that the irreducible representation which contains the normal mode in question should also contain one of the primitive translations T_x, T_y or T_z. For the cyclic group C_{2N} these are contained in $A(T_z)$ and $R_1(T_x, T_y)$. It follows that there will be four allowed transitions from the ground state (all doubly degenerate)—two in the optical branch and two in the acoustic branch. The two A modes are the zero-frequency rotation of the ring as a rigid body (acoustic) and the familiar "reststrahlen" type of motion in which adjacent atoms move out of phase (S_-^0 and therefore optical). The two R_1 modes are similar but there is a progressive modulation of atomic vibrational amplitude as we go round the ring by the factor $\cos[2\pi(n/N)]$ where n is the number of the atom starting with a given atom of each kind as $n = $ zero. When N is allowed to increase without limit, the points on the two branches for R_1 move closer and closer to the ordinate axis since $(\pi/2N)$ tends to zero. In the limit the two points are coincident with the two A points which themselves lie on the ordinate axis for all values of N. We thus have established the selection rule $\Delta \bar{k} = $ zero at least for the ground state. For transitions from excited states (i.e. hot bands and difference bands) we need to know whether A or R_1 is included in the direct product $R_k \times R_l$. It may be readily shown that a representation R_p is included in $R_k \times R_l$ if $(p+k+l)$ or $(p-k-l)$ or $(p+k-l)$ or $(p+l-k)$ equals zero. For p zero (i.e. A) one must have $k+l$ zero or $k-l$ zero, that is $\Delta \bar{k}$ transitions to a level or its degenerate companion. For $p = l$ (i.e. R_1) we again have $k+l = \pm 1$ or $k-l = \pm 1$ which, for infinite N, become $\Delta \bar{k} = $ zero transitions. We have thus shown that allowed infrared transitions occur vertically in the dispersion diagram. It should be pointed out that we have only illustrated the fundamental branches in the Figure and that a branch exists for every overtone and combination state.

The above treatment is perfectly usable in practice, especially in the far infrared where wavelengths are so much greater than interatomic distances. But to be perfectly fair it must be pointed out that the selection rules based on dipole moment integrals are only valid when the region of integration is much smaller than the wavelength. This is normally the case for small molecules and the integration is performed assuming the electric field of the radiation to be uniform over the molecule. We can still get the same result, however, if we choose a mode which has the same wavelength as the radiation, for when one changes sign so will the other. This leads immediately to the more exact selection rule discussed in Chapter 5, namely that transitions are not quite vertical but follow straight lines parallel to the dispersion curve for photons. In practice, however, a will be of the order 10^{-8} and the wavelength $\sim 10^{-2}$ cm, so that the transition will be indistinguishable from a $\Delta \bar{k} =$ zero transition at the centre of the Brillouin zone.

We must now consider the relevance of the above treatment to practical cases. Real systems such as small crystals and polymer chains do not have the perfect translational symmetry of the cyclic molecule. This is reflected in the breaking of the symmetry of the F matrix which now begins

$$
\begin{vmatrix}
f & -f & 0 & \ldots & 0 \\
-f & 2f & -f & & \\
0 & -f & 2f & & \\
\cdot & & & & \\
\cdot & & & & \\
\cdot & & & & \\
0 & & & &
\end{vmatrix}
\quad \text{instead of} \quad
\begin{vmatrix}
2f & -f & 0 & \ldots & -f \\
-f & 2f & -f & & \\
0 & -f & 2f & & \\
\cdot & & & & \\
\cdot & & & & \\
\cdot & & & & \\
-f & & & &
\end{vmatrix}
$$

The G matrix will still have high symmetry (C_{2N}) but the symmetry group of the F matrix will only be C_i. The $4N$ vibrations break up into two blocks, an A_g block and an A_u block of equal size. Nevertheless, it may still be shown that the latent roots of $\mathcal{GF}$ lie on the dispersion diagram, but the selection rules are much less rigorous for small N. Any transition to an

A_u level is allowed but it is found that the vertical transitions are the more intense. As N increases without limit, the intensity of the $\Delta \bar{k} =$ zero transition increases without limit whilst the intensities of all other transitions tend to zero. Physically this means that as N increases, the perturbation introduced by the starting and stopping of the chain becomes less and less significant.

Appendix 3

Dielectric Theory

In electronic theory one considers a system with an input and an output and the problem is to derive the transfer function relating the input to the output voltages. The input voltage is either cosinusoidal or can be reduced to cosinusoidal components by the application of Fourier's theorem. One can therefore consider a cosinusoidal component as the input: we thus have

$$V(t) = V_0 \cos \omega t \qquad (A3.1)$$

where ω is the angular frequency $= 2\pi\nu$, and ν is the time frequency in Hertz. Rather than consider an oscillating voltage which disappears when $t = (m+\frac{1}{2})/2\nu$, it is customary to introduce a complex voltage

$$\hat{V}(t) = V_0 \exp(i\omega t) = V_0 (\cos \omega t + i \sin \omega t) \qquad (A3.2)$$

and to consider this voltage as of constant modulus and rotating at angular frequency ω in the complex plane

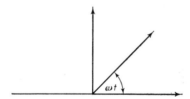

The observable quantity is then the real part of $\hat{V}(t) = V_0 \exp(i\omega t)$.

In general the transfer function is also a complex quantity (called the impedance) and one then obtains from this the phase shifts introduced by the system. In a similar manner, the oscillations of the electromagnetic field are often written in complex form, i.e.

$$\hat{E}(t) = E_0 \exp(i\omega t). \qquad (A3.3)$$

One considers a plane wave entering an homogeneous isotropic dielectric. In the absence of absorption the electric field strength (at a fixed time) throughout the dielectric is given by the simple form

$$E(x) = E(o) \cos(2\pi n \bar{\nu}_0 x) \qquad (A3.4)$$

where n is the refractive index and $\bar{\nu}_0$ is the wavenumber in free space. Introducing the complex part one can write

$$\hat{E}(x) = E(o) \exp(-2\pi i n \bar{\nu}_0 x). \tag{A3.5}$$

If the medium does absorb, then we have, by Lambert's Law,

$$I(x) = I(o) \exp(-\alpha x). \tag{A3.6}$$

Where α is the absorption coefficient in neper cm^{-1}; it follows, since $|E(x)|^2 \propto I(x)$, that

$$\hat{E}(x) = E(o) \exp(-2\pi i n \bar{\nu}_0 x + \tfrac{1}{2}\alpha x). \tag{A3.7}$$

It is now customary to introduce the complex refractive index

$$\hat{n} = n(1 - i\kappa) \tag{A3.8}$$

and, writing

$$\hat{E}(x) = E(o) \exp(-2\pi i \hat{n} \bar{\nu}_0 x), \tag{A3.9}$$

which is analogous to equation (A3.5), an explicit relationship between α and n and κ can be derived; this is

$$\alpha = 4\pi n \kappa \bar{\nu}_0. \tag{A3.10}$$

Thus, if one knows α and n, one can write down $\hat{n}$ or, if some author gives the real and imaginary parts of $\hat{n}$, one can work out the absorption coefficient. κ (kappa) is often referred to as the extinction coefficient and, since $n\bar{\nu}_0 = \lambda^{-1}$, it is the absorption coefficient per wavelength rather than per centimetre.

An alternative approach used by many authors, especially those concerned with dielectric loss, is the use of the complex dielectric constant

$$\hat{\epsilon} = \epsilon' - i\epsilon''. \tag{A3.11}$$

The two systems are readily related since one has, from Maxwell's equations,

$$\hat{\epsilon} = [\hat{n}]^2 \tag{A3.12}$$

and therefore, by substitution,

$$\hat{\epsilon} = n^2(1 - \kappa^2) - i2n^2\kappa, \tag{A3.13}$$

that is

$$\epsilon' = n^2(1 - \kappa^2) \quad \text{and} \quad \epsilon'' = 2n^2\kappa. \tag{A3.14}$$

Given ϵ' and ϵ'', n and κ can be computed and from these α can be calculated; of course, conversely, from measured values of n and α, $\hat{\epsilon}$ may be derived. The loss angle δ defined by

$$\tan \delta = \epsilon''/\epsilon' \tag{A3.15}$$

is also sometimes given. The reason for the use of $\tan \delta$ is that the power loss in a dielectric is determined by the phase angle between the voltage and the current. If this is 90°, as in a perfect dielectric, the loss is zero, and if it is 0°, as in a pure resistor, the loss is a maximum. The departure of the phase angle from 90° is seen to be $\tan^{-1}(\epsilon''/\epsilon')$ by a consideration of the rotating vectors in the complex plane. The loss in a slab of dielectric placed in a plate capacitor of vacuum capacitance C_0 can readily be established by noting that

$$\hat{C} = \hat{\epsilon}C_0 \quad \text{and that} \quad \hat{Q} = \hat{C}\hat{V} \tag{A3.16}$$

from which it follows by differentiation and taking the time average of the product of the real parts of $\hat{V}(t)$ and $d\hat{Q}/dt$ that the power loss is given by†

$$\Delta W = -\tfrac{1}{2}V^2 C_0 \omega \epsilon''. \tag{A3.17}$$

The lossy capacitor can be regarded as a perfect capacitor of capacitance $\epsilon'C_0$ in parallel with a resistor whose resistance to generate the power loss of equation (A3.17) must be given by

$$R^{-1} = \epsilon'C_0(\epsilon''/\epsilon')\omega,$$

i.e.

$$R^{-1} = \epsilon'C_0\omega \tan \delta. \tag{A3.18}$$

The capacitance of the capacitor is related to the area of its plates and their distance apart by the relation

$$C_0 = A/4\pi d, \tag{A3.19}$$

so that we have

$$\rho^{-1} = (d/A)R^{-1} = \epsilon''\omega/4\pi = \alpha cn/4\pi \tag{A3.20}$$

where ρ is the resistivity. We can therefore write down a relationship between the resistivity of a dielectric to currents flowing in conventional circuits and its absorption coefficient exhibited to free electromagnetic waves. This is numerically (for ρ in Ω cm)

$$376 \cdot 79 \, \rho^{-1} = \alpha n. \tag{A3.21}$$

It is interesting to note from this equation that, in the case of metals for which ρ might be typically 2×10^{-8}, the product αn has to be of the order 10^{10}. This is another way of looking at the very high absorption coefficients and very high reflectivities of metals.

The response of a dielectric medium to the application of an electromagnetic field can be looked at classically in a rather less phenomenological

---

† Alternatively one may write

$$\Delta W = -\tfrac{1}{2}\mathcal{R}(\hat{V}(t)\hat{\imath}(t)^*),$$

i.e. one half the real part of the product of $(\hat{V}t)$ and the complex conjugate

$$\hat{\imath}(t) = d\hat{Q}(t)/dt.$$

framework. Basically the problem is to compute the induced dipole moment produced in the system by the forced oscillation. Suppose that we have charges e and mass m held to equilibrium positions by restoring forces of force constant f, then, if an electric field E is applied, the particles will be displaced a distance x in the direction of the field given by

$$fx = eE \qquad (A3.22)$$

and therefore the additional dipole moment induced will be

$$\mu = ex = e^2 E/f. \qquad (A3.23)$$

The polarizability χ will be given by†

$$\chi = \mu/E = e^2/f. \qquad (A3.24)$$

Now consider the response to an alternating field; the most general equation of motion is

$$m\mathrm{d}^2x/\mathrm{d}t^2 + (m/\tau)\,\mathrm{d}x/\mathrm{d}t + m\omega_0^2 x = eE_0 \exp(i\omega t). \qquad (A3.25)$$

The second term is introduced to take account of frictional, collisional or other damping mechanisms and the third has been changed from $+fx$ in anticipation of the simple harmonic solution of frequency, $\omega_0 = (f/m)^{1/2}$. The solution of this equation is

$$\hat{x} = (e/m)\,E_0 \exp(i\omega t)/(\omega_0^2 - \omega^2 + i\omega\tau^{-1}). \qquad (A3.26)$$

The polarizability is thus complex and upon rationalization it may be written

$$\hat{\chi} = \frac{e^2}{m}\left\{ \frac{\omega_0^2 - \omega^2}{(\omega_0^2 - \omega^2)^2 + \omega^2\tau^{-2}} - i\left[\frac{\omega\tau^{-1}}{(\omega_0^2 - \omega^2)^2 + \omega^2\tau^{-2}} \right] \right\}. \qquad (A3.27)$$

The dielectric constant of a medium is related to the polarizability by the relation

$$\epsilon = 1 + 4\pi N\chi, \qquad (A3.28)$$

where N is the number of oscillators per cubic centimetre. The real and imaginary parts of $\hat{\epsilon}$ may therefore be written as

$$\epsilon' = 1 + (4\pi Ne^2/m)(\omega_0^2 - \omega^2)/[(\omega_0^2 - \omega^2)^2 + \omega^2\tau^{-2}], \qquad (A3.29)$$

$$\epsilon'' = (4\pi Ne^2/m)\,\omega\tau^{-1}/[(\omega_0^2 - \omega^2)^2 + \omega^2\tau^{-2}]. \qquad (A3.30)$$

When n and α are computed from these, behaviour similar to that shown in Fig. 5.19 results. This might be, at first sight, thought rather surprising since the above treatment is couched in terms of classical physics and the

† The symbol for polarizability is usually α but this is avoided here because of possible confusion with α, the absorption coefficient.

real world is populated by quantum oscillators. The strong resemblance to reality of the above treatment (and in passing it should be pointed out that equation 5.115 is a special case of our present equation A3.25) arises from the necessary connection between absorption and dispersion. The use of a complex refractive index is not just a mathematical convenience indicated by the exponential form of the propagation and attenuation equations; it is far more profound and the necessary connection between the real and imaginary parts has its origin in one of the most fundamental concepts—causality.

This argument goes as follows:[436] consider a short pulse delivered to a system at time $t = 0$. The pulse can be analysed into Fourier components extending from $t = -\infty$ to $t = +\infty$. Applying causality (namely, no output before the input), it follows that the Fourier components at the output must completely cancel at all times prior to $t = 0$. Now imagine that the system has a narrow absorption band at frequency v_0. The effect is to remove the Fourier components near v_0 or, what is the same thing, to add their complements. These will now be manifest as ripples before $t = 0$. Since this violates causality, the only possibility is that the phases of the non-absorbed components are shifted to once again produce cancellation. In other words, an absorption band is associated with a dispersion. This argument properly developed leads to the Kramers–Kronig integrals. The treatment is independent of any particular system of mechanics and the type of absorption and dispersion profiles shown in Fig. 5.19 must therefore result by any system and in particular by quantum mechanics.

From these arguments, it follows that the quantum mechanical equation of motion can be found from the classical relationship (equation A3.25) by simple substitutions. These are to replace e^2/m by $8\pi^2 v_{ij} \mid \mu_{ij} \mid ^2/3h$ and to introduce the population difference ΔN per unit volume between the lower and the upper levels. When this is done, together with two slight manipulations of the constants (for algebraical convenience), we have

$$d^2\hat{P}/dt^2 + (2/\tau)\, d\hat{P}/dt + (\omega_0^2 + \tau^{-2})\hat{P}$$
$$= \Delta N (8/3h)\, \pi^2 v_{ij} \mid \mu_{ij} \mid ^2 E_0 \exp{(i\omega t)} \quad \text{(A3.31)}$$

where $\hat{P} = E(\hat{e} - 1)/4\pi$ is the polarization, i.e. the induced moment per unit volume.

From this equation it follows that

$$\hat{P} = (\Delta N 8/3h)\, \pi^2 v_{ij} \mid \mu_{ij} \mid ^2 E_0 \exp{(i\omega t)}(\omega_0^2 + \tau^{-2} - \omega^2 + 2i\omega/\tau)^{-1} \quad \text{(A3.32)}$$

This is the analogue† of equation (A3.26) and likewise, upon rationaliza-

† Note, however, that ω_0 and τ are defined differently. The change of definition is adopted so that the factored version (equation A3.34) will have a simple form.

tion, the absorption coefficient can be written (via equations A3.10 and A3.11) in simple form, provided we assume that the refractive index does not vary over the resonance region; the answer is

$$\alpha = (\Delta N 64/3hc)\, \pi^4 \nu_{ij}\, |\, \mu_{ij}\, |\, ^2\nu \left[\frac{2\omega/\tau}{(\omega^2 + \tau^{-2} - \omega^2)^2 + 4\omega^2/\tau^2}\right]. \quad (A3.33)$$

The denominator of the term in brackets factorizes and, carrying this through, together with a conversion to wavenumbers throughout and with the approximation that $\nu_{ij} = \omega_0/2\pi$, we have

$$\alpha = \frac{8\pi^2\Delta N}{3hc}\, |\, \mu_{ij}\, |\, ^2 \left[\frac{\bar{\nu}\Delta\bar{\nu}}{(\Delta\bar{\nu})^2 + (\bar{\nu}_0 - \bar{\nu})^2} - \frac{\bar{\nu}\Delta\bar{\nu}}{(\Delta\bar{\nu})^2 + (\bar{\nu}_0 + \bar{\nu})^2}\right]. \quad (A3.34)$$

This is the Lorentz line-shape function which has been used extensively in many investigations. It is most successful at high frequencies and in the neighbourhood of the resonance; it also has the desirable feature that for $\bar{\nu} \gg \bar{\nu}_0$ the absorption coefficient approaches zero. Despite these advantages, Van Vleck and Weisskopf[370] have shown that the derivation is unsound, especially for rotational spectra, and they have pointed out that the Lorentz line-shape function does not transform into the Debye function (as expected) when $\bar{\nu}_0 \ll \bar{\nu}$. The origin of the discrepancy lies in the assumption (buried rather deeply in equation A3.31) that after a collision the values of x and dx/dt will be random. This is not usually the case since one would expect a Boltzmann distribution of molecular energies and Van Vleck and Weisskopf have shown that the line-shape formula appropriate to this assumption can be found from equation (A3.34) by replacing the term in brackets with

$$\frac{\bar{\nu}}{\bar{\nu}_0} \left[\frac{\bar{\nu}\Delta\bar{\nu}}{(\Delta\bar{\nu})^2 + (\bar{\nu}_0 - \bar{\nu})^2} + \frac{\bar{\nu}\Delta\bar{\nu}}{(\Delta\bar{\nu})^2 + (\bar{\nu}_0 + \bar{\nu})^2}\right], \quad (A3.35)$$

With this substitution, together with the evaluation of $|\, \mu_{ij}\, |\, ^2$ and allowance for statistical weight (equations 5.21 to 5.24), followed by the approximation (valid for a microwave pure rotational transition) that

$$\Delta N = N_i - N_j = N f_i [1 - \exp (E_{ij}/kT)] \approx N f_i\, h\nu_{ij}/(2kT), \quad (A3.36)$$

where N is the total number of molecules and f_i the fraction in the lower state, one finds

$$\alpha = \frac{4\pi^2 hc N \bar{\nu}_0 \mu^2}{3(kT)^2} \left[\frac{\bar{\nu}^2\Delta\bar{\nu}}{(\Delta\bar{\nu})^2 + (\bar{\nu}_0 - \bar{\nu})^2} + \frac{\bar{\nu}^2\Delta\bar{\nu}}{(\Delta\bar{\nu})^2 + (\bar{\nu}_0 + \bar{\nu})^2}\right]. \quad (A3.37)$$

This relation is frequently employed in microwave spectroscopy, but the more accurate version of the term outside the bracket given in equation (5.30) is more appropriate at submillimetric wavelengths.

A form of the Debye equation may be derived from equation (A3.37) by making the following assumptions:

$$\text{that } |\mu_{ij}|^2 = \mu^2, \quad \text{that } \nu_0 \to 0 \quad \text{and that } f_i = \tfrac{1}{2}.$$

The first of these is tantamount to saying that the rotational energy is negligible and its assumption will imply, as we have seen in Chapter 5, a breakdown in the validity of the treatment at high frequencies such as those involved in pure rotational transitions of the free molecule. The second assumption implies that the Debye equation will describe a relaxation rather than a resonance and the third follows from a consideration of the vanishingly small energy changes during the motion. With these assumptions, the right-hand side of equation (A3.37) may be multiplied by

$$2kT/(h\nu_0 c)$$

and f_i set equal to $\tfrac{1}{2}$. Alternatively, the assumptions may be inserted at an earlier state. With either approach the result when ν_0 is allowed to tend to zero is

$$\alpha = [8\pi^2 N\mu^2/(3kT)]\{\bar{\nu}^2\Delta\bar{\nu}/[\bar{\nu}^2+(\Delta\bar{\nu})^2]\} \tag{A3.38}$$

which is a form of the Debye equation. Unfortunately this simple relation is not of much value in practical situations, since the commonest use of the Debye equation is to interpret the results of microwave and radio-frequency measurements on liquids and in a condensed phase; the assumption that the refractive index variations may be ignored is certainly not tenable. Basically we may not use the approximate formula for α (equation 5.16) but must instead prefer the accurate, but very non-linear, version given by equation (5.15). Because of the non-linearity, no simple equivalent of equation (A3.38) may be written down and most workers prefer to use numerical methods in which ϵ' and ϵ'' are first calculated and these are then substituted in the accurate formula for α.

The Debye equation, in terms of the complex dielectric constant, is, however, readily obtainable within the framework developed by Van Vleck and Weisskopf. These authors have shown[370] that the correct formulation of equation (A3.32) is

$$\hat{P} = \frac{\Delta N}{3h} 8\pi^2\nu_0 |\mu_{ij}|^2 E_0 \exp(i\omega t)\left[\frac{1}{\omega_0^2 - \omega^2}\right.$$

$$-\frac{\omega}{2\tau^2\omega^2}\left(\frac{1}{(\omega_0-\omega)(\tau^{-2}+(\omega_0-\omega)^2)} - \frac{1}{(\omega_0+\omega)(\tau^{-2}+(\omega_0+\omega)^2)}\right)$$

$$\left. -\frac{i\omega}{2\tau\omega^2}\left(\frac{1}{\tau^{-2}+(\omega_0-\omega)^2} + \frac{1}{\tau^{-2}+(\omega_0+\omega)^2}\right)\right] \tag{A3.39}$$

o

from which it will be seen that the line-shape formula equation (A3.37) follows after the usual approximations. Taking this expression for $\hat{P}$ and making the substitutions for ΔN and $(\mu_{ij})^2$ appropriate to the case $\nu_0 \to 0$, we have

$$
\hat{\epsilon} - \epsilon_\infty = \frac{4\pi N f_i \mu^2}{3kT} \left[\frac{\omega_0^2}{\omega_0^2 - \omega^2} - \frac{\omega}{2\tau^2} \left(\frac{1}{(\omega_0 - \omega)(\tau^{-2} + (\omega_0 - \omega)^2)} \right. \right.
$$
$$
\left. - \frac{1}{(\omega_0 + \omega)(\tau^{-2} + (\omega_0 + \omega)^2)} \right)
$$
$$
\left. - \frac{i\omega}{2\tau} \left(\frac{1}{\tau^{-2} + (\omega_0 - \omega)^2} + \frac{1}{\tau^{-2} + (\omega_0 + \omega)^2} \right) \right]. \quad \text{(A3.40)}
$$

The term ϵ_∞ is strictly unity in the present context but we have introduced it as a symbol to take cognisance of higher-frequency dispersions. Putting now the term outside the bracket equal to $\epsilon_0 - \epsilon_\infty$ and allowing ω_0 to tend to zero, we have

$$
(\hat{\epsilon} - \epsilon_\infty)/(\epsilon_0 - \epsilon_\infty) = (1 - i\omega\tau)/(1 + \omega^2\tau^2) = (1 + i\omega\tau)^{-1} \quad \text{(A3.41)}
$$

which is the form of the Debye equation used in Chapter 5.

Although the Lorentz and the Van Vleck and Weisskopf line-shape formulae are in wide use, they have both been criticized by Brot[437] on the grounds that the behaviour of the optical constants which they predict for frequencies much less than and much greater than ω_0 does not accord with physical expectation. The use of the Van Vleck–Weisskopf formula should properly be restricted to discussions of pressure-broadened pure rotational spectra of gases, but even here the predicted constant absorption at high frequencies is not observed. A related difficulty is that the real part of the complex dielectric constant $(\hat{\epsilon} - \epsilon_\infty)$ falls monotonically to zero for the Van Vleck–Weisskopf formulism whereas physical arguments require that $\hat{\epsilon}$ approach ϵ_∞ through lower values. The Lorentz formula, on the other hand, agrees well with observation for high frequencies but is physically unacceptable at very low frequencies. The reason for this assertion is that ϵ_0, being an equilibrium property, must be independent of τ since τ is a dynamic parameter. It will be seen from inspection of equation (A3.32) that this requirement is violated for the Lorentz case. The Van Vleck–Weisskopf approach (equation A3.40) is, however, satisfactory on this count as can be seen from the behaviour of equation (A3.40) as ω tends to zero. Brot also points out that if we are considering the vibrations of a charged ensemble, an alkali halide crystal for example, the material must behave as a conductor with free carriers if ω_0 is zero. This is because the amplitude of vibration is inversely proportional to ω_0 and would become indefinitely large as $\omega \to 0$.

The d.c. conductivity of a free carrier medium is given by

$$\rho^{-1} = Ne^2\tau/m. \tag{A3.42}$$

Clearly, the Lorentz equation cannot meet this specification since ρ^{-1} is zero at zero frequency (see equation A3.20). The Van Vleck–Weisskopf formula is also unsatisfactory from this point of view, but the failure is only of academic interest since this particular line-shape theory would not be applied to vibrational spectra.

Brot concludes that the simple line-shape theory given earlier in this Appendix (equations A3.26–A3.30) is preferable to either the Lorentz or the Van Vleck–Weisskopf formulisms. Inspection of equations (A3.26) to (A3.30) will show that

$\hat{x}$ is independent of τ for $\omega = 0$,

α tends to zero as $\omega \to \infty$,

$\epsilon' - 1$ goes through a shallow minimum,

The d.c. conductivity for $\omega_0 = 0$ is correctly given by equation (A3.42).

It has to be admitted, however, that the difference between the simple theory and the Lorentz theory is rather subtle. If we define ω_0^2 for the simple theory to be equal to $(\omega_0')^2 + \tau^{-2}$, for the Lorentz theory the two treatments become formally equivalent. The physical difference is that in the simple theory the frequency of maximum absorption ($\omega = \omega_0$) is *independent* of line broadening whereas in the Lorentz theory the frequency of maximum absorption shifts to higher frequencies as the line gets broader, since

$$(\omega_{max})^2 = \omega_0^2 + \tau^{-2}. \tag{A3.43}$$

Unfortunately, very sophisticated experimental techniques will be required if this difference is to be exploited to decide between the rival claims.

A final point raised by Brot is of profound significance since it questions the basic assumptions commonly held relating to the differences between relaxational and resonance behaviour. From equations (A3.26)–(A3.30), we may write

$$(\hat{\epsilon} - 1)/(\epsilon_0 - 1) = \omega_0^2/(\omega_0^2 - \omega^2 + i\omega/\tau). \tag{A3.44}$$

This equation may be written

$$\frac{\hat{\epsilon} - 1}{\epsilon_0 - 1} = \frac{\omega_0^2}{[\frac{1}{2}\tau^{-1} - (\frac{1}{4}\tau^{-2} - \omega_0^2)^{1/2} + i\omega][\frac{1}{2}\tau^{-1} + (\frac{1}{4}\tau^{-2} - \omega_0^2)^{1/2} + i\omega]} \tag{A3.45}$$

which may be re-expressed (provided $1/2\tau > \omega_0$) as

$$(\hat{\epsilon} - 1)/(\epsilon_0 - 1) = [(1 + i\omega\tau_1)(1 + i\omega\tau_2)]^{-1} \tag{A3.46}$$

O§

where

$$\tau_1^{-1} = \tfrac{1}{2}\tau^{-1} - (\tfrac{1}{4}\tau^{-2} - \omega_0^2)^{1/2}$$

and

$$\tau_2^{-1} = \tfrac{1}{2}\tau^{-1} + (\tfrac{1}{4}\tau^{-2} - \omega_0^2)^{1/2}.$$

Equation (A3.46) is formally identical with the Rocard–Powles dispersion formula (equation 5.71) and shows that the popular notion, that relaxational or Debye-type behaviour is always associated with zero proper frequency, may not be correct.

Appendix 4

Optical Constants of some Materials at 29·712 cm⁻¹

		n	α (neper cm⁻¹)
Solids	Polyethylene	$1·461 \pm 0·023$	$0·2 \pm 0·05$
	Polypropylene	$1·500 \pm 0·02$	$0·27$
	TPX	$1·457 \pm 0·002$	$0·31$
	PTFE	$1·391 \pm 0·017$	$\sim 0·5$
	LiF	—	$5·5 \pm 0·5$
	Hexamine	$1·638$	$0·45$
	Polyethylene terephthalate	$1·69$	~ 35
	Crystalline quartz	$2·132 \pm 0·026$	$\sim 1·5$
	Vitreous silica	$1·93$	$1·8–2·6$
Liquids	Fluorobenzene	$1·46$	$21·1$
	Chlorobenzene	$1·538$	$15·2$
	Bromobenzene	$1·55$	$12·1$
	Iodobenzene	$1·60$	$9·1$
	Benzene	$1·512$	$2·68$
	Methyl benzene	$1·503$	$2·73$
	Ethyl benzene	$1·500$	$2·12$
	Sym-Tetrabromoethane	$1·643$	$8·51$
	Carbon tetrachloride	$1·492$	$1·37$
	Cyclohexane	$1·419$	$0·11$
	p-Xylene	$1·497$	$1·92$
	Chloroform	$1·480$	$17·14$
	Bromoform	$1·610$	$9·02$
	Methylene dichloride	—	104
	Methylene dibromide	—	$54·8$
	Methylene diiodide	$1·749$	$23·5$
	Silicon tetrachloride	$1·460$	$1·63$
	Tin tetrachloride	—	$1·68$
	Tin tetrabromide	$1·798$	$3·87$
	Water (20°C)	$2·132$	220
	Heavy water (20°C)	$2·017$	199

The absorption coefficients of commercial plastics vary widely due to the presence of various additives such as plasticizers, anti-oxidants etc. Fused silica likewise has a variable absorption coefficient depending on the nature of the material and the method of manufacture. The refractive indices are much less sensitive. In the absence of specified possible error, the range of accuracy may be assumed to be ± 5 per cent for α. The measurements are principally due to Chamberlain and his colleagues, but some by Fleming are included.

Appendix 5

Rotational Perturbations in the CN Radical

The first excited state of the CN radical $A^2\Pi$ lies at only 9241 cm^{-1} above the ground state $X^2\Sigma$ and is overlapped therefore by the vibrational levels of the ground state. Since $A^2\Pi$ is also a strongly bound state, its vibrational levels overlap those of the second excited state $B^2\Sigma$ which lies at 25 752 cm^{-1} above the ground state. The situation is illustrated in Fig. A5.1 and it

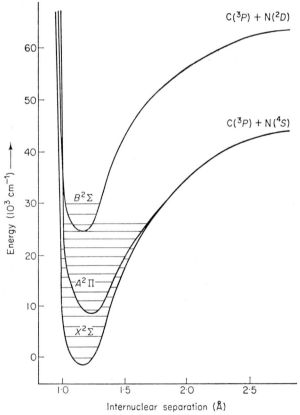

FIG. A5.1. Potential curves for the CN Radical.

will be seen that two close coincidences occur between $n = 11$ of $X^2\Sigma$ and $n = 7$ of $A^2\Pi$ and between $n = 0$ of $B^2\Sigma$ and $n = 10$ of $A^2\Pi$. The latter is a particularly close coincidence with a separation between the rotational origins of each vibrational level of only 44 cm^{-1}. In order to discuss the consequences of such a close approach it is necessary to consider the rotational structure, the spin-splitting fine structure and the hyperfine structure of each vibrational level. The angular momenta present in the molecule are that due to rotation, that due to the orbital motion of the odd electron, that due to the spin of the odd electron and finally that due to the spin of the ^{14}N nucleus. The problem of how these vector quantities add together has been worked out[438] by Hund. $^2\Sigma$ molecular states always belong to Hund's case (b) in which, of course, there is no orbital angular momentum and the electron spin is not coupled to the internuclear axis at all. Under these circumstances the rotational quantum number (called N since J is the *total* angular momentum) is a good quantum number. The rotational structure is thus quite simple, consisting of a series of levels having energies (in frequency units)

$$E = \nu_0 + B_v N(N+1) - D_v N^2(N+1)^2 \qquad (A5.1)$$

where ν_0 is the term energy. Each level is a close doublet, the two members having the same parity but different values of J, namely $J = N + \frac{1}{2}$ and $J = N - \frac{1}{2}$. These differ slightly in energy because of the interaction between the magnetic moment of the electron and the magnetic field due to rotation of the molecule. The splitting is given by $\Delta\nu = \gamma \ (N - \frac{1}{2})$, so it is to be expected to become more observable for high values of N. For a $^2\Sigma \to {}^2\Sigma$ transition such as the violet system of CN, the selection rules $\Delta N = \pm 1$, $\Delta J = \pm 1$ hold effectively, since $\Delta J = 0$ transitions are very weak. It follows that each line of the P and R branches will be a doublet with a splitting equal to the difference of that in the upper and lower levels. This splitting never exceeds $0 \cdot 2$ cm^{-1}, even for $N > 20$, and is only within the resolving power of quite good optical spectrographs. Each component of the spin doublet is itself made up of three very close hyperfine components due to interaction with the magnetic and quadrupole moments of the spin 1 ^{14}N nucleus. Hyperfine structure is not observable by conventional optical spectroscopy, although in certain cases it is detectable by microwave methods (see Chapter 2). In the context of spin-splitting, it should be pointed out that the very large (2 cm^{-1}) values encountered with molecules such as O_2 and SO arise from the spin–spin interaction of the two odd electrons in these diradicals: very much smaller values are found for the majority of radicals such as CN where there is only one odd electron.

The $A^2\Pi$ state is a multiplet since the total electronic angular momentum Ω can have the two values

$$\Omega = \Lambda \pm S, \qquad (A5.2)$$

i.e. $\frac{3}{2}$ and $\frac{1}{2}$. These two components, labelled $^2\Pi_{3/2}$ and $^2\Pi_{1/2}$, are separated by 50 cm^{-1} for the $n = 10$ level of $A^2\Pi$. The coupling of angular momenta in this state is of an intermediate case so that only J is defined; however, for each component there is a series of rotational levels each of which is a close doublet. The two levels forming the doublet have the same value of J but differ in parity—the two components are said to form a Λ doublet. This is quite analogous to l-type doubling in linear polyatomic molecules. The positions of the rotational levels for a state intermediate between Hund's case (a) and case (b) such as $A^2\Pi$ of CN are given by

$$E = \nu_0 + B_v[(J+\tfrac{1}{2})^2 - \Lambda^2 \pm \tfrac{1}{2}(4(J+\tfrac{1}{2})^2 + Y(Y-4)\Lambda^2)^{1/2}]$$
$$+ \text{higher terms} \quad (A5.3)$$

where Y is equal to the spin-orbit coupling constant A divided by the rotational constant B_v, and Λ, the orbital angular momentum, is unity for Π states. The $A^2\Pi$ state of CN is inverted ($A = -52 \cdot 2$) so the energy states derived by taking the positive sign for the radical form $^2\Pi_{1/2}$ and those derived from the negative sign make up $^2\Pi_{3/2}$. For the latter the lowest level ($J = \frac{1}{2}$) does not exist since J must of necessity be larger than Ω. It is also interesting to note that the first few rotational levels of $^2\Pi_{3/2}$ lie below the band origin ν_0. For large $(J+\frac{1}{2})$ compared to $(Y(Y-4)\Lambda^2/4)^{1/2}$ the energy expression (A5.3) reduces to

$$E = \nu_0 + B_v[N(N+1) - \Lambda^2] + \text{higher terms} \quad (A5.4)$$

or, in other words, gives simple rotor levels. The energy levels of $B^2\Sigma$, $A^2\Pi_{3/2}$ and $A^2\Pi_{1/2}$ relative to the $N = 0$ level of $B^2\Sigma$ ($n = 0$) are shown in Fig. A5.2. The spin and Λ doubling are not shown resolved in this Figure but the two components of each level are indicated by the two J values and the $(+ -)$ parity respectively.

On inspection it will be seen that three close coincidences occur—together with another not shown in the Figure; these involve the levels $J = 3\frac{1}{2}(+)$ and $7\frac{1}{2}(-)$ of $A^2\Pi_{3/2}$ and $J = 10\frac{1}{2}(-)$ and $15\frac{1}{2}(-)$ of $A^2\Pi_{1/2}$, together with their counterparts in $B^2\Sigma$. It has been shown by Kronig[439] that rotational levels of different electronic states may interact with one another leading to a quantum mechanical mixing when certain selection rules are satisfied. These are

1. Both levels must have the same value of J.
2. Both levels must have the same multiplicity.
3. The Λ values must not differ by more than unity.
4. Both levels must have the same parity.

In addition, there are two more rules that determine the magnitude of the

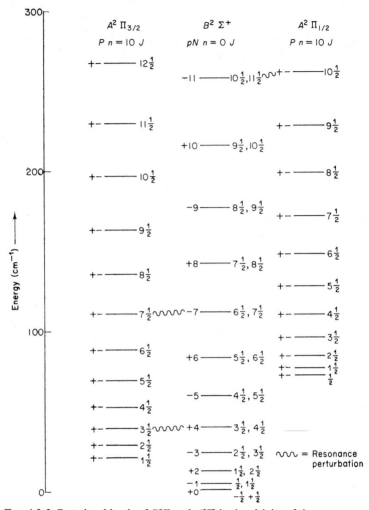

FIG. A5.2. Rotational levels of $B^2\Sigma$ and $A^2\Pi$ in the vicinity of the resonance.

effect if it is possible by the above four: these are

5. The two levels should agree in total energy very exactly ($<0\cdot5$ cm^{-1}).
6. The two vibrational wave functions should overlap as much as possible.

A study of Figs. A5.1 and A5.2 will show that all these rules are satisfied for the case under consideration, with the possible exception of $J = 10\frac{1}{2}(-)$ for which (5) is not very well fulfilled.

Under the resonance, the wave functions of the two states mix and the eigenvalues are displaced, one up and the other down; this is shown in Fig. A5.3 for the $J = 7\frac{1}{2}(-)$ and $3\frac{1}{2}(+)$ resonances. To the right of this diagram the hypothetical positions of the levels before resonance has occurred are shown schematically, i.e. the positions one would calculate from a study of the frequencies of the unperturbed rotational lines in an electronic band spectrum. In the middle are shown the observed positions. It will be seen

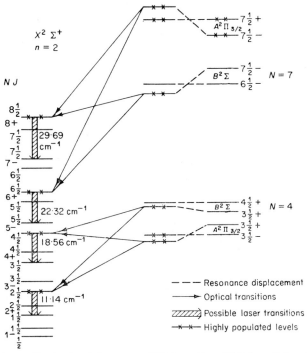

Fig. A5.3. Anomalies in the violet system $B^2\Sigma$ $(n = 0) \rightarrow X^2\Sigma$ $(n = 2)$ band of CN and possible laser action in the lower state. The diagram is not to scale and in particular the spin and Λ doubling are greatly exaggerated.

that in the electronic spectrum the $B^2\Sigma$ $n = 0 \rightarrow X^2\Sigma$ bands will show an anomaly in that the lines corresponding to $N' = 4, 7, 11$ and 15 will appear as doublets (one line from each of the perturbed levels) and that neither component will lie at the expected frequency. Experimentally this is confirmed but, in addition, when the experiments are performed at low pressures an extra phenomenon is observed, namely that the doublets are very much stronger than the regular members.[439] This is because the $A^2\Pi$ state is much more densely populated than the $B^2\Sigma$ state—for reasons which are still not fully agreed upon. As a consequence, there will be rapid transfer from A to B at the perturbed levels and transitions from these to the ground state will be intense.

Because of the highly selective nature of the intense transitions in the $B^2\Sigma \rightarrow X^2\Sigma$ system, population inversions can be brought about in the ground state and this phenomenon was initially postulated as an explanation of the laser action at 337 μm in cyanic vapours. The population differences will be most significant in the higher vibrational levels of $X^2\Sigma$ where thermal effects are negligible and for this reason attention has been focussed on the $B^2\Sigma$ ($n = 0$) to $X^2\Sigma$ ($n = 2$) transition. This is shown on the left of Fig. A5.3. For the $X^2\Sigma$ ($n = 2$) state it will be seen that the only levels to be significantly populated are with N numbering first—(16, 16½), (14, 14½), (8, 8½), (6, 6½), (5, 4½), (3, 2½). Several population inversions are therefore brought about and could give rise to possible lasing transitions. The largest population inversion occurs between the levels $N = 8$ and $N = 7$ and the transition (8, 8½)$\rightarrow$(7, 7½) is expected from optical spectroscopic data to occur at $29 \cdot 69 \pm 0 \cdot 01$ cm^{-1}. The existence of this demonstrated population inversion, together with the close coincidence with the measured laser wavenumber (29·712 cm^{-1}) led to the confident assignment of CN as the emitting species. The presence of large quantities of the radical in the discharge was obvious from the intense visible emission in the violet ($B^2\Sigma \rightarrow X^2\Sigma$) and red ($A^2\Pi \rightarrow X^2\Sigma$) systems of CN. The first indication that this might not be correct, despite the impressive evidence, came from Mathias[440] who stated that for emissions to occur at 337 μm it was necessary for hydrogen to be present. Broida also had reservations[441] based on kinetic arguments but when he, together with others,[442] predicted emission at $18 \cdot 56$ cm^{-1} if CN were the source, and this was experimentally demonstrated,[443] the case seemed settled. Still further confirmations came from the observation[443] of 337 μm radiation from non-hydrogenic systems such as BrCN and ICN. Studies of the 337 μm emission under conditions of the highest possible resolution indicated that it was a singlet and some criticisms of the CN mechanism were voiced on this count, but it will be seen from Fig. A5.3 that the selection rules only permit the transition to the $J = 7\frac{1}{2}$ spin component of the $N = 7$ level and the line must be a singlet. It remained to consider the hyperfine structure of the levels involved. This has been measured directly by Broida and his colleagues[74] (see Chapter 2) for the perturbed $B^2\Sigma$ levels and large hyperfine splittings are observed of the order of 10^{-2} cm^{-1}. However, as pointed out by Radford,[76] the hyperfine splittings in the ground state will be much smaller. Physically, the explanation is that in the ground state the odd electron is localized on the carbon atom in a non-bonding orbital pointing away from the nitrogen atom. The odd electron density at the nitrogen nucleus is therefore small and hyperfine splittings of about 10^{-4} cm^{-1} are anticipated. Such small splittings were beyond the early workers in this field and were probably within the line-width of the crude unstabilized lasers available at that time.

Nevertheless, and despite all this evidence, it is now established that the emitter of the 337 μm radiation is in fact HCN. The HCN mechanism is described in Chapter 6 where also the crucial evidence in its favour is spelled out. There remain a considerable number of unsolved problems in understanding the highly efficient nature of this laser. Clearly some interesting results may be gleaned from studying the radiative and collisional equilibria within the plasma. What is most remarkable is that, although lasing systems are quite rare, there exist two perfectly plausible mechanisms which predict emission near 337 μm from two different entities both of which are known to be present in the discharge. Careful work has shown that the emission from systems which had no apparent hydrogen in them did, in fact, arise from HCN formed by interaction of primary discharge products with hydrogenic compounds adsorbed on the walls of the tube. The emission at 18·56 cm^{-1} has been shown[444] to arise from some entity which contains iodine. All these facts indicate how difficult it may be to make correct identifications of emitting species when the complex chemistry of an electric discharge is involved and when there are the highly non-linear characteristics of a laser to be considered.

References

This listing is not intended to be exhaustive nor to reflect any views on the importance or historical priority of any paper; it is hoped, however, that it will provide a guide to easily accessible sources of further information.

1. Gordy, W. (1959). "Millimeter and Submillimeter Waves in Physics" presented at the Symposium on Millimeter Waves, Polytechnic Institute of Brooklyn, 1959, and published in the Microwave Research Institute Symposia Series, Vol. IX.
2. Glagolewa-Arkadiewa, A. (1924). *Nature (London)*, **113**, 640.
3. Nichols, E. F., and Tear, J. D. (1923). *Phys. Rev.* **21**, 587, and *Proc. Nat. Acad. Sci. USA*, **9**, 211.
4. The earliest paper in English is Rubens, H., and Snow, B. W. (1893). *Phil. Mag.* **35**, 35.
5. Rubens, H., and Nichols, E. F. (1897). *Phys. Rev.* **5**, 98, and **5**, 152.
6. du Bois, H., and Rubens, H. (1911). *Phil. Mag.* **22**, 322.
7. Rubens, H., and Baeyer, O. (1911). *Phil. Mag.* **21**, 689.
8. Palik, E. D. (1960). *J. Opt. Soc. Amer.* **50**, 1329.
9. Czerny, M. (1925). *Z. Phys.* **34**, 227.
10. Badger, R. M. (1928). *Nature (London)*, **121**, 942.
11. Barnes, R. B. (1932). *Phys. Rev.* **39**, 562.
12. Cartwright, C. H. (1934). *Z. Phys.* **90**, 480.
13. Strong, J. (1932). *Rev. Sci. Instrum.* **3**, 810.
14. Randall, H. M. (1938). *Rev. Mod. Phys.* **10**, 72.
15. Townes, C. H., and Schawlow, A. L. (1955). "Microwave Spectroscopy." McGraw-Hill, New York.
16. Gordy, W. (1948). *Rev. Mod. Phys.* **20**, 668.
17. Jones, G., and Gordy, W. (1964). *Phys. Rev.* **135**, A295; see also Helminger, P., De Lucia, F. C., and Gordy, W. (1970). *Phys. Rev. Lett.* **25**, 1397; De Lucia, F. C., Helminger, P., and Gordy, W. (1971). *Phys. Rev.* **A3**, 1849.
18. Gebbie, H. A., and Vanasse, G. A. (1956). *Nature (London)*, **178**, 432.
19. Strong, J. (1957). *J. Opt. Soc. Amer.* **47**, 354.
20. Strong, J., and Vanasse, G. A. (1959). *J. Opt. Soc. Amer.* **49**, 844; Vanasse, G. A., and Strong, J. (1958). Appendix F to "Concepts of Classical Optics" (Ed. J. Strong). Freeman, San Francisco.
21. Gebbie, H. A. (1961). "Advances in Quantum Electronics" (Ed. J. R. Singer), p. 155. Columbia University Press, New York.
22. Golay, M. (1947). *Rev. Sci. Instrum.*, **18**, 347, 357.
23. For a general account of this field see Putley, E. H. (1967). Detectors, *in* "Spectroscopic Techniques" (Ed. D. H. Martin). North Holland, Amsterdam.
24. Bloor, D. (1970). *Infrared Phys.*, **10**, 1.
25. See, for example, Gebbie, H. A., and Twiss, R. Q. (1966). *Rep. Progr. Phys.* **XXIX**, 729.

26. Much of this section is inspired by the far more complete and elegant treatment in Born, M., and Wolf, E. (1959). "Principles of Optics". Pergamon Press, Oxford.
27. Jacquinot, P. (1954). *J. Opt. Soc. Amer.* **44**, 761.
28. Bratt, P., Engeler, W., Levinstein, H., Mac Rae, A., and Pehek, J. (1961). *Infrared Phys.* **1**, 27.
29. Simpson, O., Sutherland, G. B. B. M., and Blackwell, D. E. (1948). *Nature (London)*, **161**, 281; see also (1970). "Infrared Detectors" (Eds R. K. Willardson and A. C. Beer), *in* "Semiconductors and Semimetals" series, Vol. 5, Academic Press, London and New York.
30. See, for example, Fellgett, P. (1967). *J. de Physique*, C.2, **28**, 165.
31. Gebbie, H. A. (1969). *Appl. Opt.* **8**, 501.
32. In fact Vol. 8, No. 3, March 1969.
33. Jacquinot, P., ibid. p. 497.
34. Wilkinson, G., and Martin, D. H. (1967). *In* "Spectroscopic Techniques" (Ed. D. H. Martin), p. 69. North Holland, Amsterdam.
35. Kneubuhl, F. K. (1969). *Appl. Opt.* **8**, 505.
36. Wood, R. W. (1910). *Phil. Mag.* **20**, 770.
37. See reference 26, pp. 387–392.
38. Moser, J. F., Steffen, H., and Kneubuhl, F. K. (1968). *Helv. Phys. Acta*, **41**, 607; see also reference 35.
39. Wood, R. W. (1902). *Phil. Mag.* **4**, 396; (1912). *Phil. Mag.* **23**, 310; (1935). *Phys. Rev.* **48**, 928.
40. Ritchie, R. H., Arakawa, E. T., Cowan, J. J., and Hamm, R. N. (1968). *Phys. Rev. Lett.* **21**, 1530.
41. Czerny, M., and Turner, A. F. (1930). *Z. Phys.* **61**, 792.
42. Wilkinson, G. (1962). *In* "Spectroscopy" (Ed. M. J. Wells), p. 157, Institute of Petroleum, London; see also reference 34.
43. Kneubuhl, F. K., Moser, J. F., and Steffen, H. (1966). *J. Opt. Soc. Amer.* **56**, 760.
44. Dowling, J. M., and Hall, R. T. (1967). *J. Opt. Soc. Amer.* **57**, 269.
45. Kneubuhl, F. K., Moser, J. F., and Steffen, H. (1967). *J. Opt. Soc. Amer.* **57**, 271.
46. Iwahashi, I., Matsumoto, K., Matsudaira, S., Minami, S., and Yoshinaga, H. (1969). *Appl. Opt.* **8**, 583.
47. Ozier, I., Ho, W., and Birnbaum, G. (1969). *J. Chem. Phys.* **51**, 4873.
48. Whiffen, D. H. (1964). *Trans. Faraday Soc.* **60**, 1.
49. Fabry, C., and Perot, A. (1899). *Ann. Chim. Phys.* **16**, 115; see also reference 26, pp. 329–341.
50. Connes, P. (1956). *Rev. Opt. Theor. Instrum.* **35**, 37.
51. Ulrich, R., Renk, K. F., and Genzel, L. (1963). *IEEE Trans. Microwave Theory Tech.* MTT–11, 363.
52. Putley, E. H., and Martin, D. H. (1967). *In* "Spectroscopic Techniques" (Ed. D. H. Martin), p. 113. North Holland, Amsterdam.
53a. Coleman, P. D. (1963). *IEEE Trans. Microwave Theory Tech.* MTT–11, 271.
53b. Dees, J. W. (September 1966). *Microwave Journal*, p. 48.
53c. Robinson, L. C. (1969). *Advan. Electron. Phys.* **26**, 171.
54. "Millimetre and Sub-millimetre Waves" (1969). (Ed. F. A. Benson), Iliffe, London.
55. Gordy, W. (1965). *In* "Molecular Spectroscopy VIII", p. 403. Butterworths, London.

56. For a survey of this field see the Chapter by A. Mardon in reference 54.
57. Ohl, R. S., Budenstein, P. P., and Burrus, C. A. (1959). *Rev. Sci. Instrum.* **30**, 765.
58. Daneu, V., Sokoloff, D., Sanchez, A., and Javan, A. (1969). *Appl. Phys. Lett.* **15**, 398.
59. Rank, D. H., Eastman, D. P., Rao, R. S., and Wiggins, T. A. (1962). *J. Opt. Soc. Amer.* **52**, 1.
60. Herzberg, G. (1945). "Infrared and Raman Spectra". Van Nostrand, New York.
61. Trambarulo, R., and Gordy, W. (1950). *J. Chem. Phys.* **18**, 1613.
62. Sheridan, J., and Gordy, W. (1950). *Phys. Rev.* **79**, 513.
63. Johnson, C. M., Trambarulo, R., and Gordy, W. (1951). *Phys. Rev.* **84**, 1178.
64. Smith, A. G., Gordy, W., Simmons, J. W., and Smith, W. V. (1949). *Phys. Rev.* **75**, 260.
65. Simmons, J. W., Anderson, W. E., and Gordy, W. (1950). *Phys. Rev.* **77**, 77.
66. Errata to reference 65, (1952). *Phys. Rev.* **86**, 1055.
67. Senitzky, B., and Piltch, M., quoted in Senitzky, B., Gould, G., and Cutler, S. (1963). *Phys. Rev.* **130**, 1460.
68. Marcuse, D. (1961). *J. Appl. Phys.* **32**, 743.
69. Barnes, F. S., and Maley, D. (1961). *Electronics*, **34**, 45.
70. De Lucia, F., and Gordy, W. (1969). *Phys. Rev.* **187**, 658.
71. Westerkamp, J. F. (1954). *Phys. Rev.* **93**, 716; Maki, A. G., and Lide, D. R. (1967). *J. Chem. Phys.* **47**, 3206.
72. Maki, A. G., and Blaine, L. R. (1964). *J. Mol. Spectrosc.* **12**, 45.
73. Törring, T. (1961). *Z. Phys.* **161**, 179.
74. Evenson, K. M., Dunn, J. L., and Broida, H. P. (1964). *Phys. Rev.* **136**, A1566.
75. Chantry, G. W., Gebbie, H. A., and Chamberlain, J. (1965). *Nature (London)*, **205**, 377.
76. Radford, H. E. (1964). *Phys. Rev.* **136**, A1571.
77. Strauch, R. G., Cupp, R. E., Derr, V. E., and Gallagher, J. J. (1966). *Proc. IEEE*, **54**, 506.
78. Cupp, R. E., Kempf, R. A., and Gallagher, J. J. (1968). *Phys. Rev.* **171**, 60.
79. Bates, H. E., Gallagher, J. J., and Derr, V. E. (1968). *J. Appl. Phys.* **39**, 3218.
80. See, for example, Steel, W. H. (1967). "Interferometry". Cambridge University Press, London.
81. Slater, J. C., and Frank, N. H. (1933). "Introduction to Theoretical Physics", p. 254. McGraw-Hill, New York.
82. For a full treatment of this and many other related points see Vanasse, G. A., and Sakai, H. (1967). "Progress in Optics", Vol. VI, p. 261. North Holland, Amsterdam.
83. Connes, J., and Connes, P. (1966). *J. Opt. Soc. Amer.* **56**, 896.
84. Born, M., and Wolf, E. (1959). "Principles of Optics", p. 40. Pergamon Press, Oxford.
85. Chamberlain, J., Chantry, G. W., Findlay, F. D., Gebbie, H. A., Gibbs, J. E., Stone, N. W. B., and Wright, A. J. (1966). *Infrared Phys.* **6**, 195.
86. Chantry, G. W., Fleming, J. W., Fuller, D. W. E., and Gebbie, H. A., to be published in *Infrared Phys*.
87. For another good example see Dowling, J. M., and Hall, R. T. (1966). *J. Mol. Spectrosc.* **19**, 108.

88. Chantry, G. W., Gebbie, H. A., Hamlin, A. G., and Lomas, B. (1970). *Infrared Phys.* **10**, 95.
89. See, for example, Gebbie, H. A., and Stone, N. W. B. (1964). *Infrared Phys.* **4**, 85.
90. Chantry, G. W., Evans, Helen M., Chamberlain, J., and Gebbie, H. A. (1969). *Infrared Phys.* **9**, 85.
91. Burroughs, W. J., reported by Gebbie, H. A. (1965). *In* "Molecular Spectroscopy VIII", p. 579. Butterworths, London.
92. Richards, P. L., and Tinkham, M. (1960). *Phys. Rev.* **119**, 575.
93. Chamberlain, J., Gebbie, H. A., Pardoe, G. W. F., and Davies, M. (1968). *Chem. Phys. Lett.* **1**, 523.
94. Genzel, L. (1960). *J. Mol. Spectrosc.* **4**, 241; Happ, H., and Genzel, L. (1961). *Infrared Phys.* **1**, 39.
95. Milward, R. C. (1969). *In* "Molecular Spectroscopy", p. 81. Institute of Petroleum, London.
96. Herzberg, G. (1945). "Infrared and Raman Spectra", p. 58. Van Nostrand, New York.
97. White, J. U. (1942). *J. Opt. Soc. Amer.* **32**, 285; Stephens, E. R. (1961). *Infrared Phys.* **1**, 187.
98. Fleming, J. W. (1970). *Infrared Phys.* **10**, 57.
99. Chantry, G. W., Anderson, A., and Gebbie, H. A. (1964). *Spectrochim. Acta*, **20**, 1223.
100. Anderson, A. and Gebbie, H. A., unpublished work.
101. Gebbie, H. A., Burroughs, W. J., and Bird, G. R. (1969). *Proc. Roy. Soc.* (*London*), **A310**, 579.
102. Gibbs, J. E., and Gebbie, H. A. (1965). *Infrared Phys.* **5**, 187.
103. Connes, J. (1961). *Rev. Opt. Theor. Instrum.* **440**, 45, 116, 171, 231; see also references 106 and 113.
104. Strong, J., and Vanasse, G. A. (1960). *J. Opt. Soc. Amer.* **50**, 113.
105. Milward, R. C. (1969). *Infrared Phys.* **9**, 59.
106. Richards, P. L. (1967). *In* "Spectroscopic Techniques" (Ed. D. H. Martin), p. 58. North Holland, Amsterdam.
107. Richards, P. L. (1964). *J. Opt. Soc. Amer.* **54**, 1474.
108. This concept is discussed (with a change of sign for the imaginary component) in Born and Wolf (reference 26, p. 613); see also references 110 and 113.
109. Chamberlain, J., Findlay, F. D., and Gebbie, H. A. (1965). *Nature* (*London*), **206**, 886.
110. Chamberlain, J. (1967). *J. Quant. Spectrosc. Radiat. Transfer*, **7**, 151.
111. Chamberlain, J. and Gebbie, H. A. (1965). *Nature* (*London*), **206**, 602.
112. Prichard, W. H., and Orville-Thomas, W. J. (1963). *Trans. Faraday Soc.* **59**, 2218.
113. Chamberlain, J., Gibbs, J. E., and Gebbie, H. A. (1969). *Infrared Phys.* **9**, 185.
114. Chamberlain, J., and Gebbie, H. A. (1965). *Nature* (*London*), **208**, 480.
115. Chamberlain, J., Werner, E. C. B., Gebbie, H. A., and Slough, W. (1967). *Trans. Faraday Soc.* **63**, 2605.
116. Gebbie, H. A., Burroughs, W. J., Harries, J. E., and Cameron, R. M. (1968). *Astrophys. J.* **154**, 405.
117. Stone, N. W. B. (1970). *Optics Technology*, **2**, 8.

118. McCarthy, D. E. (1963). *Appl. Opt.* **2**, 591; (1963). Ibid., **2**, 596; (1965). Ibid. **4**, 317, 507; (1968). Ibid. **7**, 1997.

119. Burroughs, W. J., and Harries, J. E. (1970). *Nature (London)*, **227**, 824.

120. See, for example, Manley, T. R., and Williams, D. A. (1965). *Spectrochim. Acta*, **21**, 737.

121. Chantry, G. W., Evans, Helen M., Fleming, J. W., and Gebbie, H. A. (1969). *Infrared Phys.* **9**, 31.

122. For a survey see Larsen, T. (May 1962). *IRE Trans. Microwave Theory Tech.* p. 191.

123. Auton, J. P. (1967). *Appl. Opt.*, **6**, 1023.

124. Möller, K. D., and McKnight, R. V. (1963). *J. Opt. Soc. Amer.* **53**, 760.

125. Connes, P. (1959). *Rev. Opt. Theor. Instrum.* **38**, 157, 416; (1960). *Ibid.* **39**, 402; Verges, J. (1967). *J. Phys.* **28**, 176.

126. Girard, A. (1967). *J. Phys.* **28**, 172.

127. See the standard works such as references 15 and 60, and also, for additional details, Allen, H. C., and Cross, P. C. (1963). "Molecular Vib-Rotors: The Theory and Interpretation of High Resolution Infrared Spectra". John Wiley, New York.

128. Lichtenstein, M., Derr, V. E., and Gallagher, J. J. (1966). *J. Mol. Spectrosc.* **20**, 391; Burroughs, W. J., Harries, J. E., and Gebbie, H. A. (1969). *Nature (London)*, **222**, 658; Helminger, P., De Lucia, F. C., and Gordy, W. (1971). *Bull. Amer. Phys. Soc.* **16**, 531.

129. Birch, J. R., Burroughs, W. J., and Emery, R. J. (1969). *Infrared Phys.* **9**. 75.

130. Chantry, G. W., Gebbie, H. A., Popplewell, R. J. L., and Thompson, H. W. (1968). *Proc. Roy. Soc.* **A304**, 45.

131. Helminger, P., and Gordy, W. (1969). *Phys. Rev.* **188**, 100; Helminger, P., De Lucia, F. C., and Gordy, W. (to be published).

132. Gebbie, H. A., Stone, N. W. B., Bird, G. R., and Hunt, G. R. (1963). *Nature (London)*, **200**, 1304.

133. Zwanzig, R. (1965). *Ann. Rev. Phys. Chem.* **16**, 67.

134. This equation may be extracted after a little manipulation from the dispersion relations given by Fahrenfort, J. (1963). *In* "Infrared Spectroscopy and Molecular Structure" (Ed. Mansel Davies), pp. 380 and 381. Elsevier, Amsterdam.

135. For a review see O'Dwyer, J. J. (1967). "Progress in Dielectrics" (Ed. J. B. Birks), Vol. 7, p. 1. Heywood, London.

136. Lassier, B., and Brot, C. (1969). Motions in molecular crystals. *Discuss. Faraday Soc.* **48**, 39.

137. Birnbaum, G. and Cohen, E. R. (1970). *J. Chem. Phys.* **53**, 2885.

138. Wilson, E. B., Jr., and Wells, A. J. (1946). *J. Chem. Phys.* **14**, 578.

139. Burroughs, W. J., Jones, R. G., and Gebbie, H. A. (1969). *J. Quant. Spectrosc. Radiat. Transfer*, **9**, 799.

140. Crawford, M. F., Welsh, H. L., and Locke, J. L. (1949). *Phys. Rev.* **75**, 1607 and **76**, 580.

141. Welsh, H. L., Crawford, M. F., McDonald, J. C. F., and Chisholm, D. A. (1951). *Phys. Rev.* **83**, 1264.

142. Birnbaum, G., Maryott, A. A., and Wacker, P. F. (1954). *J. Chem. Phys.* **22**, 1782.

143. Colpa, J. P., and Ketelaar, J. A. A. (1958). *Mol. Phys.* **1**, 14.

144. Herzberg, G. (1949). *Nature (London)*, **163**, 170.

145. Kiss, Z. J., Gush, H. P., and Welsh, H. L. (1959). *Can. J. Phys.* **37**, 362; Kiss, Z. J., and Welsh, H. L. (1959), *Can. J. Phys.* **37**, 1249; van Kranendonk, J., and Kiss, Z. J. (1959). *Can. J. Phys.*, **37**, 1187.

146. Egelstaff, P. A., Haywood, B. C., and Webb, F. J. (1967). *Proc. Phys. Soc. London*, **90**, 681.

147. Gebbie, H. A., Stone, N. W. B., and Williams, D. (1963). *Mol. Phys.* **6**, 215.

148. Gebbie, H. A., and Stone, N. W. B. (1963). *Proc. Phys. Soc.* **82**, 543.

149. Birnbaum, G., and Maryott, A. A. (1962). *J. Chem. Phys.* **36**, 2032.

150. Maryott, A. A., and Birnbaum, G. (1962). *J. Chem. Phys.* **36**, 2026.

151. Ho, W., Kaufman, I. A., and Thaddeus, P. (1966). *J. Chem. Phys.* **45**, 877.

152. Harries, J. E. (1970). *Proc. Phys. Soc. London* (to be published); (1970). *J. Phys. B.* **3**, 704.

153. Buckingham, A. D., Disch, R. L., and Dunmur, D. A. (1968). *J. Amer. Chem. Soc.* **90**, 3104.

154. Ozier, I., and Fox, K. (1968). *Phys. Lett.* **27A**, 174.

155. Birnbaum, G., and Rosenberg, A. (1968). *Phys. Lett.* **27A**, 272.

156. Birnbaum, G., and Rosenberg, A. (1968). *J. Chem. Phys.* **48**, 1396.

157. Heastie, R., and Martin, D. H. (1962). *Can. J. Phys.* **40**, 122.

158. Pöschl, G., and Teller, E. (1933). *Z. Phys.*, **83**, 143; Neece, G., and Poirier, J. C. (1965). *J. Chem. Phys.* **43**, 4282.

159. Palin, D. E., and Powell, H. M. (1947). *J. Chem. Soc.* 208.

160. Van Vleck, J. H. (1961). *J. Phys. Chem. Solids*, **20**, 241.

161. Burgiel, J. C., Meyer, H., and Richards, P. L. (1965). *J. Chem. Phys.* **43**, 4291.

162. Rowland Davies, P. (1969). Motions in molecular crystals. *Discuss. Faraday Soc.* **48**, 181.

163. Born, M., and Huang, K. (1954). "Dynamical Theory of Crystal Lattices". Oxford, New York.

164. Mitra, S. S., and Gielisse, P. J. (1964). "Progress in Infrared Spectroscopy" (Ed. H. A. Szymanski), Vol. 2, p. 47. Plenum Press, New York and London.

165. Lyddane, R. H., Sachs, R. G., and Teller, E. (1941). *Phys. Rev.* **59**, 673.

166. For a recent survey of ferroelectric crystals see Barker, A. S. (1970). *In* "Far Infrared Properties of Solids" (Eds S. S. Mitra and S. Nudelman), Plenum Press, New York and London.

167. Cowley, R. A. (1964). *Phys. Rev.* **134A**, 981.

168. Cochran, W. (1960). *Advan. Phys.* **9**, 387.

169. Nilsen, W. G., and Skinner, J. G. (1968). *J. Chem. Phys.* **48**, 2240.

170. Woods, A. D. B., Cochran, W., and Brockhouse, B. N. (1960). *Phys. Rev.* **119**, 980.

171. Fleury, P. A., and Worlock, J. M. (1967). *Phys. Rev. Lett.* **18**, 665; (1968). *Phys. Rev.* **174**, 613; Fleury, P. A., Scott, J. F., and Worlock, J. M. (1968). *Phys. Rev. Lett.* **21**, 16.

172. Anastassakis, E., Iwasa, S., and Burstein, E. (1966). *Phys. Rev. Lett.* **17**, 1051.

173. Kälin, R., Balthes, H. P., and Kneubuhl, F. K. (1970). *Solid State Commun.* **8**, 1495; (1970) *Helvetica. Physica Acta*, **43**, 487.

174. See, for example, Anderson, A., and Gebbie, H. A. (1965). *Spectrochim. Acta*, **21**, 883.

175. Anderson, A., Gebbie, H. A., and Walmsley, S. H. (1964). *Mol. Phys.* **7**, 401; (1962). *Phil. Mag.*, **7**, 1243.

176. Fleming, J. W., Turner, P. A., and Chantry, G. W. (1970). *Mol. Phys.* **19**, 853.

177. Chantry, G. W., Gebbie, H. A., and Mirza, H. N. (1967). *Spectrochim. Acta,* **23A**, 2749.
178. Chantry, G. W., Anderson, A., and Gebbie, H. A. (1964). *Spectrochim. Acta,* **20**, 1223.
179. Chantry, G. W., Anderson, A., and Gebbie, H. A. (1964). *Spectrochim. Acta,* **20**, 1465.
180. Debye, P. (1912). *Ann. Phys.* **39**, 789.
181. Debye, P. (1929). "Polar Molecules," Chemical Catalogue, New York.
182. Cole, R. H. (1955). *J. Chem. Phys.* **23**, 493.
183. Rivail, J. L., and Goulon, J. (to be published).
184. Cole, K. S., and Cole, R. H. (1941). *J. Chem. Phys.* **9**, 341.
185. Poley, J. Ph. (1955). *J. Appl. Sci. B,* **4**, 337.
186. Hill, N. E. (1963), *Proc. Phys. Soc.* **82**, 723; see also Wyllie, G. (1971). *J. Phys. C.* **4**, 564.
187. Davies, M., Pardoe, G. W. F., Chamberlain, J., and Gebbie, H. A. (1968). *Trans. Faraday Soc.* **64**, 847.
188. Leroy, Y., Constant, E., Abbar, C., and Desplanques, P. (1967). *Advan. Mol. Relaxation Processes,* **1**, 273.
189. Rocard, Y. (1933). *J. Physique Radium,* **4**, 247.
190. Powles, J. G. (1948). *Trans. Faraday Soc.* **44**, 802.
191. Sack, R. A. (1957). *Proc. Phys. Soc.* **B70**, 402, 414.
192. Kubo, R. (1957). *J. Phys. Soc.* (*Japan*), **12**, 570; (1958). "Lectures in Theoretical Physics", Vol. 1, Chap. 4. Interscience Publishers, New York.
193. Gebbie, H. A., Stone, N. W. B., Findlay, F. D., and Pyatt, E. C. (1965). *Nature* (*London*), **205**, 377.
194. Chantry, G. W., and Gebbie, H. A. (1965). *Nature* (*London*), **208**, 378.
195. Wyss, H. R., Werder, R. D., and Günthard, Hs. H. (1964). *Spectrochim. Acta,* **20**, 573.
196. Chantry, G. W., Gebbie, H. A., Lassier, B., and Wyllie, G. (1967). *Nature* (*London*), **214**, 163.
197. Davies, M., Pardoe, G. W. F., Chamberlain, J., and Gebbie, H. A. (1968). *Chem. Phys. Lett.* **2**, 411; (1970). *Trans. Faraday Soc.* **66**, 273.
198. Whiffen, D. H. (1949). *Trans. Faraday Soc.* **45**, 124.
199. Kroon, S. G., and Van der Elksen, J. (1967). *Chem. Phys. Lett.* **1**, 285.
200. Chamberlain, J. (1968). *Chem. Phys. Lett.* **2**, 464.
201. Bradley, C. C. (1969). "High Pressure Methods in Solid State Research". Butterworths, London.
202. Pardoe, G. W. F. (1970). *Trans. Faraday Soc.* **66**, 2699.
203. Bradley, C. C., Gebbie, H. A., Gilby, A. C., Kechin, V. V., and King, J. H. (1966). *Nature* (*London*), **211**, 839.
204. Darmon, I., Gerschel, A., and Brot, C. (1971). *Chem. Phys. Lett.* **8**, 454.
205. Lassier, B., Brot, C., Chantry, G. W., and Gebbie, H. A. (1969). *Chem. Phys. Lett.* **3**, 96.
206. Brot, C., Lassier, B., Chantry, G. W., and Gebbie, H. A. (1968). *Spectrochim. Acta,* **24A**, 295.
207. Gutowsky, H. S., and McCall, D. W. (1960). *J. Chem. Phys.* **32**, 548.
208. Darmon, I., Brot, C., Chantry, G. W., and Gebbie, H. A. (1968). *Spectrochim. Acta,* **24A**, 1517.
209. Lassier, B., and Brot. C. (1968). *Chem. Phys. Lett.* **1**, 581.
210. Gee, G. (1970). The glassy state in polymers, *Contemp. Phys.* **11**, 313.
211. Buckingham, K. A., and Reddish, W. (1967). *Proc. IEE,* **144**, 1810.

212. Reddish, W. (1966). *J. Polym. Sci.* **C14**, 123.
213. Deutsch, K., Hoff, E. A. W., and Reddish, W. (1954). *J. Polym. Sci.* **13**, 565.
214. See McCrum, N. G., Read, B. E., and Williams, G. (1967). "Anelastic and Dielectric Effects in Polymeric Solids", pp. 180–182 and 357–376. John Wiley, London.
215. Chantry, G. W., Fleming, J. W., Pardoe, G. W. F., Reddish, W., and Willis, H. A. (1971). *Infrared Phys.* **11**, 109.
216. Dean, G. D., and Martin, D. H. (1967). *Chem. Phys. Lett.* **1**, 415.
217. Krimm, S., and Bank, M. I. (1965). *J. Chem. Phys.* **42**, 4059.
218. Chantry, G. W., Fleming, J. W., Smith, Patricia M., Cudby, M., and Willis, H. A. (1971). *Chem. Phys. Lett.* **10**, 473.
219. Snyder, R. G., and Schachtschneider, J. H. (1964). *Spectrochim. Acta,* **20**, 853.
220. Wilson, E. B., Jr., Decius, J. C., and Cross, P. C. (1955)."Molecular Vibrations: The Theory of Infrared and Raman Vibrational Spectra". McGraw-Hill, New York.
221. Long, D. A., Spencer, T. V., Waters, D. N., and Woodward, L. A. (1957). *Proc. Royal Soc.* **A240**, 499.
222. Butcher, F. K., Gerrard, W., Mooney, E. F., Rees, R. G., Willis, H. A., Anderson, A., and Gebbie, H. A. (1964). *J. Organometal. Chem.* **1**, 431.
223. Chantry, G. W. (1971). Interferometry: experimental techniques and applications to inorganic structures. *In* "Essays in Structural Chemistry". Macmillan, London.
224. Kagarise, R. E., and Rank, D. H. (1952). *Trans. Faraday Soc.* **48**, 394.
225. Kagarise, R. E. (1956). *J. Chem. Phys.* **24**, 300.
226. Chantry, G. W., Gebbie, H. A., Griffiths, P. R., and Lake, R. F. (1966). *Spectrochim. Acta,* **22**, 125.
227. Hunt, R. H., and Leacock, R. A. (1966). *J. Chem. Phys.* **45**, 3141.
228. Oelfke, W. C., and Gordy, W. (1969). *J. Chem. Phys.* **51**, 5336.
229. See Brasch, J. W., Mikawa, Y., and Jakobsen, R. J. (1968). *Appl. Spectrosc. Rev.* **1** (2), 187. (For a list of references.)
230. Fately, W. G., and Miller, F. A. (1961). *Spectrochim. Acta,* **17**, 857.
231. Lin, C. C., and Swalen, J. D. (1959). *Rev. Mod. Phys.* **31**, 841.
232. Reference 15, p. 323.
233. Carlson, G., Witkowski, R., and Fateley, W. G. (1966). *Spectrochim. Acta,* **22**, 1117.
234. Harries, J. E., Burroughs, W. J., and Gebbie, H. A. (1969). *J. Quant. Spectrosc. Radiat. Transfer,* **9**, 799.
235. See, for example, Jones, W. J., Seel, R. M., and Sheppard, N. (1969). *Spectrochim. Acta,* **25A**, 385.
236. Plyler, E. K., Yates, D. J. C., and Gebbie, H. A. (1962). *J. Opt. Soc. Amer.* **52**, 859.
237. For a more complete account of the topics raised in this section see Heald, M. A., and Wharton, C. B. (1965). "Plasma diagnostics with microwaves". John Wiley, New York.
238. Chamberlain, J., Gebbie, H. A., George, A., and Beynon, J. D. E. (1969). *J. Plasma Phys.* **3**, 75.
239. Parkinson, G. J., Dangor, A. E., and Chamberlain, J. (1968). *Appl. Phys. Lett.* **13**, 233; see also Peterson, R. W., and Jahoda, F. C. (1971). *Appl. Phys. Lett.* **18**, 440.
240. Kotthaus, J. P., and Dransfeld, K. (1969). *Phys. Lett.* **30A**, 34.

241. Joyce, R. R., and Richards, P. L. (1969). *Phys. Rev.* **179**, 375.
242. As examples of discussions of the electronic structure of ruby see the articles by Brossel, J., and Margerie, J., and by Artman, J. O., and Murphy, J. C. (1963). *In* "Paramagnetic Resonance" (Ed. W. Low), Vol. II. Academic Press, London and New York.
243. Birnbaum, G. (1964). "Optical Masers" (*in* "Advances in Electronics and Electron Physics" series, Supplement 2). Academic Press, New York and London.
244. Siegman, A. E. (1964). "Microwave Solid-State Masers". McGraw-Hill, New York.
245. Hadni, A. (1970). *In* "Far Infrared Properties of Solids" (Eds S. S. Mitra and S. Nudelman). Plenum Press, New York and London.
246. Wheeler, R. G., Reames, F. M., and Wachtel, E. J. (1968). *J. Appl. Phys.* **39**, 915.
247. Wright, J. C., and Moos, H. W. (1969). *Phys. Lett.* **29A**, 495.
248. Prinz, G. A., and Wagner, R. J. (1969). *Phys. Lett.* **30A**, 520.
249. See, for example, Richards, P. L. (1964). *J. Appl. Phys.* **35**, 850.
250. Cipriani, J., Racine, S., and Dupeyrat, R. (1971). *Phys. Lett.* **34A**, 187.
251. Richards, P. L. (1965). *Bull. Amer. Phys. Soc.* **10**, 33.
252. Blocker, T. G., Kinch, M. A., and West, F. G. (1969). *Phys. Rev. Lett.* **22**, 853.
253. Sievers, A. J., and Tinkham, M. (1963). *J. Appl. Phys.* **34**, 1235.
254. Palik, E. D., and Stevenson, J. R. (1963). *Phys. Rev.* **130**, 1344.
255. Couder, Y. (1969). *Phys. Rev. Lett.* **22**, 890.
256. Button, K. J., Gebbie, H. A., and Lax, B. (1966). *IEEE J. Quantum Electronics*, QE. 2, 202.
257. Bardeen, J., Cooper, L. N., and Schrieffer, J. R. (1957). *Phys. Rev.* **108**, 1175.
258. Josephson, B. D. (1965). *Advan. Phys.* **56**, 14; (1962). *Phys. Lett.* **1**, 251; (1964). *Rev. Mod. Phys.* **36**, 216. See Richards, P. L., University of California, Lawrence Radiation Laboratory, UCRL 19035 (to be published).
259. Grimes, C. C., Richards, P. L., and Shapiro, S. (1968). *J. Appl. Phys.* **39**, 3905.
260. Richards, P. L., and Sterling, S. A. (1969). *Appl. Phys. Lett.* **14**, 394.
261. McDonald, D. G., Kose, V. E., Evenson, K. M., Wells, J. S., and Cupp, J. D. (1969). *Appl. Phys. Lett.* **15**, 121.
262. McDonald, D. G., Risley, A. S., Cupp, J. D., and Evenson, K. M. (1971). *Appl. Phys. Lett.* **18**, 162.
263. McDonald, D. G., Evenson, K. M., Wells, J. S., and Cupp, J. D. (1971). *J. Appl. Phys.* **42**, 179.
264. Slater, J. C. (1951). "Quantum Theory of Matter", Chap. 12. McGraw-Hill, New York.
265. (1970). "Infrared Detectors" (Eds R. K. Willardson and A. C. Beer), *in* "Semiconductors and Semimetals" series, Vol. 5. Academic Press, London and New York.
266. Putley, E. II. (1964). *Phys. Status Solidi*, **6**, 571; (1965). *Appl. Optics*, **4**, 649.
267. Kinch, M. A., and Rollin, B. V. (1963). *Brit. J. Appl. Phys.* **14**, 672.
268. Brown, M. A. C. S., and Kimmitt, M. F. (1963). *Brit. Commun. Electron.* **10**, 608.
269. Stolen, R. H. (1969). *Appl. Phys. Lett.* **15**, 74.
270. Birch, J. R. (to be published), and Birch, J. R., and Bradley, C. C. (to be published).

271. Waynant, R. W., Shipman, J. D., Elton, R. C., and Ali, A. W. (1970). *Appl. Phys. Lett.* **17**, 383.
272. Burgess, J. S., Bell, E. E., and Nielson, H. H. (1953). *J. Opt. Soc. Amer.* **43**, 1058.
273. Herzberg, G. (1945). "Infrared and Raman Spectra", p. 279. Van Nostrand, New York.
274. Maki, A. G., and Blaine, L. R. (1964). *J. Mol. Spectrosc.* **12**, 45; see also Maki, A. G., Olson, W. B., and Sams, R. L. (1970). *Ibid.* **36**, 433.
275. Gebbie, H. A., Stone, N. W. B., and Findlay, F. D. (1964). *Nature (London)*, **202**, 685.
276. Lide, D. R., and Maki, A. G. (1967). *Appl. Phys. Lett.* **11**, 2.
277. Hocker, L. O., and Javan, A. (1967). *Phys. Lett.* **25A**, 489.
278. Pollack, M. A. (1969). *IEEE J. Quantum Electronics,* **QE5**, 558.
279. Lichtenstein, M., Corcoran, V. J., and Gallagher, J. J. (1967). *IEEE J. Quantum Electronics,* **QE3**, 696.
280. McCaul, B. W. (1970). *Appl. Opt.* **9**, 653.
281. Mathias, L. E. S., Crocker, A., and Wills, M. S. (1968). *IEEE J. Quantum Electron.* **QE4**, 205.
282. Maki, A. G. (1968). *Appl. Phys. Lett.* **12**, 122.
283. Lide, D. R. (private communication).
284. Hocker, L. O., and Javan, A. (1968). *Appl. Phys. Lett.* **12**, 124.
285. Crocker, A., Gebbie, H. A., Kimmitt, M. F., and Mathias, L. E. S. (1964). *Nature (London)*, **201**, 250.
286. Witteman, W. J., and Bleekrode, R. (1964). *Phys. Lett.* **13**, 126; Flesher, G. T., and Muller, W. M. (1966). *Proc. IEEE.* **54**, 543; Muller, W. M., and Flesher, G. T. (1966). *Appl. Phys. Lett.* **8**, 217.
287. Pollack, M. A., Bridges, T. J., and Tomlinson, W. J. (1967). *Appl. Phys. Lett.* **10**, 253.
288. Hartmann, B., and Kleman, B. (1968). *Appl. Phys. Lett.* **12**, 168; Benedict, W. S. (1968). *Appl. Phys. Lett.* **12**, 170; Pollack, M. A., and Tomlinson, W. J. (1968). *Appl. Phys. Lett.* **12**, 173.
289. Benedict, W. S., Pollack, M. A., and Tomlinson, W. J. (1969). *IEEE J. Quantum Electronics,* **QE5**, 108.
290. Frenkel, L., Sullivan, T., Pollack, M. A., and Bridges, T. J. (1967). *Appl. Phys. Lett.* **11**, 344; Pollack, M. A., Frenkel, L., and Sullivan, T. (1968). *Phys. Lett.* **26A**, 381.
291. Pollack, M. A., Bridges, T. J., and Strnad, A. R. (1967). *Appl. Phys. Lett.* **10**, 182.
292. Bridges, T. J., and Chang, T. Y. (1969). *Phys. Rev. Lett.* **22**, 811.
293. Fox, A. G., and Li, T. (1961). *Bell System Tech. J.* **40**, 453.
294. Gordon, J. P., Zeiger, H. Z., and Townes, C. H. (1955). *Phys. Rev.* **99**, 1264.
295. Stone, N. W. B., Gebbie, H. A., Fuller, D. W. E., Lott, A. R., and Bradley, C. C. (1968). *Nature (London)*, **217**, 1042.
296. Bradley, C. C., and Fuller, D. W. E. (private communication), but see Fuller, D. W. E., Hines, J., and Compton, B. (1969). *Electron. Lett.* **5**, No. 19.
297. Herriott, D. R. (1963). *J. Opt. Soc. Amer.* **52**, 31.
298. Bradley, C. C., and Knight, D. J. E. (1970). *Phys. Lett.* **32A**, 59.
299. Lamb, W. E. (1964). *Phys. Rev.* **134**, A1429.
300. Winton, R. S., and Gordy, W. (1970). *Phys. Lett.* **32A**, 219.
301. Cohen, E. R., and Dumond, J. W. M. (1965). *Rev. Mod. Phys.* **37**, 537.
302. Froome, K. D. (1958). *Nature (London)*, **181**, 258; (1958). *Proc. Roy. Soc. (London)*, **A247**, 109.

303. Daneu, V., Hocker, L. O., Javan, A., Ramachandra Rao, D., and Szöke, A. (1969). *Phys. Lett.* **29A**, 319.
304. Bradley, C. C., Edwards, G., and Knight, D. J. E. (to be published).
305. Hocker, L. O., Small, J. G., and Javan, A. (1969). *Phys. Lett.* **29A**, 321.
306. Evenson, K. M., Wells, J. S., Matarrese, L. M., and Elwell, L. B. (1970). *Appl. Phys. Lett.* **16**, 159.
307. Evenson, K. M., Wells, J. S., and Matarrese, L. M. (1970). *Appl. Phys. Lett.* **16**, 251.
308. Sokoloff, D. R., Sanchez, A., Osgood, R. M., and Javan, A. (1970). *Appl. Phys. Lett.* **17**, 257.
309. McCubbin, T. K. (unpublished but quoted in reference 58).
310. Barger, R. L., and Hall, J. L. (1969). *Phys. Rev. Lett.* **22**, 4.
311. Gebbie, H. A., and colleagues (unpublished work).
312. Kotthaus, J. P. (1968). *Appl. Opt.*, **7**, 2422.
313. Briner, E., and Hoefer, H. (1940). *Helv. Chim. Acta*, **23**, 1054.
314. Fuller, D. W. E. (private communication), but see Muller, W. M., and Flesher, G. T. (reference 286).
315. Fuller, D. W. E. (private communication).
316. See *New Scientist*, **32**, 505 (1966); and also Ferris, J. P., and Kuder, J. E. (1970). *J. Amer. Chem. Soc.* **92**, 2527.
317. Schwaller, P., Steffen, H., Moser, J. F., and Kneubuhl, F. K. (1967). *Appl. Opt.* **6**, 827.
318. Duxbury, G. (1968). (Unpublished work.)
319. Del Greco, F. P., and Kaufman, F. (1962). *Discuss. Faraday Soc.* **33**, 139.
320. Broida, H. P., and Kane, W. R. (1953). *Phys. Rev.* **89**, 1053.
321. This paragraph describes unpublished work from NPL but some published details may be found in Yamanaka, M., Yoshinaga, H., and Kon, S. (1968). *Jap. J. Appl. Phys.* **7**, 250.
322. Gebbie, H. A., Stone, N. W. B., Slough, W., Chamberlain, J., and Sheraton, W. A. (1966). *Nature* (*London*), **211**, 62.
323. Strauch, R. G. (1969). *Electron. Lett.* **5**, 246.
324. See, for example, Corcoran, V. J., Smith, W. T., and Gallagher, J. J. (1969). *IEEE J. Quantum Electron.*, **QE5**, 292; Stafsudd, O. M., and Yeh, Y. C. Ibid. p. 377.
325. McNice, G. T., and Derr, V. E. (1969). *IEEE J. Quantum Electron.* **QE5**, 569.
326. Wickersham, A. F. (1958). *J. Appl. Phys.* **29**, 1537. Ulrich, R. (1968). *J. Appl. Opt.* **7**, 1987.
327. Ulrich, R., Bridges, T. J., and Pollack, M. A. (1970). *Appl. Opt.* **9**, 2511.
328. Bradley, C. C. (private communication).
329. Smith, P. W. (1965). *IEEE J. Quantum Electron.* **QE1**, 343.
330. Moeller, G., and Dane Rigden, J. (1966). *Appl. Phys. Lett.* **8**, 69.
331. Jeffers, W. Q. (1967). *Appl. Phys. Lett.* **11**, 178.
332. Brannen, E., Hoeksema, M., and Sarjeant, W. J. (1969). *Can. J. Phys.* **47**, 597.
333. Sargent, M., Lamb, W. E., and Fork, R. L. (1967). *Phys. Rev.* **164**, 436; (1967). *Phys. Rev.* **164**, 450; Tomlinson, W. J., and Fork, R. L. (1967). *Phys. Rev.* **164**, 466.
334. Yamanaka, M., Yoshinaga, H., and Kon, S. (1968). *Jap. J. Appl. Phys.* **7**, 827.250
335. Birch, J. R., and Jones, R. G. (1970). *Infrared Phys.* **10**, 217.
336. Chamberlain, J. and others (to be published).
337. Bradley, C. C., Button, K. J., Lax, B., and Rubin, I. G. (1968). *IEEE J. Quantum Electron.* **QE4**, 733.

338. See Goodman, R. R. (1961). *Phys. Rev.* **122**, 397, for a good discussion based on the theory of Luttinger, J. M., and Kohn, W. (1955). *Phys. Rev.* **97**, 869.
339. Stickler, J. J., Zeiger, H. J., and Heller, G. S. (1962). *Phys. Rev.* **127**, 1077.
340. Button, K. J., Brecher, A., Lax, B., and Bradley, C. C. *Phys. Rev.* (to be published).
341. Pidgeon, C. R., and Brown, R. N. (1966). *Phys. Rev.* **146**, 575.
342. Button, K. J., Lax, B., and Bradley, C. C. (1968). *Phys. Rev. Lett.* **21**, 350.
343. Button, K. J., Landwehr, G., Bradley, C. C., Grosse, P., and Lax, B. (1969). *Phys. Rev. Lett.* **23**, 14.
344. Dickey, D. H., Johnson, E. J., and Larsen, D. M. (1967). *Phys. Rev. Lett.* **18**, 599.
345. Waldman, J., Larsen, D. M., Tannenwald, P. E., Bradley, C. C., Cohn, D. R., and Lax, B. (1969). *Phys. Rev. Lett.* **23**, 1033.
346. Brandt, R. C., and Brown, F. C. (1969). *Phys. Rev.* **181**, 1241.
347. Bradley, C. C., Burroughs, W. J., Gebbie, H. A., and Slough, W. (1967). *Infrared Phys.* **7**, 129.
348. Strauch, R. G., Stephenson, D. A., and Derr, V. E. (1969). *Infrared Phys.* **9**, 137.
349. Benedict, W. S., Clough, S. A., Frenkel, L., and Sullivan, T. (1970). *J. Chem. Phys.* **53**, 2565.
350. Duxbury, G., and Jones, R. G. (1971). *Mol. Phys.* **20**, 721.
351. Duxbury, G., and Burroughs, W. J. (1970). *J. Phys. B.* **3**, 98.
352. Uehara, K., Shimizu, T., and Shimoda, K. (1968). *IEEE J. Quantum. Electron.* **QE4**, 728.
353. Duxbury, G., and Jones, R. G. (1971). *Chem. Phys. Lett.* **8**, 439.
354. Brewer, R. G., Kelly, M. J., and Javan, A. (1969). *Phys. Rev. Lett.* **23**, 559.
355. Brewer, R. G. (1970). *Phys. Rev. Lett.* **25**, 1639.
356. Tinkham, M., and Strandberg, M. W. P. (1955). *Phys. Rev.* **97**, 937; (1955). **97**, 951.
357. Burkhalter, J. H., Anderson, R. S., Smith, W. V., and Gordy, W. (1950). *Phys. Rev.* **79**, 651.
358. McKnight, J. S., and Gordy, W. (1968). *Phys. Rev. Lett.* **21**, 1787.
359. Mizushima, M., and Hill, R. M. (1954). *Phys. Rev.* **93**, 745; Zimmerer, R. W., and Mizushima, M. (1961). *Phys. Rev.* **121**, 152.
360. Babcock, H. D., and Herzberg, L. (1948). *Astrophys. J.* **108**, 167.
361. Wilheit, T. T., and Barrett, A. H. (1970). *Phys. Rev.* **A1**, 213.
362. Beringer, R., and Castle, J. G. (1951). *Phys. Rev.* **81**, 82.
363. Hill, R. M., and Gordy, W. (1954). *Phys. Rev.* **93**, 1019.
364. Evenson, K. M., Broida, H. P., Wells, J. S., Mahler, R. J., and Mizushima, M. (1968). *Phys. Rev. Lett.* **21**, 1038.
365. Wells, J. S., and Evenson, K. M. (1970). *Rev. Sci. Instrum.* **41**, 226.
366. Evenson, K. M., Wells, J. S., and Radford, H. E. (1970). *Phys. Rev. Lett.* **25**, 199.
367. Evenson, K. M., and Wells, J. S. (to be published).
368. Evenson, K. M., Radford, H. E., and Moran M. M. (1971). *Appl. Phys. Lett.* **18**, 426.
369. Karplus, R., and Schwinger, J. (1948). *Phys. Rev.* **73**, 1020; see also Snyder, H. S., and Richards, P. I. (1948). *Phys. Rev.* **73**, 1178.
370. Van Vleck, J. H., and Weisskopf, V. F. (1945). *Rev. Mod. Phys.* **17**, 227.
371. Senitzky, B., Gould, G., and Cutler, S. (1963). *Phys. Rev.* **130**, 1460.

372. Senitzky, B., and Cutler, S. (January 1964). *Microwave Journal*, 62.
373. Liebe, H. J. (1968). *IEEE Trans. Microwave Theory Tech.* MTT–16, 860.
374. Duxbury, G., Jones, R. G., Burroughs, W. J., Bradley, C. C., and Stone, N. W. B. (1970). Symposium on Submillimeter Waves, Polytechnic Institute of Brooklyn.
375. Bradley, C. C., Jones, R. G., Birch, J. R., and Duxbury, G. (1970). *Nature (London)*, **226**, 941.
376. Jones, R. G., Bradley, C. C., Chamberlain, J., Gebbie, H. A., Stone, N. W. B., and Sixsmith, H. (1969). *Appl. Opt.* **8**, 701.
377. See Bloembergen, N. (1965). "Non-linear Optics", Benjamin, New York.
378. Franken, P., and Ward, J. F. (1963). *Rev. Mod. Phys.* **35**, 23.
379. Zernike, F., and Berman, P. R. (1965). *Phys. Rev. Lett.* **15**, 999.
380. Yajima, T., and Inoue, K. (1968). *Phys. Lett.* **26A**, 281; (1969), *IEEE J. Quantum Electron.* **QE5**, 140.
381. Abella, I. D., and Cummins, H. Z. (1961). *J. Appl. Phys.* **32**, 1177.
382. Faries, D. W., Gehring, K. A., Richards, P. L., and Shen, Y. R. (1969). *Phys. Rev.* **180**, 363.
383. Richards, P. L. (private communication).
384. Woodbury, E. J., and Ng, W. K. (1962). *Proc. Inst. Radio Eng.* **50**, 2367; Eckhardt, G., Hellwarth, R. W., McClung, F. J., Schwarz, S. E., Weiner, D., and Woodbury, E. J. (1962). *Phys. Rev. Lett.* **9**, 455.
385. See Chantry, G. W. (1971). Polarizability theory of the Raman effect, *in* "The Raman Effect" (Ed. A. Anderson), Vol. I. Marcel Dekker, New York.
386. Hellwarth, R. W. (1963). *Phys. Rev.* **130**, 1850.
387. Buckingham, A. D. (1965). *J. Chem. Phys.* **43**, 25.
388. Garmire, E., Pandarese, F., and Townes, C. H. (1963). *Phys. Rev. Lett.* **11**, 160.
389. Gelbwachs, J., Pantell, R. H., Puthoff, H. E., and Yarborough, J. M. (1969). *Appl. Phys. Lett.* **14**, 259.
390. Puthoff, H. E., Pantell, R. H., Huth, B. G., and Chacon, M. A. (1968). *J. Appl. Phys.* **39**, 2144.
391. Yarborough, J. M., Sussman, S. S., Puthoff, H. E., Pantell, R. H., and Johnson, B. C. (1969). *Appl. Phys. Lett.* **15**, 102.
392. Yarborough, J. M., and Ammann, E. O. (1971). *Appl. Phys. Lett.* **18**, 145.
393. Johnson, B. C., Puthoff, H. E., Soo Hoo, J., and Sussman, S. S. (1971). *Appl. Phys. Lett.* **18**, 181.
394. Chang, T. Y., Van Tran, N., and Patel, C. K. N. (1968). *Appl. Phys. Lett.* **13**, 357.
395. Van Tran, N., and Patel, C. K. N. (1969). *Phys. Rev. Lett.* **22**, 463.
396. Slusher, R. E., Patel, C. K. N., and Fleury, P. A. (1967). *Phys. Rev. Lett.* **18**, 77; Patel, C. K. N., and Slusher, R. E. (1968). *Phys. Rev.* **167**, 413, and (1969). **177**, 1200.
397. Patel, C. K. N., and Shaw, E. D. (1970). *Phys. Rev. Lett.* **24**, 451; (1971). *Phys. Rev.* **3**, 1279.
398. Patel, C. K. N., Shaw, E. D., and Kerl, R. J. (1970). *Phys. Rev. Lett.* **25**, 8.
399. Mould, H. M., Price, W. C., and Wilkinson, G. R. (1959). *Spectrochim. Acta*, **13**, 313.
400. Shaw, E. D., and Patel, C. K. N. (1971). *Appl. Phys. Lett.* **18**, 215.
401. Brueck, S. R. J., and Mooradian, A. (1971). *Appl. Phys. Lett.* **18**, 229.
402. Patel, C. K. N. (1971). *Appl. Phys. Lett.* **18**, 274.
403. Snavely, B. B. (1969). *Proc. IEEE*, **57**, 1374.

404. Chantry, G. W., Gebbie, H. A., and Hilsum, C. (1964). *Nature (London)*, **203**, 1052.
405. For some references see Soffer, B. D., and McFarlane, B. B. (1967). *Appl. Phys. Lett.* **10**, 266.
406. Strome, F. C., and Webb, J. P. (1971). *Appl. Opt.* **10**, 1348.
407. For one solution and references to others see Erickson, L. E., and Szabo, A. (1971). *Appl. Phys. Lett.* **18**, 433.
408. Dewey, C. F., and Hocker, L. O. (1971). *Appl. Phys. Lett.* **18**, 58.
409. Yarborough, J. M., and Massey, G. A. (1971). *Appl. Phys. Lett.* **18**, 438.
410. Hordvik, A. Schlossberg, H. R., and Stickley, C. M. (1971). *Appl. Phys. Lett.* **18**, 448.
411. McFarlane, R. A., Faust, W. L., Patel, C. K. N., and Garrett, C. G. B. (1964). *Proc. IEEE*, **52**, 318; Patel, C. K. N., Faust, W. L., McFarlane, R. A., and Garrett, C. G. B. (1964). *Appl. Phys. Lett.* **4**, 18; Patel, C. K. N., Faust, W. L., McFarlane, R. A., and Garrett, C. G. B. (1964). *Proc. IEEE*, **52**, 713.
412. Mathias, L. E. S., Crocker, A., and Wills, M. S. (1967). *IEEE J. Quantum Electron.* **QE3**, 170.
413. Levine, J. S., and Javan, A. (1969). *Appl. Phys. Lett.* **14**, 348.
414. Dyubko, S. F., Svich, V. A., and Valitov, R. A. (1968). *JETP Lett.* **7**, 320.
415. Hard, T. M. (1969). *Appl. Phys. Lett.* **14**, 130.
416. Hassler, J. C., and Coleman, P. D. (1969). *Appl. Phys. Lett.* **14**, 135.
417. Polanyi, J. C. (1961). *J. Chem. Phys.* **34**, 347; Findlay, F. D., and Polanyi, J. C. (1964). *Can. J. Chem.* **42**, 2126.
418. Kasper, J. V. V., and Pimentel, G. C. (1964). *Appl. Phys. Lett.* **5**, 231.
419. Pimental, G. C. (1967). Infrared study of transient molecules in chemical lasers, published *in* "Molecular Spectroscopy"—General lectures to the IXth European Congress, Madrid. Butterworths, London.
420. Deutsch, T. F. (1967). *Appl. Phys. Lett.* **11**, 18.
421. Deutsch, T. F. (1967). *IEEE J. Quantum Electron.* **QE3**, 419.
422. Akitt, D. P., and Yardley, J. T. (1970). *IEEE J. Quantum Electron.* **QE6**, 113.
423. Wood, O. R., and Schwarz, S. E. (1967). *Appl. Phys. Lett.* **11**, 88.
424. Chang, T. Y., Wang, C. H., and Cheo, P. K. (1969). *Appl. Phys. Lett.* **15**, 157.
425. Chang, T. Y., Bridges, T. J., and Burkhardt, E. G. (1970). *Appl. Phys. Lett.* **17**, 249.
426. Mathias, L. E. S., Crocker, A., and Wills, M. S. (1965). *Phys. Lett.* **14**, 33.
427. Lide, D. R. (1967). *Phys. Lett.* **24A**, 599.
428. Akitt, D. P., and Wittig, C. F. (1969). *J. Appl. Phys.* **40**, 902.
429. Chang, T. Y., Bridges, T. J., and Burkhardt, E. G. (1970). *Appl. Phys. Lett.* **17**, 357.
430. Shimizu, F. (1970). *J. Chem. Phys.* **52**, 3572.
431. Shimizu, F. (1970). *Appl. Phys. Lett.* **16**, 368.
432. Karlov, N. V., Konov, Yu. B., Petrov, Yu. N., Prokhorov, A. M., and Stel'makh, O. M. (1968). *JETP Lett.* **8**, 12.
433. Bott, I. B. (1965). *Phys. Lett.* **14**, 293.
434. Hinkley, E. D., and Kelley, P. L. (1971). *Science*, **171**, 635.
435. Melngailis, I., Stillman, G. E., Dimmock, J. O., and Wolfe, C. M. (1969). *Phys. Rev. Lett.* **23**, 1111.

436. Toll, J. S. (1956). *Phys. Rev.* **104**, 1760; Stern, F. (1963). *Solid State Phys.* **15**, 299.

437. Brot, C. (1969). *Phys. Lett.* **30A**, 101.

438. For a good discussion of the Hund treatment see Herzberg, G. (1950). "Spectra of Diatomic Molecules" (2nd edition), pp. 219ff. Van Nostrand, New York.

439. See reference 438, pp. 280ff, and also Wager, A. T. (1943). *Phys. Rev.* **64**, 18; and Radford, H. E., and Broida, H. P. (1963). *J. Chem. Phys.* **38**, 644.

440. Mathias, L. E. S., Crocker, A., and Wills, M. S. (1965). *Electron. Lett.* **1**, 45.

441. Broida, H. P., Evenson, K. M., and Kikuchi, T. T. (1965). *J. Appl. Phys.* **36**, 3355.

442. Chantry, G. W. (unpublished work).

443. Steffen, H., Steffen, J., Moser, J. F., and Kneubuhl, F. K. (1966). *Phys. Lett.* **20**, 20; and (1966) **21**, 425.

444. Yamanaka, M., Kon, S., Yamamoto, J., and Yoshinaga, H. (1968). *Jap. J. Appl. Phys.* **7**, 554.

Author Index

367

Subject Index

Compound Index

A

A (argon), 162–163, 168

ADP (ammonium dihydrogen phosphate), 290, 303

Ag_3AsS_3 (proustite), 302, 303

AgBr (silver bromide), 274

Ag_3SbS_3 (pyrargyrite), 302

Al_2O_3 (alumina), 129–130, 213

B

$BaTiO_3$ (barium titanate), 172

BBr_3 (boron tribromide), 309

BCl_3 (boron trichloride), 309

BF_3 (boron trifluoride), 309

Be (beryllium), 225–226

BeO (beryllium oxide), 129

C

$Ca(C_{18}H_{35}O_2)_2$ (calcium stearate), 133

CaF_2 (calcium fluoride), 129–130

$CaTiO_3$ (calcium titanate, perovskite), 171

$C(CH_3)_4$ (neopentane), 188

$C(CH_3)_3Cl$ (t-butyl chloride), 188

$C(CH_3)Cl_3$ (methylchloroform), 188

$C_6(CH_3)_{6-n}Cl_n$, 189–190

CCl_4 (carbon tetrachloride), 85, 96, 182–183, 188

CCl_3H (chloroform), 175, 179

CD_4 (per deuteromethane), 161

CF_4 (carbon tetrafluoride), 148, 160–161, 308

CF_3H (fluoroform), 308

CH, 283

CH_4 (methane), 160–161, 241, 260, 262, 263

C_2H_2 (acetylene), 148

C_6H_6 (benzene), 141, 175, 183, 185

$C_2H_2Br_4$ (tetrabromoethane), 200–201

CH_3CCH (methyl acetylene), 33

CH_2CF_2 (difluorethylene), 276, 287–289

$C_6H_5CH_3$ (toluene), 189

CH_2CHF (vinyl fluoride), 310

CH_3CHO (acetaldehyde), 203, 205

C_6H_5Cl (chlorobenzene), 182, 184, 186

CH_3CN (acetonitrile), 262, 263

C_2H_5CN (propionitrile), 262

CH_3F (methyl fluoride), 257, 310, 311

C_2H_5F (ethyl fluoride), 205

CH_3NH_2 (methylamine), 206

CH_3NO_2 (nitromethane), 206, 263

CH_3OH (methanol), 310

$CH.OOH$ (formic acid), 206

CdHgTe (cadmium mercury telluride), 233

CdTe (cadmium telluride), 274

ClCN (cyanogen chloride), 257

CN, 37, 243, 245, 343ff

CO (carbon monoxide), 32, 257

CO_2 (carbon dioxide), 148, 159–160, 207, 240, 241, 298

CoF_2 (cobaltous fluoride), 218

COS (carbonyl sulphide), 187, 257

Cr^{3+} (chromic ion), 214–216

CS (carbon monosulphide), 37, 41

CsBr (caesium bromide), 18

CsI (caesium iodide), 64, 128, 129, 139

D

DCl (deuterium chloride), 173

DCN (deuterium cyanide), 34, 246

D_2O (deuterium oxide), 275–277

D_2O_2 (deuterium peroxide), 203–205

DTTCI (diethyl thiatricarbocyanine iodide), 302

$DyPO_4$ (dysprosium phosphate), 216–217

F

FeF_2 (ferrous fluoride), 218

G

GaAs (gallium arsenide), 28, 219, 232, 298, 315

383